THE NEW NATURALIST
A SURVEY OF BRITISH NATURAL HISTORY

MOUNTAINS AND MOORLANDS

The aim of this series is to interest the general reader in the wild life of Britain by recapturing the inquiring spirit of the old naturalists. The Editors believe that the natural pride of the British public in the native fauna and flora, to which must be added concern for their conservation, is best fostered by maintaining a high standard of accuracy combined with clarity of exposition in presenting the results of modern scientific research. The plants and animals are described in relation to their homes and habitats and are portrayed in the full beauty of their natural colours by the latest methods of colour photography and reproduction

THE NEW NATURALIST

MOUNTAINS AND MOORLANDS

W. H. PEARSALL D.SC. F.R.S.

Quain Professor of Botany in the
University of London at University College

WITH REVISIONS BY WINIFRED PENNINGTON

(MRS. T. G. TUTIN)

with 47 colour photographs
by John Markham, B. A. Crouch and others
34 black and white photographs
and 46 maps and diagrams

COLLINS
ST JAMES'S PLACE LONDON

First Edition   *1950*
Reprinted   *1960*
Reprinted   *1965*
Revised Edition   *1971*

Printed in Great Britain
Collins Clear-Type Press
London and Glasgow

CONTENTS

COLOUR PLATES

It should be noted that throughout this book Plate numbers in arabic figures refer to Colour Plates, while roman numerals are used for Black-and-White Plates

PLATES IN BLACK AND WHITE

TEXT FIGURES

xi

EDITORS' PREFACE

T H E R E are really two Britains—two different countries, their boundary a line that strikes diagonally across England from Yorkshire to Devon. To the north and west of this line is the region of mountains and old rocks ; to its south and east the newer, fertile land of the plains. These regions differ vastly in their climate, rocks, soils, scenery, plants, animals—and men.

It is of the mountains and moorlands that W. H. Pearsall writes. Moorland, mountain-top and upland grazing occupy over a third of the total living-space of the British Isles, and, of all kinds of land, have suffered least interference by man. Mountains and moorlands provide the widest scope for studying natural wild life on land.

In the present volume Professor Pearsall has brought together the results of over thirty years' work among the high hills, the lakes and the moorlands of northern and western Britain. He is a botanist, but these pages show that animals have appealed to him almost as much as plants, a double interest that is rarer than it should be among naturalists. It is doubtful whether any other author could, single-handed, have presented such a well-balanced picture of the wild life of an area as Professor Pearsall has done in this volume.

Although he is now banished to the gently undulating south (he is head of the Botany Department at University College, London) the whole of Professor Pearsall's previous working life has been spent within call of the mountains and moorlands about which he writes— at Manchester, at Leeds, and finally as Professor of Botany at Sheffield University. During this period he has made many outstanding contributions to ecological research, especially in the Lake District, but it is obvious from his book that the severely scientific discipline that these researches demand has by no means extinguished his deep love of the countryside in which they were carried out. On the contrary, the aesthetic and the scientific approaches have reinforced each other, as they should—but frequently do not—in any fully developed naturalist.

For many people, perhaps the most arresting point in the book will be the idea that since the end of the Ice Age our mountains and

xiii

moorlands have been subject to a process of inevitable change, one of the trends being towards the growth of bog and peat-moss at the expense of grassland and woodland, and towards a general impoverishment of soils; further, that during the last 3,000 years or so this and other changes have been progressively accentuated by man's interference, so that the difference between the natural history of our moorlands to-day and a bare two centuries ago is very marked. Indeed, work such as Professor Pearsall's is putting the history of our country in a new light. His chapter on the future possibilities of our uplands is equally striking.

Before the growth of modern transport most people in the south of England had little chance of knowing how those in the rest of Britain lived; there was little opportunity for studying and appreciating the lives of those who lived in the unspoilt countryside of the north and west. But to-day the mountains and moorlands of Highland Britain are within reach of every one, and we hope that Professor Pearsall's book will help to quicken—and guide—interest in those parts of this country which now provide the main (almost the only remaining) opportunity for observing and investigating wild life and human problems in Britain as it was before modern man's heavy hand was laid upon it.

THE EDITORS

AUTHOR'S PREFACE

T H I S book is an expression of many happy days in the field and is thus a tribute to the many naturalist friends who have consciously or unconsciously helped towards it by sharing their interests and enthusiasms. I should like to think that they may find some satisfaction in its dedication and that they would feel that they had in part contributed towards its creation.

When so much is owed to others, it may seem invidious to mention any by name. But the largest part of the animal population is composed of insects and for these specialised knowledge is unavoidable, even for a general review. I count myself extremely fortunate in having been able to obtain the sort of information I wanted, and also pertinent criticisms, from Mr. C. A. Cheetham, Professor J. W. Heslop Harrison and Mr. W. D. Hincks, the last of whom also verified the names according to the *Check List of British Insects*. Mr. W. H. R. Tams very kindly gave much help in the preparation of Plate 30, p. 245. The Editors too have been generous in help and criticism ; and, finally, a tribute must be made to the photographic skill of Mr. John Markham.

In spite of this, I fear that this may be thought an odd book, remarkable more for its omissions than its scope. It tries to integrate certain aspects of upland biology of which it may safely be said that about ten years' intensive work would be required to do them reasonably well. The real integration, perhaps, is that it tells about some of the things that have interested its author.

W. H. P.

University College, London

PREFACE TO REVISED EDITION

Professor Pearsall died in October 1964. A lifetime of active work as a field ecologist, university teacher and administrator, ecological advisor and one of those most concerned with the foundation of the Nature Conservancy, had left him too little time to write. *Mountains and Moorlands* remains as his major work for the general reader; it is a classic, and must not be touched by a lesser hand. But in the twenty years since its publication, further research has inevitably modified certain concepts. When I was asked by Collins to revise *Mountains and Moorlands* for this edition, it seemed to me that Chapter 10, on ecological history, should be largely rewritten in the light of new work and the emergence of the technique of radiocarbon dating since 1950. Chapter 10 was partly based on the work of Dr. Verona Conway and myself, and the revised edition of this chapter has been approved by Dr. Conway and by Mrs. Pearsall. I am grateful to Miss Clare Fell for advice on changes in the interpretation of the archaeological record in North-west England since R. G. Collingwood's account of 1933, which formed the basis of Professor Pearsall's discussion of the ecological history of North-west England. In other chapters I have changed only a few sentences, to conform with new discoveries, and have provided additional bibliography to cover relevant work published since 1950. Chapter 15, a brief account of the work of the Nature Conservancy in Highland Britain, has been added to the book because of Professor Pearsall's concern with the Nature Conservancy—he was for many years Chairman of its Scientific Policy Committee—and because of the relevancy of the work of the Conservancy to the matters discussed in Chapter 14 of *Mountains and Moorlands*, which was written before that work had begun.

The nomenclature of plants has been revised to conform with current usage; on the advice of various colleagues, the revised nomenclature, with two exceptions, conforms with that found in Clapham, Tutin and Warburg's *Excursion Flora of the British Isles*, Second Edition; the Census Catalogue of British Mosses, by E. F. Warburg, Third Edition, published by the British Bryological Society in 1963; the Census Catalogue of British Hepatics, by J. A. Paton, Fourth Edition, published by the British Bryological Society in 1965; and A New Check-list of British Lichens, by P. W. James, in The Lichenologist, Volume 3, 1965. The exceptions are that *Scirpus caespitosus* has been retained, instead of *Trichophorum caespitosum*, as in Clapham, Tutin and Warburg, and that *Cladonia sylvatica agg.* has been retained, as it includes the two species, *Cladonia arbuscula* and *C. impexa*, of the Check-list.

W. P.

University of Leicester and
The Freshwater Biological Association

PLATE I

Seton Gordon

Ruadh Stac and Blaven, Skye: a granite mountain and a gabbro ridge. August

PLATE 2

ENGLISH LAKE DISTRICT

B. A. Crouch

a. Wastwater, Scafell Pike and (*right*) Scafell
showing a water-eroded gully with gravel fan below

B. A. Crouch

b. Wastwater Screes: a gully and stone-shoot

CHAPTER I

INTRODUCTION

> " The grounde is baren for the moste part of wood
> and corne, as forest grounde ful of lynge, mores
> and mosses with stony hilles."
>
> (LELAND)

A VISITOR to the British Isles usually disembarks in lowland
England. He is charmed by its orderly arrangement and by its open
landscapes, tamed and formed by man and mellowed by a thousand
years of human history. There is another Britain, to many of us the
better half, a land of mountains and moorlands and of sun and cloud,
and it is with this upland Britain that these pages are concerned. It
is equal in area to lowland Britain but its population is less than that
of a single large town. It lies now, as always, beyond the margins of
our industrial and urban civilisations, fading into the western mists
and washed by northern seas, its needs forgotten and its possibilities
almost unknown.

Nevertheless, to the biologist at least, highland Britain is of sur-
passing interest because in it there is shown the dependence of organism
upon environment on a large scale. It includes a whole range of
habitats with restricted and often much specialised faunas and floras.
At times, these habitats approach the limits within which organic life
is possible, and they are commonly so severe that man has avoided
them. Thus we can not only study the factors affecting the distribution of plants and animals as a whole, but we can envisage something
of the forces that have influenced human distribution. Moreover, in
these marginal habitats we most often see man as a part of a biological
system rather than as the lord of his surroundings.

This book, then, deals primarily with mountains and moorlands
as habitats for living organisms. Many plants and animals are
mentioned, usually without detailed descriptions, except where they
can be seen to be a characteristic part of the environmental system as a
whole, or where they illustrate typical relations between organisms
and environment. For this reason also no attempt is made to
give full lists. It is also inevitable that the plant-soil relationship
occupies in outline a large part of the story because this is the feature
which links the animate with the inanimate.

M.M.   B

It would hardly be possible to frequent upland Britain without becoming an admirer of its beauty. Its scenery is due to the interplay of its geological structure, of its climate and vegetation, and of human influences. It thus becomes important to the biologist as an *integration* of the interplay of these habitat factors and often his first interest will be to look keenly at the scenery for clues in the analysis of the environmental factors. As Professor Dudley Stamp has pointed out in his volume *Britain's Structure and Scenery*, the scenery of the British Isles is remarkable in its diversity, and this conclusion applies with special force to the British Highlands. Diversity of aspect means diversity of habitat and of biological pattern. It offers a fruitful and as yet hardly explored field for the naturalist's work and one which is particularly attractive because very valuable results can be obtained without highly specialised knowledge or apparatus.

While the study of the relations between organism and environment is no new aspect of biological inquiry, it is nowadays dignified by a special name and is called the science of ecology. The ecological study of mountains and moorlands may be in its infancy but their fauna and flora have long been objects of interest to naturalists. It is evident from the routes they followed and the lists of plants they collected from 1660 onwards, that John Ray and his associates were no strangers to the high northern hills, but the first record of an ascent of a British mountain we owe to another botanist—stout Thomas Johnson—whose account of the ascent of Snowdon in 1639 all naturalists will enjoy, especially perhaps the concluding sentence : " Leaving our horses and outer garments, we began to climb the mountain. The ascent at first is difficult, but after a bit a broad open space is found, but equally sloping, great precipices on the left, and a difficult climb on the right. Having climbed three miles, we at last gained the highest ridge of the mountain, which was shrouded in thick cloud. Here the way was very narrow, and climbers are horror-stricken by the rough, rocky precipices on either hand and the Stygian marshes, both on this side and that. We sat down in the midst of the clouds, and first of all we arranged in order the plants we had, at our peril, collected among the rocks and precipices, and then we ate the food we had brought with us."

Johnson lived in troubled times and he was later to die of his wounds as a Cavalier soldier. If interest in the Alps may be said to have started as a result of de Saussure's scientific expedition to Mont

Blanc in 1787, we may perhaps fairly regard Johnson as a British de Saussure at a far earlier date, though on a more modest and unassuming scale.

Fig. 1.—Map of areas discussed, showing some of the Nature Reserves in Highland Britain.

CHAPTER 2

STRUCTURE

T H E British Highlands are composed of blocks of hard and old rocks that occupy the north and west of these islands. While the biologist is not primarily concerned with the manner in which these rocks originated and attained their present condition, the geological structure of the uplands is a matter of some importance to him because it determines the character of the soil and the nature of the habitats available for living organisms. Consequently, a slight acquaintance with geological structure and processes forms part of the necessary background of the present subject and one, moreover, which is of interest in helping us to understand the great scenic and biological diversity of different parts of Highland Britain.

Almost every mountain observer has been struck by the evidence of decay which centres around the larger peaks. There is shattered rock round their summits (Pl. III, p. 12), while below every crag we find scree and from every gully there runs a stone-shoot (Pl. 2b, p. 1), formed from débris coming down from above. In the mornings the ceaseless downward trickle of stones or the occasional rock-fall proclaims the constant attrition to which the steeper hills are subject. Thus to the distant observer the mountains may seem to be permanent, " the immortal hills," but to those who know and move among them a different impression is formed, in which breakdown and change play by far the most prominent part.

The causes of this constant weathering of the rock surfaces are primarily the uneven contractions and expansions of the rocks caused by fluctuations of temperature, the action of rain and frost and the force of gravity. Any cracks that develop become filled with water and are expanded when the water freezes and widened when it thaws. The actions of rain and of gravity tend to remove the smaller rock fragments so that nothing accumulates to protect the constantly exposed surface. Thus the surface continues to be weathered away until the slope approaches an angle of rest (usually between 30° and 40°). Rainwash, soil-creep and the gradual downward movement of larger stones continue, long after this angle is reached, to move the materials towards the valley.

Still more important in the long run are the effects of running

PLATE I

C. H. Wood

Aerial view of Yewdale, Coniston, showing rock structures. The flatter land in the foreground with fields, woods and horizontal stratification is on softer flags and grits (Bannisdale series); all the mountains behind, rising with steeply inclined gullies from the foreground, are on the hard Borrowdale volcanic rocks

PLATE II

J. Tully

Tryfan: the eastern "scarp slope" and "heathery terrace". The rock climbs are above the terrace water, for this not only tends to move materials downwards, but it may also remove them from the area altogether. In the course of time, therefore, every mountain torrent erodes a gully of its own construction, and the coarser materials eroded are deposited below the gully on a gravel fan or delta (Pl. 2a, p. 1), while the finer materials are carried ultimately to the plains beyond the mountain area. It follows that the land-forms in the uplands tend to be those which have survived the processes of weathering and erosion. In terms of these ideas, the uplands, whether moorland or mountain, have survived because the rocks of which they are formed are harder or have resisted removal rather than because they are being or have been lifted up. At the same time there must have been some original mountain-building process.

Many facts can be used to illustrate this argument. Almost every visitor to the English Lake District becomes familiar with a type of scenery in which there is a foreground of lower and rounded hills, backed by a skyline of larger and steeper mountains. This is well shown in the photograph of Esthwaite Water in Plate 3b, p. 16, and this type of scenery has a simple explanation. The rounded hills in the foreground are composed of rocks less resistant to weathering and the high mountains of harder or more resistant rocks, in this case the hard volcanic " tuffs " or ashy beds of the Borrowdale Volcanic series which make up much of the mountain core of the Lake District. Both to the north and the south of these hard rocks lie softer slates and grits. Although to the uninitiated these rocks present a generally similar appearance, they exhibit considerable difference in hardness. As the harder Borrowdale rocks have weathered much more slowly, they now generally form much higher ground than do the adjacent softer rocks. The actual junction of the harder and softer rocks is shown in Plate I, p. 4, where it will be seen that the harder rocks are mountain slopes, the softer being soil-covered and cultivated.

There are many equally good examples elsewhere of the influence of the hardness or softness of rocks upon land forms. A second illustration may be taken from Scotland, where, north of the Highland line, there are to be found long stretches of steeply inclined and metamorphosed grits, hard and resistant rocks which give the line of the summits, Ben Lomond, Ben Ledi, and Ben Vorlich. The valleys intersecting this area lie on beds of softer rocks, shales, limestones and phyllites, which have suffered correspondingly greater erosion and so have been cut down below the general upland level.

The general concept of mountain structure thus illustrated can be applied on a larger scale, for it has been pointed out already that the distribution of mountains and moorlands in Britain is essentially that of the older and harder rocks. These lie, as we have seen, to the north-west of the British Isles, and their range covers all the main mountain areas. The causes of this distribution lie in the far-distant past when large-scale earth movements were taking place, and there seems to have remained since a tendency for the north and west of the British Isles to stand as a raised system. While any attempt to trace these mountain building movements lies outside the scope of the present discussion, it may be interesting to indicate something of their effects on upland structure.

In the simplest cases, of which the Pennine range in Northern England is a good example, the upland area represents essentially a fold in the earth's crust. In the Pennines, this fold runs approximately north and south and a transverse section through it would show the general arrangement represented in Fig. 2a, with the newer rocks (including the Coal Measures) represented on either side of the fold, that is in Lancashire and Yorkshire, but absent from the top of the Pennines themselves. There is evidence of various types which points strongly to the probability that newer rocks, from the Coal Measures upwards, have in fact been removed by erosion from along the crest.

Thus the Craven Uplands, including Ingleborough at their southern end, are separated from the main block of the Southern Pennines by the great Craven Fault system. Just south of this fault, at Ingleton, coal was formerly mined from strata lying *above* those which correspond to the rocks on the top of Ingleborough. The assumption seems clear, therefore, that these Coal Measures have been removed by erosion from the area north of the Craven Fault.

The Craven Uplands are interesting in another respect also. The

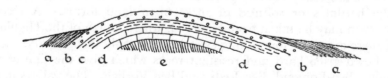

FIG. 2a —General character of Pennine anticline. (Diagrammatic.) *a*, Coal Measures; *b*, Millstone Grit; *c*, Yoredale Shales, etc.; *d*, Carboniferous limestone; *e*, Ordovician and Silurian.

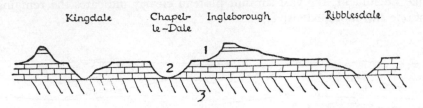

FIG. 2b —Dissection of Craven Pennines by river valleys : 1, Yoredale rocks ; 2, Carboniferous limestone ; 3, Ordovician and Silurian. (Diagrammatic.)

three parallel summits of the mid-Pennines, from east to west—Great Whernside (2310 ft.), Penyghent (2273 ft.) and Ingleborough (2373 ft.), but also, to the north-west, Whernside (2414 ft.) and Grey Gareth (2250 ft.), reproduce almost identical characteristics in structure and altitude. They are separated by a series of river valleys, Wharfdale, Littondale and Ribblesdale, then also by Chapel-le-Dale and Kingdale, which have very obviously been cut down through the original rock formations, here almost horizontal (see Fig. 2b). A reconstruction of the mid-Pennines on an east-to-west section thus shows these mountains as the surviving elements of the Pennine fold, resting on a mass of the still older Silurian rocks, upon which also the rivers now run. North and south of these Craven Uplands, the Pennines have commonly the character of a high moorland plateau (see Fig. 28). It is only when these plateaux have been greatly dissected by erosion and by river action, that distinctive mountain peaks are frequent. This has happened not only in Craven but also at the southern extremity of the Pennine range where dissection has also split up the plateau into peaks such as Kinder Scout and Bleaklow.

Now whatever their origin may otherwise be, it is extremely common to find that mountain masses have the character of dissected plateaux. There is perhaps no better example of this in Britain than the Cairngorms as a whole. The observer standing at any considerable distance from these mountains (so as to be able to see most of the major summits) will inevitably be struck by the fact that the group as a whole presents a nearly level or gently domed-shaped profile. This may be seen particularly well from near Aviemore (see Fig. 3), and it is suggested by the skyline in Plate 5, p. 22. In other words, these peaks, so impressive at close quarters, are due to the cutting up of the high plateau by deep and steep valleys. Even on isolated peaks like Lochnagar, the vast summit plateau clearly indicates the remains of one still more extensive.

FIG. 3.—Silhouette of the northern face of the Cairngorms—a dissected plateau.

Imagine the processes of erosion and dissection proceeding over many square miles of nearly horizontal strata, until much more has been removed than is left, and it will be possible to understand the origin of the extreme examples of mountain or plateau dissection to be seen in Western Ross and Sutherland. Here, formerly, nearly horizontal layers of Torridonian sandstone covered an ancient surface of hard and resistant crystalline rocks. To-day, such mountains as Suilven and Canisp represent the last remains of these sandstone masses, most of which have long since vanished. In this category also must no doubt be placed Lugnaquilla (3039 ft.) in south-eastern Ireland—the last remnant of rocks overlying a large boss of granite.

There is one other point about the effects of erosion which is worthy of brief mention. If a mountain mass or ridge were composed of uniform materials and if it were equally eroded on all sides, the shape of the mountain would tend to approach more and more closely, as time went on, to that of a perfect cone. This generalised type of mountain is not perhaps very common in Britain—though isolated hills like Muckish and Errigal in Donegal are of this general type as well as many of the rather lumpy mountains in the Scottish Highlands, especially perhaps Schiehallion. The Paps of Jura, illustrated in Plate 3a, p. 16, show the disintegration of a quartzite ridge in this way. A common British variant of this simple type is one in which the summit is distinctly flat-topped or tabular. This is particularly to be seen in some of the examples already mentioned. The three most prominent Pennine summits, Cross Fell, Ingleborough (Pl. 17, p. 96) and Kinder Scout all have this form as do the Sutherland mountains Suilven and Canisp, and MacLeod's Tables, west of

Dunvegan in Skye. It is due to the presence at the summit level of a horizontal stratum of hard and resistant rock, usually Millstone Grit in the Pennines and Torridonian Sandstone, capped by Cambrian quartzite in Sutherland, the latter containing so much white quartz that the rock may be mistaken for a snow-cap when seen from a distance. (Pl. III, p. 12).

The Craven Uplands show in a particularly striking manner the dependence of mountain scenery and vegetation on the geological structure. The rocks are horizontally stratified and they consist of an upper zone, mainly of Yoredale sandstones and shales, below which lies a great thickness of Carboniferous Limestone, once called the Mountain Limestone from its association with upland areas in Britain. Where the overlying rocks have been removed by erosion, the hard limestone may form extensive plateaux, and because it is almost pure calcium carbonate, it yields practically no soil on weathering. It is traversed in all directions by deep vertical fissures and is consequently dry (Pl. XXII, p. 133). The surface, aptly called " limestone pavement," is usually devoid of vegetation except where traces of glacial drift occur, but a luxuriant flora lives in the shelter of the fissures. The limestone plateaux are often bounded by almost vertical " scars " (Pl. XVIII, p. 236). A very striking type of scenery is thus produced, a feature not only of the Craven Uplands and mid-Pennines in general, but also of large areas in Western Ireland (Clare and Mayo).

In contrast, the Carboniferous Sandstones (including Millstone Grit) and shales are non-calcareous and are almost always covered by the moorland vegetation which is so characteristic a feature of the high plateaux of the northern and southern Pennines. In Craven, where these rocks are exposed along with the limestones, the contrast between the two sorts of rock is often very striking, and is well illustrated in Plate 4, p. 17. Thus both the physical and chemical qualities of the rocks may affect the scenery and vegetation.

The simple conical form that is to be expected where rocks of approximately uniform texture are equally eroded on all sides, is lost not only when the harder rock strata occur, but also wherever the mountain is composed of strata that are not horizontal. Thus both Blencathra and Dow Crags in the Lake District show one gently sloping aspect (see Fig. 4) which is that of the " dip " or slope of the rock strata, while on their steep faces the rock weathers into blocks, more or less at right angles to the dip of the strata, so that a

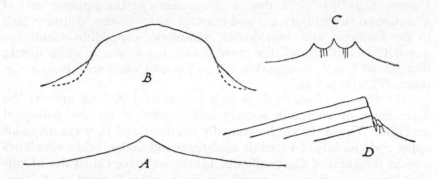

FIG. 4.—Some types of mountain form. A, Symmetrical weathering of uniform rock ; B, Recent oversteepening below ancient upper form ; C, Ridge with softer interbedded rock ; D, Dip and scarp slopes.

steep angle tends to persist. In Wales, Tryfan also shows this type of structure in a still more spectacular manner (Pl. II, p. 5) and it is very generally to be seen in the different mountain areas, often recurring, again and again, wherever the rock strata act as guiding planes for the inevitable erosion.

Sometimes hard rocks arranged in this manner overlie much softer ones. Such is the essential structure of Mam Tor, the " Shivering Mountain " in Derbyshire, and also of Alport Castles not far away. In both cases, hard sandstones and grits in the upper part of the escarpment have below them soft shales which are constantly washing and weathering away. Thus, on Mam Tor, the upper parts of the escarpment is constantly being undermined and so are constantly falling. Alport Castles, in contrast, represent an immense wedge of the mountain detaching itself from the face behind and falling outwards with infinite slowness, pushing before it into the valley a great wave of earth, as is well shown in Plate 6, p. 23. There are no better examples in Britain of the instability of mountain structures than these two Derbyshire hills.

In other British mountain areas, the comparatively simple arrangements of rocks seen in the examples already discussed are obscured and other considerations become important. An upfold like that met with in the Pennines is called an *anticline* (see Fig. 1) and a corresponding valley-shaped fold (or depression) would be called a *syncline*.

Now it is a striking fact that the mountain summits very often represent the remains of a syncline. Naturally this is only in areas where great erosion has taken place. The reason for the persistence of the synclinal folds as mountains is that when folding takes place as a result of lateral pressure, the synclinal folds will be compressed and so will tend to become harder. Anticlinal folds, on the other hand, will come under tension and so will tend to crack.

Thus when weathering and erosion takes place, the anticline, being shattered, is more easily attacked and suffers more, while the syncline, being compressed and hardest, therefore tends to be more slowly affected. It is thus logical, if somewhat unexpected, to find that great peaks or perhaps particularly ridges often represent the remains of a syncline, though the synclinal structure may not always be evident because the main ridge of the mountain often represents the long axis of the synclinal fold.

The classical example of synclinal mountain structure, of which a fine picture exists in Lord Avebury's *Scenery of England,* is that of Y-Wyddfa, the main peak of Snowdon, as seen from between the Crib Goch and Crib y Ddysgl under suitable conditions—with a powdering of recent snow. This face is usually in shade and not easily photographed to bring out the rock structure, but the essential features are shown in Fig. 5.

Another fine and well-known section illustrating synclinal structure is exposed on the Clogwyn du'r Arddu, to the north-west of the main

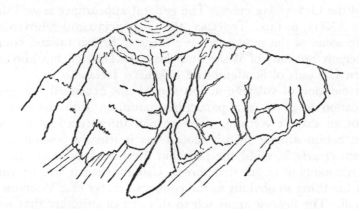

FIG. 5.—Rock structure showing syncline on Y-Wyddfa—the Snowdon summit.

summit, where a great synclinal fold makes up the whole of the precipice. These rather simple illustrations serve to illustrate a very important fact that where great earth-movements have taken place the contortions of the rock strata may greatly affect their hardness and resistance to erosion.

Snowdon itself represents the bottom of a great fold whose crest lay somewhere to the south-east. In that locality some 20,000 ft. of rock must have been removed by erosion. The human mind can hardly appreciate the length of time, not less than hundreds of millions of years, which erosion on this scale must have taken. The rocks now exposed belong to two ancient systems which we have already encountered in discussing an earlier illustration (Pl. 3b, p. 16). They are in geological terminology of Ordovician and Silurian age (see *Britain's Structure and Scenery* by L. Dudley Stamp). The central core of Wales, as of the Lake District, consists of Ordovician rocks which are solidified volcanic ashes and stones (*tuffs*) and lava flows, with interbedded marine strata indicating a submarine origin. These make up some of our boldest mountain scenery, though there is nothing to suggest that the individual mountains such as Snowdon, Cader Idris or Scafell have ever been volcanoes. Associated with the Ordovician tuffs and lavas are extensive sedimentary rocks of later Silurian age which are mainly fine grits or shales, and these, though generally softer, are as a rule rather poorer in bases like lime. They form somewhat more rounded hills (sometimes described as *moels*, their Welsh name), to-day almost always grass-covered like the lower slopes of the Ordovician crags. The general appearance is well shown in Plate XXIII, p. 140. Together, the Ordovician and Silurian rocks make up some of the most extensive areas of British upland country, characteristic not only of Wales and the Lake District, but also of the Southern Uplands of Scotland and Southern Ireland.

The mention of volcanic action should not necessarily suggest an identification of parts of a particular mountain with the cone and crater of an extinct volcano. The correct interpretation of signs of volcanic action among British mountains is usually possible only if one keeps clearly in mind the fact that most mountains are likely to be the remnants of larger structures. Usually then it will be vain to look for anything so obvious as the cone and crater of a Vesuvius or a Stromboli. The nearest approach to this sort of structure that we are likely to find in Britain is seen in some of the Laws of Southern Scotland.

PLATE III

Torridonian sandstone "scones" and Cambrian quartzite above, at the summit of Cul Mor, Wester Ross

James Fisher

PLATE IV

W. A. Poucher

The Old Man of Storr, Skye, from above, showing cliffs of Tertiary basalts

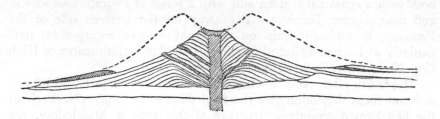

FIG. 6.—A Scottish " Law "—eroded remains of ancient volcanic vent. The shaded areas are basalt (lava flows)—the laminated areas are volcanic tuffs (ashes).

These usually represent the vents of small volcanoes which have become plugged with solidified lava whilst the surrounding cone has been more or less completely removed by erosion. A simplified section is given in Fig. 6. One of the most complete examples, Largo Law in Fife, is essentially similar but has two main vents. The figure shows the position of the vents and the lava flows which are marked by " basaltic " rocks. Around these are the remains of the cones formed by tuffs or solidified volcanic ashes and stones. The mineral composition of these volcanic tuffs is characteristic, so that they can be recognised where no volcanic cone is evident. It is this type of identification that is used in the case of the Ordovician tuffs already mentioned, where the scale of output was immeasurably larger and no certain vent can be found.

Igneous rocks apart from volcanic lavas more usually fall into one of two main morphological types. The largest areas are occupied by *plutonic* rocks, representing enormous masses of molten rock which has solidified without reaching the surface. There are secondly " dykes " and " sills," both representing intrusions of molten rock among other pre-existing strata. In the case of *dykes* the intruded material runs through cracks or planes at right angles to the general stratification —in the case of *sills* the molten rock follows between the bedding planes and therefore runs parallel to the general " dip " of the rock. Sills are often more resistant than the rocks into which they have been intruded, and when this is the case they may form striking cliffs. Especially well-known examples are some of the sills in the Edinburgh district, of which perhaps Salisbury Crags are the most impressive. In Northern England the Whin Sill not only forms natural escarpments on which part of the Roman Wall stands, but it is associated both with a remarkable flora and with a series of majestic cascades in and near Upper Teesdale. Far away on the western side of the Pennines, it outcrops again on the great western escarpment, particularly at Roman Fell and in the spectacular amphitheatre of High Cup Nick, where it is eighty feet thick.

Dykes are often on a much smaller scale, but when found among resistant rocks they often give rise to striking gullies and cols. Perhaps the best-known mountain structure of this type is Mickledore, the great gap separating Scafell from Scafell Pike.

The larger intrusions of igneous rock are very often great bosses of granite which may be many miles across. Classical examples are those in Galloway, which give the mountains of Criffel and of Cairnsmore of Fleet. To this type of structure belong the summit of Crib Goch and also Penmaen Mawr in Wales, the latter familiar to every one who drives along the coastal road. Generally similar is the huge granite mass of Dartmoor. In all these cases the granite boss is harder than the surrounding country rock and so has been left more elevated than the areas around. Where the surrounding rocks are hard, however, granite bosses may contribute no noteworthy structure to a mountain region, and this is the case in the Lake District, for example, where the Shap, Eskdale or Ennerdale granites are all relatively inconspicuous among the hard slates into which they were intruded.

Along the western seaboard of Scotland granite intrusions occur among other traces of volcanic or plutonic activity. The Western Isles and many of their mountains include the remains of vast flows of basaltic lavas which formerly stretched from Antrim, through Staffa, Mull and Arran to Skye, and, indeed, as far north as the Faeroe Islands and Iceland. Geologically, these lava beds are of Tertiary Age and very much more recent than the tuffs of the Lake District and Wales. Even to-day the beds lie nearly horizontal, and though they form the well-known columns of Staffa and the Giant's Causeway and are often exposed in sea-cliffs (those of Eigg and of Portree Harbour, for example), they do not as a whole contribute much to our mountain scenery. Nevertheless, the familiar view of the mountains of Mull, Sgurr Dearg and its neighbours seen from Oban, consists almost wholly of rocks of this type, forced upward by later volcanic action in Central Mull. Still farther north, in Skye, the Storr Rocks (Plate IV, p. 13) and the Quirang are, moreover, both composed of these

Tertiary lavas overlying softer Jurassic shales, and the whole of the coastal scenery is dominated by them.

Much more important scenically were the great subsequent upwellings of molten igneous matter in this area, which are associated with the noble mountain scenery of Skye, Rhum and Arran. In Skye, the principal contrast is between the Black Coolin and the Red Hills. The crags of the former are composed mainly of a hard and basic rock called *gabbro*, with a coarsely crystalline structure that delights the climber's heart. The Red Hills, in contrast, are granite and this has weathered far more rapidly and uniformly to give mountains of smooth and rounded aspect. The contrast, known to every visitor to Skye, is extremely well shown in the fine photograph (Pl. 1, p. xvi) of Blaven and Ruadh Stac, the former of gabbro and the latter of granite. The gabbro is intersected by igneous " dykes " which, running mainly north-west and south-east, serve to accentuate the differences, for these are more easily eroded than gabbro and so tend to form the gullies in the great gabbro ridges. Plate VII, p. 48, gives an excellent impression of the distant aspects of the rock and the ridges.

Somewhat similar contrasts are to be seen in Rhum, where the outstanding peaks of Hallival and Askival are composed of ultra-basic and coarsely crystalline rocks of an unusual type. Their craggy outlines contrast noticeably with the grassy and rounded appearance of the hills farther west, such as Fionchre and Bloodstone Hill, both mainly built of more easily weathered basalt. A similar contrast is seen between the peaks of igneous rock and the gentle moorland contours of the Torridonian sandstones in the northern part of the island, which form a foreground as seen from Skye. In northern Arran, too, there were great intrusions of igneous rocks. The granite of Goatfell stands out boldly, as seen from Brodick Bay, against a foreground of softer sandstones.

The igneous geology of these western mountains is extremely complex and cannot adequately be discussed here except where it plays a part in determining the characteristic features of a mountain mass. But a few words may perhaps be spared for Ben Nevis (4406 ft.) which, as the highest mountain in Britain, deserves at least a passing mention. Ben Nevis represents a central plug of rock, surrounded by two cylinders of intrusive granite, that is presumably by two cylindrical faults, filled up from below by molten rock. The cap of the mountain core consists of ancient lavas (Old Red Sandstone Period) overlying Dalradian schists, and it is supposed that this central core of rock must have sunk considerably into the molten rock now represented by the granite cylinders. Going east from Ben Nevis, Carn Mor Dearg lies on the inner cylinder of granite and Aonach Mor (3,999 ft.) on the outer cylinder. From the north-west, both types of granite can be distinguished on the route from Fort William to the summit of Ben Nevis.

A similar complex system centres round Glen Etive, with the Buchailles of Etive representing a cap of rhyolites and tuffs on a core surrounded by cylinders of granite. Ben Cruachan lies wholly on one of the granite intrusions and so too does the greater part of the Moor of Rannoch.

From the point of view of their influence on the animal and plant life, a highly important property of the volcanic and igneous rocks is whether or not they are rich in basic substances like lime, potash and magnesia.

The geological classification expresses these features inversely in terms of the amount of the non-basic material, silica, which is present, as shown in the following table :

Table 1

SILICA CONTENT OF IGNEOUS ROCKS

Silica content (per cent)	75-65 *Acid*	65-55 *Intermediate*	55-45 *Basic*	45-35 *Ultra-basic*
PLUTONIC ROCKS	Granite	Syenite Diorite	Gabbro	Peridotite Serpentine
VOLCANIC ROCKS	Pumice Rhyolite Obsidian	Andesite	Basalt	

Biologically, the basic and ultra-basic rocks provide habitats which are generally more interesting largely because they yield richer soil. The favourable feature of a high base content is, it is true, often partly counteracted by the hardness of the rocks and an accompanying resistance to weathering and erosion, as in the examples already given from Skye and Rhum. But many British basalts are not only basic but they also weather especially easily to yield a comparatively rich

PLATE 3

F. Fraser Darling

a. The Paps of Jura from Colonsay: conical mountains resulting from the
denudation of a quartzite ridge

H. F. Alsop

b. Esthwaite Water, North Lancashire: hard rocks (the Langdale Pikes) and
softer ones in foreground. October

PLATE 4

John Markham

Whernside, Yorkshire: limestone pavement, and moorlands on the sandstones
and shales above. November

soil. The Ordovician tuffs are often intermediate in character and may include much andesitic material. In contrast, most British granites contain on an average over 70 per cent of silica and they yield soils which may consist of little but sand and which, as a result, are correspondingly infertile. The biologist thus soon learns to regard granite areas as a distinctive upland type, just as they are geologically and scenically. On the other hand, he has learnt to approach areas dominated by basic or ultra-basic rocks with a certain amount of optimism. Their more varied vegetation and fauna runs parallel with the higher base-status of the soils and rocks, and the latter, indeed, often contain large amounts of bases such as potash, magnesia and iron oxides instead of the lime that prevails in many sedimentary rocks. By analogy with other parts of the world, it is probable that the presence of certain plants and animals on the basic and ultra-basic rocks is associated with these peculiarities of chemical composition of the latter.

The great variety of rock type and of rock arrangement which runs through the Western Islands is less apparent on the Scottish mainland. There the mountain masses of the Grampians are mainly composed of hard and ancient rocks, so greatly contorted by subsequent earth movement that their arrangement is often obscure and it is consequently less easy to describe in broad general terms their relation to mountain structure. They are geologically, for the most part, schists or gneisses (which are, respectively, metamorphosed and distorted shales or sandstones and grits) or finely crystalline igneous rocks. But the simple principles which have been stressed above are generally applicable when the structure of any individual mountain or upland area is considered. Without considering these in detail, it may be noted that the Grampians include three main areas of differing structural type, which have biological interest. Towards the south and west there is an area in which mica-schists predominate. This is a rock which weathers easily, yielding an open and uniform soil. It is marked by a group of characteristic and somewhat lumpy, grass-covered mountains lying roughly along a curved line between Ben Lawers, Ben Doireann and Ben Alder, which possess a well-recognised biological type.

The chief contrast in the Grampians is, however, between the eastern and western halves of the country. The former, exemplified particularly by the Cairngorms, is mainly a high though deeply dissected plateau, which constitutes the greatest continuous area of high ground in the British Isles. The Cairngorms are evidently in the early stages of a new erosion cycle, and their typical outlines, already discussed in connection with Plate 5, p. 22, contrast remarkably with those of Dartmoor, for example, also a granite mass, but one characterised by land-forms indicating far advanced weathering and erosion (see Pl. XXXI, p. 272).

In the western part of the Highlands, erosion and dissection have proceeded far more effectively, so that more often the mountains are partly isolated peaks or broken ridges. The change has undoubtedly been hastened not only by greater precipitation and glacial erosion in these areas, but also by the presence of numerous faults, running roughly from north-east to south-west, which have offered full play to eroding influences and have given us a series of loch-filled valleys. The most notable of these fault-lines is that of the Great Glen. Nevertheless, in spite of the much greater amount of erosion, the general level of the summits among the western mountains is very uniform and is indicative of that of the original plateau from which they must have been derived.

The Scottish Highlands illustrate very well a point that was emphasised a long time ago by the late Professor J. E. Marr. In general, as upland surfaces recover from disturbances, they will tend to develop systems of gentle slopes and to approach, as Dartmoor is doing, characteristic forms of "subdued relief." Among the upper levels of our British mountain regions it is possible to see a large proportion of land forms which are predominantly those of subdued relief. This implies that these forms must be of great age, for on account of the great hardness of the rocks, it must have taken an enormous time for the outlines to have "softened" in such an extreme manner. From arguments such as these, it may be assumed that the general form of our mountain regions is often ancient, and this usually applies particularly to the positions of the main summits and the river valleys. Superimposed on these ancient features we have also features which are the result of comparatively recent agencies. Foremost among these are the effects of ice and of glaciation.

Much British mountain scenery is that characteristic of a glaciated and ice-eroded country. That there is a marked contrast with other regions will be at once apparent if one compares a typical British upland scene with one, for example, from the Grand Canyon of Colorado.

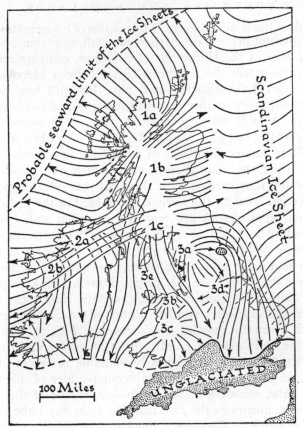

Probable seaward limit of the Ice Sheets

Scandinavian Ice Sheet

1a
1b
1c
2a
2b
3a
3e
3b
3d
3c

100 Miles

UNGLACIATED

FIG. 7.—Ice movements in the British Isles.

GLACIATION

The most striking feature in the recent geological history of the British Isles was the series of great Quaternary Glaciations, which terminated only some 10,000 years ago. For biologists this is a convenient starting-point for recent biological history, but it was scenically of equal or greater importance. In order to obtain a picture of what Britain was like during the Glacial period, we should have to try to imagine it buried beneath a great ice-sheet many hundreds of feet thick, and covering, at its maximum extent, almost the whole of these islands north of the River Thames. The centres of ice formation were the areas with greatest precipitation (then snowfall, now rain), particularly the greater area of the Highlands of Scotland, centring on Rannoch Moor, to a less extent the Southern Uplands from Merrick outwards and the smaller Lake District, and also, but still less, Snowdonia. From these and other smaller centres the ice flowed outwards, though very slowly. A huge existing ice-sheet, that in Antarctica, to-day is still moving at the rate of a yard and a half a day when it reaches the sea as the Ross Barrier, hundreds of miles from its source.

We can trace the main directions in which our British ice-sheets moved, because they carried with them all the soil and rock detritus that had accumulated on the surface of the land in the preceding ages. Any unusual types of rock are readily recognised and, because they have characteristic fossils or special mineral constituents, limestone and igneous or volcanic rocks are especially useful for this purpose. Rocks thus found far from their place of origin are termed erratics, and the photograph in Plate VI, p. 33, shows a well-known example, one of the Norber boulders in West Yorkshire, slate rocks carried by ice from an adjacent valley and left on top of the Carboniferous Limestone which normally overlies the slates (see Fig. 2). In England, erratics of the Shap granite, coming from a small area in the eastern Lake District, have been particularly valuable in tracing the movements of Lake District ice. A magnificent boulder of this rock some ten feet in cube, standing in the main quadrangle of the University of Manchester, illustrates the fact that ice from the Lake District left debris as far south as Cheshire. Farther west there was an ice-flow carrying Galloway granite to Flint and Shropshire. Similar evidence shows that some Lake District ice went east over Stainmoor, leaving boulders of Shap granite as far away as the Yorkshire coast. The accompanying map (Fig. 7), constructed mainly from evidence of this type, shows the main lines of ice movement in Britain during this period. It will be noticed from this map that the ice movements did not always follow the obvious lines of outward radiation. In Lancashire and Wales, for example, the ice was deflected southwards and eastwards by Scottish and Irish sea-borne ice. In Scotland particularly, and to some extent in Yorkshire and Northumbria, the outward-moving ice was dammed up and deflected by Scandinavian ice coming across the North Sea. Moreover, in the partial northerly deflection of the northern ice there is evidence that it overrode mountains 3,000 ft. high.

On the west coast of the Highlands, the ice-marks not only reach this altitude, but, allowing for the depth of adjacent lochs, it can be estimated that the ice-field must at times have been some 4,000 ft. thick. Similarly in the Lake District, where the area of high precipitation is much smaller, the ice-fields were some 2,000 ft. thick. Indeed, on Scafell and Helvellyn the marks of glaciation may be seen up to a height of 2,500 ft. It is not easy to imagine the scale of this ice-covering. The nearest thing to it at present may be the Greenland ice-cap ; that in Antarctica is apparently larger.

Even at its maximum extent, it did not wholly cover the country (see Fig. 7). There could not have been much ice south of the Thames, and Dartmoor seems to have been quite unglaciated. Moreover, the highest mountains, and, indeed, many of the lower outlying ones, projected through the ice as *nunataks.* They can often be recognised by their greater altitude and bolder shape, which contrasts markedly with that of the lower, rounded and glaciated hills. In the later stages of the Ice Age, at least, considerable areas of the Southern Pennines may have been generally ice-free, though no doubt supplied with local snowfields. The main ice-flow at this time seems to have been deflected by the Howgill and Bowland Fells, or westward down into the Cheshire Plain. The existence of ice-free areas makes the comparison with Greenland more valuable and it allows us to assume that there were probably at least some plants and animals there.

In their movements, the ice-sheets not only scoured away existing soils and rock debris, but they also scraped away rock. Thus in glaciated regions, every projecting rock tends to be smoothed and scratched on the exposed side, even if it retains rough surfaces on the lee side. Such rocks are termed " roches moutonnées," and often they allow us to infer the direction of local ice movements even better than do erratics. Although it did not invariably do so, the moving ice tended to follow existing valley lines and hence these were scoured out and deepened, particularly towards the valley heads where the ice was normally deeper. Often rock basins were formed which now contain lakes (Pl. 8, p. 27). The form of these glaciated valleys (and of the lakes) is very characteristic: they tend to be " canal-sided " in plan and U-shaped in section. The effect of these great ice-sheets is not only to deepen and broaden the main valleys but also in doing so to remove the lower and gentler slopes on each side. Thus spurs are cut off and lateral valleys are cut short, while the lateral streams they contain now tend to enter the main valley by sudden rapids or water-falls. " Hanging valleys " of this type and " truncated spurs " are a characteristic feature of British mountain scenery. The photograph of Loch Avon in Plate 8, p. 27, shows a fine example of a hanging valley, while truncated spurs can be seen in Plate 10, p. 65.

Additional results of this form of erosion are, first, that vast quantities of detritus are removed and scattered over the adjacent country; and, secondly, that the existing forms of low relief are " sharpened " as it were and made more mountainous in aspect (see Pl. 23, p. 160). The gentle plateau-like profiles of some of our mountain areas, as seen from a distance, give no hint as to the steepness and wildness of the ridges and valleys they prove to contain. At the same time, the removal of pre-existing soils and gentle slopes has generally left the valleys in what is essentially a " montane " condition of bare rock or rock detritus in marked contrast to the deep and long-established soils that must have prevailed in pre-glacial conditions.

As to the materials left behind by the ice, the most obvious are usually coarse rock-waste in the valleys, often material which had fallen from adjacent hills on to the ice during the last stages of its retreat. The effects of these last remaining valley glaciers were com-parable indeed to those observed in existing high alpine regions, but they were insignificant as compared with those of the great inland ice-sheets. The detritus accumulated by these sheets in their ground moraines and left behind when they finally melted, has largely deter-mined the appearance of the existing British lowlands and indeed of the lower valleys, obliterating all pre-existing soils or underlying rock, and often smothering the pre-glacial features under layers of " drift " 30 or 40 ft. thick (Pl. V, p. 32). Although it may contain rock-waste of almost every type, the drift usually consists of some form of boulder clay in which ice-worn and scratched boulders are mixed with what is really rock-flour. The prominent clay fraction of this drift, whatever its general texture, usually suffices to make it " set " readily, and accordingly it often tends to be impervious to water. Not only has this type of material been scattered to great depths all over the lowlands adjacent to our mountain areas, but, in thinner sheets, it will also often be found to be plastered over almost any area of low relief in the mountains themselves. Consequently most gentle slopes in the upland districts, if not left scoured clean by ice action, are covered with drift which is often of a clayey nature.

PLATE 5

John Markham

The Lairig Ghru, Inverness-shire: showing the Cairngorms as a dissected plateau and a foreground vegetation of native pine-forest and heather-moor. May

PLATE 6

Cyril Newberry

Alport Castles, Derbyshire: the largest land-slip in Britain. July 1946

These drifts and morainic deposits usually contain material carried from a distance and, like the erratics, unrelated in characters to the locally underlying rock. Plate 9, p. 65, for example, shows some glacial ground moraines of a non-calcareous nature bearing moorland vegetation, although the underlying rock is limestone, on which such vegetation does not normally occur. A similar effect is clearly shown in Plate 17, p. 96, where drift overlying limestone has blocked up the drainage so thoroughly that peat, bearing moorland vegetation, has developed over the limestone. Of course the reverse can also take place. In many places, calcareous clays have been distributed over non-calcareous strata, and thus as a general rule considerable caution is necessary in glaciated regions in attempting to relate soil or vegetation types to underlying rock.

Of course, at the close of the glacial period, there was a great deal of resorting of the rubbish left behind by the melting ice. The vast quantities of moving water which must have resulted during the melting process obviously redistributed the morainic materials on an enormous scale. Consequently to-day we often see streams running down valleys that now seem far too large for them or issuing across deltas which, quite obviously, they could never have produced in their present condition. A particularly striking condition at that time must have been the numerous large lakes held up among the ice-sheets, often in what are now quite unexpected places. At least one of the high limestone hills in Yorkshire, Moughton Fell, has lake silts on its summit, and such sediments or delta cones deposited in water are not uncommon on the flanks of the wider valleys. A classical British example, Lake Pickering, lying to the south of the Cleveland Hills in North Yorkshire, is associated with the name of the late Professor P. F. Kendall, who showed how the existence of the ice-dammed lake could be recognised. While we are not concerned here with the detailed history of these bodies of water, it should be recognised that they left behind various sediments, including impervious ones, that helped to create local stagnation of the drainage system ; and, as we shall see, so gave a definite character to the sites they had occupied.

The great glaciation merits more attention than we can really give it, and this not only because it moulded our scenery. It is far more important because it represents a characteristic phase in the history of our mountains and moorlands as we now know them, as well as the agency which has perhaps more than anything else determined their present biological character. Whatever may ultimately prove to be the underlying cause of such an ice-age, it cannot effectively develop, as Sir George Simpson has emphasised, without the heavy precipitation (then as snow, now as rain) that characterises British mountains. From this point of view, the Ice Age seems to be as characteristic of British highlands as is the present climate. From the historical point of view, the Ice Age is important because it means that the starting-point from which our present fauna and flora is derived must have been largely an arctic-alpine group of organisms. From still a third point of view—of particular interest to the botanist—the glacial epoch left behind it an upland country largely sterilised by the removal of existing soils and fertile deposits. Some areas, such as large parts of the Hebrides and of Sutherland, were in fact left sterile, and even to-day remain as an almost bare and undulating rock surface occupied only by small tarns and moorland of the bleakest type. This is a common condition among the mountains. But speaking generally, even among the mountains and particularly among the foothills round each mountain group, areas of gentle slope were usually plastered over with clayey drifts or sediments. The result was a great deterioration of the natural drainage in many areas. Even the limestone hills, as we have seen above, Plates 9, p. 64 and 17, p. 96, though naturally extremely porous, often suffered in this way, and in many cases cannot be superficially distinguished from the non-calcareous rocks around them in this respect. Elsewhere, and particularly in the valleys, the erosion of the lower slopes by ice and by glacial streams left behind a sharpened relief of a much more montane character and, incidentally, often paved the way for a new cycle of erosion.

RECENT EROSION

The forms of the mountains we see to-day are clearly the results of three agencies—of the original rock structure as modified by large-scale earth movements, of the long continued erosion which, acting on the original structure, has fixed the positions and outlines of the main valleys and summits, and, lastly, of the sharpening of land forms and the removal of pre-glacial screes and soils by ice action. As a habitat for living organisms, the surface of a mountain is as important as its skeleton, and this is affected not only by the legacy of slope and structure already described, but still more by the recent or post-glacial effects of erosion. Speaking generally, the upland surfaces are either physically *stable* or *unstable*, and it is the large proportion of unstable surfaces which is particularly characteristic of upland areas. Nevertheless, even the stable surfaces, those more comparable in slope and form with lowland areas, show peculiarities, for they are often rock surfaces, either scraped clean during glaciation (as in the Northern Scottish examples just mentioned) or sometimes, like limestone pavements, composed of rock which yields little or no soil on weathering. Even the soil-covered stable surfaces are often areas covered by poor glacial drifts or with impervious rock strata beneath, and now mostly peat-covered.

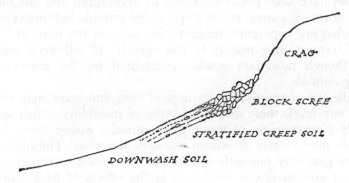

CRAG

BLOCK SCREE

STRATIFIED CREEP SOIL

DOWNWASH SOIL

FIG. 8.—Arrangement of main zones below a rock outcrop.

The unstable surfaces naturally tend to lie along the main lines of erosion, and they include both the places over-steepened by ice action as well as those showing the immediate effects of stream erosion. The most widespread type of unstable surface is the steep scree-slope with its capping of crag. This generally shows a gradation of form and composition such as is illustrated in Fig. 8. The upper part is usually the steepest, and consists of coarser detritus, while the lower part shows finer detritus and gentler slope. As on any steep slope, rainwash leads to the accumulation of the finest materials on the lower parts.

The downward movement of material continues long after an angle of primary stability (usually between 30° and 40°) is reached ; and there are numerous interesting manifestations of this movement.

The larger stones, in particular, are usually persistent " creepers," expanding more on the lower side when the temperature rises and contracting more on the upper margin when cooling takes place. They often continue to move downwards long after the rest of the surface has been stabilised by vegetation.   When such stones are elongated in shape they generally tend to progress with their long axes more or less parallel to the slope, as may be seen in Plate 25, p. 208. Although the larger boulders move most persistently on partly stabilised screes, they usually move more slowly than the finer material on loose scree slopes, where the finer materials often accumulate around the upper side of the boulders, giving a step-like arrangement. Obstacles such as tufts of grass lead to a similar effect, so that some form of terracing is particularly characteristic of steep mountain slopes, even after they have been partly stabilised by vegetation, and one has only to look down on a steep grassy slope under suitable lighting conditions to see what are apparently innumerable more or less parallel " sheep-track " terraces, due mainly to the agencies of soil-creep and rain-wash, though nowadays much accentuated by the movements of grazing animals.

While the characteristic features of crag and scree may occur at almost any level, there are other types of instability which are par-ticularly characteristic of the higher altitudes above 2,000 ft., and generally most clearly shown on the high summits. The high moun-tains are generally but little affected by the action of running water, and their erosion is due far more to the effects of frost and snow, sometimes collectively distinguished as *nivation*.

The surface of the higher and steeper summits is commonly covered with rock detritus, sometimes to a depth of several feet (Pl. III., p. 12). This material, often called mountain-top detritus, is formed by the disintegration of the native rock by the action of frost. The size of the individual fragments, as in the case of screes, depends largely upon the hardness and the physical character of the underlying rocks.

The frost detritus or mountain-top detritus is the most characteristic of summit surfaces. Its appearance is well illustrated in a number of the plates included here (Pls. 11a, p. 80; 12, p. 81; 25, p. 208) and its loose surface indicates the constant struggle between the stabilising effect of vegetation and the instability due to wind exposure and the action of frost, snow and gravity. In the plates given here, the striking instability of very slight slopes at high levels is clearly shown. In the

PLATE 7

ENGLISH LAKE DISTRICT

B. A. Crouch

b. Little Arros Moor, Coniston: a home of Neolithic man

B. A. Crouch

a. Pier's Gill, Wasdale: a high gully leading to a gorge below a hanging valley

PLATE 8

John Markham

Loch Avon, Banffshire: a glaciated valley showing ice-smoothed slopes and a hanging valley examples pictured in Plates 11a, p. 80 and 25, p. 208 the slopes have an inclination of only about 10° to 15°, although the surfaces show little tendency to be fixed by vegetation. A slope of 30° at lower altitudes would quickly become completely covered by vegetation and hence more thoroughly stabilised.

The instability of the surfaces at high altitudes is not confined to those that are predominantly or wholly stony. It is equally evident on many of the more rounded mountains (" moels ") and on those on which the friable nature of the underlying rock has permitted some soil formation. Here solifluction effects may become extremely marked. When soil highly charged with water first freezes and then melts, the expansion accompanying freezing makes the soil very unstable when it thaws, so that downward movement on even the gentlest of slopes becomes possible, the semi-fluid surface slipping easily over the frozen sub-soil. On steeper slopes, large volumes of muddy detritus may be stripped off the flank of a mountain through this agency, and at high levels soil-covered slopes, however slight, almost invariably show signs of movement produced in this way (Pl. XIb, p. 60). The most frequent signs are different forms of terracing, and these occur on quite gentle slopes and where vegetation is present. The swollen soil behaves almost as a series of fluid drops, each partly restrained by the turf, which prevents complete movement, bounding the whole on the lower side in the form of a step, the earth being exposed on the upper flatter part.

Of the reality and importance of these influences, no one who has frequented mountain summits in spring can have any doubt. The mountain soils at that time are " puffed up," as it were, so that the foot sinks deeply into them. The frequent freezing and thawing has the effect of mixing the soil surface, and, in particular, it causes frost-heaving by which the stones present are extruded, so that the surface is commonly more stony than the material beneath.

The processes seen at work on the higher mountain summits bear a considerable resemblance to those observed in arctic regions. On flat or nearly flat surfaces in the Arctic, solifluction effects are associated with the production of curious " stone polygons " in which a central area of mud, often associated with smaller rock detritus, is surrounded by a polygonal boundary of larger stones. Possibly because of the prevalent slopes, polygons of this sort are not very common on British mountains, although they have been recorded by Professor J. W.

Gregory from Merrick in the Southern Uplands and by Dr. J. B. Simpson from Ben Iadain in Morven. An interesting area may be seen at about 3,100 ft. on the broad saddle connecting Foel Grach with Carnedd Llewellyn. This shows that the polygons are found only on a flat surface, giving way to " stone stripes " as soon as the

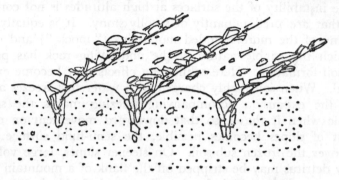

FIG. 9.—Distribution of materials below " stone stripes." (Diagrammatic.)

surface acquires an appreciable slope. Stone stripes, or the somewhat similar " striped screes " which appear in coarser and more sloping material, were first described in this country by Professor S. E. Hollingworth from examples in the Lake District, where, once one learns to look for them, they are not uncommon. The larger stones collect in rows parallel to the slope as is shown in Fig. 9. The stone stripes, like polygons, overlie soil, and presumably the stones have been extruded from the soil by the movements due to freezing and thawing. Apparently both polygons and stripes occur where frozen layers of soil persist below the thawed surface. The British mountain polygons and stone stripes are often quite small. Those shown in Plate XI, p. 60, were only about a foot apart, though where the movements are on a larger scale they may be three or four times this size. There are especially striking ones on the eastern face of Yr Elen in Snowdonia which can easily be seen from a distance of over a mile.

Many of these solifluction areas illustrate the general feature that the unstable areas on high mountains are often as characteristic of gentle slopes as of steep slopes. Thus the average angle at which an equivalent degree of stability is reached seems to be much less at 2,500 ft. and upwards than at, say, 1,000 ft. No doubt the slower growth of vegetation at higher altitudes also contributes to this condition.

Nevertheless, if it is invariably the case, the difference must have a considerable influence on the shape of a mountain. Wherever the rock structure allows comparable rates of weathering, we might perhaps expect to get a shape of the type illustrated in Fig. 4, rather than the simple cone. The preliminary steepening of the lower slopes must, of course, be due to more remote causes.

There are probably other processes by which rock and soil movement may be brought about at high levels, though they do not seem to have been much studied in this country. Some are undoubtedly associated with places where snow lies long. Where such a slope persists below a region of surface instability, rock-waste may move rapidly downward across the snow surface, collecting in a band at its base. Further, long-persistent snow-banks almost always terminate below in erosion channels, which, at the higher levels, may give permanent drainage channels cutting back towards the mountain crest. The interest of these features is not only biological (see p. 227), but it lies also in their possible bearing on the origin of the high-level corries (or cwms or cirques) so often found in the larger British mountains. In the extreme form these are rock basins and undoubtedly relics of the small high-level glaciers and *nevé* which must have lingered on for long after the main ice-sheets had passed away. Corries seem to be most frequent on the east of a main summit or ridge, and it may be that in the first place their position was the result of a semi-permanent snow-bank which started an erosion system. In the later stages it has been supposed that the upper *nevé* exerts a plucking action on the frost-shattered mountain face, through the periodic filling and downward contraction of the bergschrund, if one may use this term in such a case. In this way continuous over-steepening of the head of the erosion system may have resulted in the formation of the crags encircling the corrie. It seems probable that corrie-formation was most vigorous during and just after the Ice Age, but as it usually lies above the other main erosion effects of the ice-sheets it may be appropriate to regard it as an extreme effect of persistent snow-lie.

In attempting to summarise what has been obtained from this survey, it becomes clear that physical instability is the most noticeable feature of upland surfaces, and it is equally evidently a chief characteristic of the high-level or montane region—although it also accompanies any steep slope as well as the borders of active erosion systems such as streams. Physically stable areas in the uplands differ little from lowland areas, except in other features such as those of climatic origin.

We also see that British mountains are often likely to show an upper zone of comparatively gentle slopes, representing the ancient land forms, moulded long ago, but often kept alive or unstable through the agencies we call nivation. The lower slopes have often been over-steepened in comparatively recent times as a result of glaciation or of the extensive erosion which must have been associated with the melting of the ice. This common plan, if we may call it so, results in the appearance of numerous rather round-topped mountains, although it is modified in innumerable ways as a result of the varieties of rock which make up the mountain blocks and of the different sorts of bedding planes which may be found in different areas.

There is still another way of looking at these matters. The present cycle of erosion as it affects the upland surfaces may be considered to have started at the end of the Ice Age. The upland surface at that time, except where covered by drifts or morainic materials, must have been very different from what it is to-day. It must have been mostly exposed rock which, presumably under the sub-Arctic post-glacial conditions, quickly developed frost-shattering and the characteristic erosion forms found to-day in the Arctic and at high altitudes. To-day much of the corresponding surface is soil- or peat-covered, and only the montane or unstable areas preserve what must have been a wide-spread condition in the immediate post-glacial period. It will be seen, therefore, if this argument is correct, that the study of the montane areas is likely to be of especial interest. We shall expect to find that the biological character of the unstable areas is widely different from that found elsewhere and perhaps in some respects reminiscent of a condition that was more widespread in post-glacial times.

CHAPTER 3

CLIMATE

THE differences between upland habitats and those of the lowlands are only partly structural. Partly they are climatic and this
aspect must now be considered. British mountains are only of moderate
size but they lie near the sea and across the path of the strong Atlantic
breezes from the west. For this reason, wind and cloud and rain play
a large part in the weather conditions and they combine to give a
characteristic " atmosphere " to British mountain scenery, something
of which is conveyed in the photograph of Glen Einich in Plate VIII,
p. 49. Equally familiar to inhabitants and noticed by many visitors
is the building up of evening cloud after sunset (Pl. XXIX, p. 256),
while even in the finest weather the day is likely to break beneath a
curtain of morning mist, well shown in the charming photograph of
Llyn Padarn, Plate 10, p. 65. The visual impressions we thus carry
with us can readily be confirmed from the precise data collected by
meteorologists, and to them we may now turn.

We are fortunate in having detailed records which enable us to
assess these effects over long periods and thus to present them as the
main features of mountain climate in Britain. They were made between
1884 and 1903, when an observatory was maintained near the top of
Ben Nevis (4,406 ft.), and though they thus give the extreme climatic
limits for British mountains, they enable other more scattered observations to be checked and utilised.

In the first place, the records confirm the impression that strong
winds are frequent. During thirteen years, an average of 261 gales
a year with wind velocities exceeding 50 miles an hour was recorded
at the summit of the mountain. This large number should be compared with the conditions at sea-level, when, even on the exposed
western seaboard, few places average annually more than forty winds
of such a velocity. The comparison between montane and lowland
conditions may, however, be made in another form. A more recent
estimate of wind-speeds has been made on Crossfell (2,930 ft.), a much
lower summit in the Northern Pennines. There, it was estimated that
the average wind velocity was at least twice that prevailing in the
adjacent lowlands, a result comparable to similar estimates on Ben
Nevis.

The Ben Nevis records also serve to illustrate the cloudiness of the mountain sky, for during the years of observation the summit was clear of mist and cloud for less than 30 per cent of the time and, as the table shows, had correspondingly low figures for exposure to sunshine (Table 2, p. 33). These are, however, only different aspects of a more fundamental feature, the great humidity of the atmosphere. The average relative humidity of the air on Ben Nevis was 94 per cent of saturation with water vapour, showing little variation throughout the year, except in June, when it fell temporarily to 90 per cent, still an exceptionally high average figure.

As might be expected, this high atmospheric humidity was associated with high rainfall. Over a long period this averages 161 in. annually at the summit, and it was rather higher during the thirteen years of comparative observations given in Table 2, p. 33. The maximum recorded was 242 in. in 1909, and as much falls on Ben Nevis during the three " dry " months, April, May and June, as would represent the whole annual rainfall in Eastern England. High rainfall is, of course, a general feature of British mountains. Thus there is the well-known example of the Seathwaite District in Cumberland where Stye Head Tarn, east of Great Gable (2,900 ft.) has an annual average of 153 inches with a recorded maximum of 250 inches in 1928. The computed average for Glas Llyn (2,500 ft.), 500 yards north-east of the summit of the Snowdon ridge, is 198 inches. The Snowdon summit, Y-Wyddfa, in fact, competes with the head of Glen Garry (in Western Inverness), east of Sgurr na Ciche (3,140 ft.), for the distinction of being the wettest place in the British Isles. Both are considered to have an average annual rainfall of some 200 inches. Ben Nevis or Scafell and its Pike, have more of the character of isolated peaks, so that the prevalent winds can slip around them and less rain results.

The last feature of the Ben Nevis records to which attention must be directed is the range of temperatures, also given in Table 2, where they are compared with those at Fort William (at the base of the mountain).

In this table, the figures given at the foot of the columns for the year are averages in the case of temperature, and annual totals for hours of sunshine and rainfall. As there are many summits between 2,000 and 2,900 ft. to the south and west of Fort William, the rainfall there is already much higher than it would be on the outermost sea-

PLATE V

W. H. Pearsall

Glacial drift exposed in a gravel-pit, Carnforth, West Lancashire, including gravel, sand and boulder clay. The variable size of the rounded boulders is characteristic of material transported in the lower part of an ice-sheet. The white boulders are of Carboniferous limestone, the darker ones of Carboniferous sandstone or occasionally of slate

PLATE VI

John Markham

The Norber boulders, West Yorkshire. Slaty erratics transported by ice from an adjacent valley and left perched on Carboniferous limestone which normally overlies the slate coast, and sunshine records are accordingly lower, so that the contrast between the lowland and montane conditions is much diminished.

Table 2

METEOROLOGICAL DATA OVER THE SAME
I 3 - YEAR PERIOD

	Ben Nevis (4406 ft.)			Fort William (30 ft.)		
Month	Temperature (°F)	Sunshine (hours)	Rainfall (inches)	Temperature (°F)	Sunshine (hours)	Rainfall (inches)
Jan.	23·4	19.6	19·0	38·7	24·1	8·7
Feb.	24·1	41·9	15·1	38·8	49·7	6·9
Mar.	24·3	59·8	16·8	40·4	95·2	7·0
Apr.	28·3	82·5	9·6	45·1	139·5	4·0
May	33·2	128·3	8·3	49·7	180·1	3·5
June	40·0	124·7	7·8	55·4	173·2	3·5
July	41·7	90·3	11·3	57·1	131·0	4·6
Aug.	40·8	58·9	14·0	56·5	111·4	6·9
Sept.	38·0	58·1	16·9	53·2	98·5	8·2
Oct.	31·4	46·4	17·8	46·6	75·2	7·9
Nov.	29·5	30·0	16·0	44·0	28·5	7·5
Dec.	25·7	17·1	21·2	40·1	12·7	11·3
Year	31·7	757·6	170·8	47·1	1119·1	80·0

The temperature figures given in the table are for mean monthly temperatures and they bring out very clearly the striking difference in temperature conditions which higher altitude entails. At the summit, the mean monthly temperatures are at or well below the freezing point of water for eight months in the year. Even during the four " summer " months, June to September, the mean monthly temperatures barely rise above those experienced during winter at the foot of the mountain. The temperature conditions are therefore severe.

It may justifiably be urged that this represents the extreme case among British mountains and that we need a more general method of representing the usual effects of temperature. Roughly speaking, an increase of altitude of 300 ft. entails a fall in the mean temperatures of about 1° F. Assuming now that 2,000 ft. represents an approximate lower limit to the mountain zone in Britain, we can obtain representative temperatures at this altitude by taking the average of the Ben Nevis and the Fort William temperatures and adding 0·6° F. to reduce the values approximately to those at 2,000 ft. The results are included in Fig. 10.

It is interesting to note, however, that essentially similar results can be obtained for different parts of the British uplands using the varying records of temperatures made at various altitudes and calculating from them the probable values at 2,000 ft. The following table summarises the mean temperatures so obtained for January and July :

Table 3

Station	Altitude	Mean temperatures °F at named altitude		Calculated temperatures °F at 2,000 ft.	
		Jan.	July	Jan.	July
Ben Nevis	4406	23·4	41·7	31·8	50·1
Dun Fell	2735	29	49	31·4	51·4
Moor House	1840	33	53	32·5	52·5
Braemar	1111	34·9	55·1	31·9	52·1

The Dun Fell and Moor House stations are two set up in the Northern Pennines by Prof. Gordon Manley, for which the data are less complete, though it will be seen that they suggest that the temperature conditions are essentially similar to those at Braemar, which represents the Eastern Scottish Highlands. The conditions at 2,000 ft. are generally similar therefore, with lower summer temperatures in the west. They may perhaps be regarded as sub-Arctic, resembling those just above sea-level in South Iceland.

The graphs in Figure 10 thus serve to illustrate what are for practical purposes the upper and lower limits of temperature for the British mountain climate. In effect, the increases in altitude produce little relative change in the levels of summer and winter temperatures but they sink, as it were, the whole temperature curve, in relation to any temperature level which may be chosen. Such a level, for example, is that represented in the graph by the horizontal line at 42° F. This level is given, because it is a temperature level which has been used

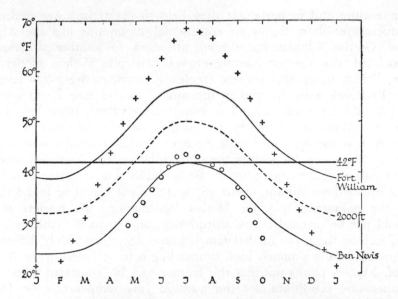

FIG. 10.—Mean monthly temperature in °F. at Fort William and at the summit of Ben Nevis (4,406 ft.)—continuous lines. The broken line gives calculated figures at 2,000 feet. The circles are summer temperatures in West Greenland and the crosses are data for Vermont (U.S.A.).

by meteorologists to represent the mean temperature above which the normal crop-plants of cool temperate climates start to grow. While the choice of such a level is somewhat arbitrary and does not by any means deal satisfactorily with the physiological problems involved, it is convenient to use this convention for the purpose of making comparisons. We could thus estimate that for plants of the type named above, the growing season at Fort William would be about eight months, say 243 days, while at 2000 ft. it would be about 142 days, and at the summit of Ben Nevis it would be quite negligible.

One of the difficulties of using such a simple method of treatment is that the higher summer temperatures at low altitudes have also a strong and cumulative effect on the rate of plant growth, as indeed do other features of the temperature cycle, such as freedom from frost. Thus lower summer temperatures markedly reduce the intensity of growth and hence the total annual amount is also very greatly affected. The strong westerly winds on British mountains tend to regulate the temperature and in particular they help to maintain lower summer temperatures than obtain on continental mountains like the Alps. Prof. Gordon Manley has drawn attention to another difference associated with the temperature curves. In spite of their moderate size, British mountains become treeless at comparatively low levels, usually below 2,000 ft., and in the same way the zone up to which useful cultivation can extend is comparatively low, often less than 1000 ft. While this is partly due to the operation of other climatic factors, it is also associated with the nature of the annual temperature cycle. If we were to go to some place such as New England, where the mean annual temperature in the lowlands is of the same order as that in Northern Britain, about 46° to 47° F., it would be found that on the mountains, e.g. on Mount Washington, the treeless zone would not be reached below altitudes of some 5000 ft. Although in Switzerland the mean annual temperatures are more widely different from our own, a similarly high timber-line is to be found in the Alps. Prof. Manley points out that this feature can be associated with the temperature conditions, for the average July temperature on Dun Fell (2,735 ft.) in Northern England is almost the same, about 48° F., as that on Mount Washington in New England at 6,284 ft.

A biological explanation of this difference is seen in the *form* of the temperature curves, and to illustrate the fact an additional temperature curve is given in Fig. 10. This is a typical curve for the lowlands of New England (Vermont) taken from Prof. Manley's paper. The effect of adjusting this for changes in altitude would be to lower it to an appropriate extent. To give the equivalent curve for a height of 4406 ft., that of Ben Nevis, would require a reduction throughout of 14·7° F. Even if this were done, a large part of the annual temperature cycle would remain above 42° F. There would be a growing season at this altitude of at least 60 days and a mean July temperature of 53·8° F. Thus a considerable amount of plant growth, even from crop-plants, would be possible under New England conditions, while none could be expected with the temperature cycles obtaining in the Western Highlands of Scotland.

This method of considering the matter emphasises the importance of the low summer temperatures in British mountains as an obstacle to plant growth and as a feature which distinguishes them from localities of comparable altitude in continental areas either in North America or in Europe. In fact if we wish to find a climate equivalent in summer to that of our high mountain zone in temperature and in humidity, we must go to places in Arctic regions, preferably to those near the sea and remarkable for their frequent summer fogs, like West Greenland. But even these only rarely attain the constantly high air humidity which was observed on Ben Nevis. This, it is true, probably represents the extreme in Britain, though, judging from the rainfall records, it must be closely paralleled on the other main mountain masses in the west. Farther east and notably in the Cairngorms, where rainfall is less, air humidity is probably more variable and hence more like the Arctic stations of which we have record.

It is rather striking that the low summer temperatures found on British mountains are not associated with the presence of permanent snow, although on the highest peaks drifts may persist throughout the summer on north-facing slopes and in deep gullies. Two such drifts are well known and almost permanent, one on the north face of Ben Nevis and the other in the great corrie of Braeriach (4,246 ft.) in the Cairngorms. The latter, after having been known for some fifty years, finally disappeared for a time in the summer of 1935.

On Ben Nevis the top is usually free from accumulated snow for about 75 days in the year, though some snow may fall on about one day in ten, even in July and August. Thus, though even the highest summits are below the permanent snow-line, they are evidently very near to it. In these circumstances it might be expected that the extent and duration of " snow-lie " in early summer would have a good deal of influence on the distribution of living organisms in the highest montane zone. No detailed study of this matter has, however, yet been made in Britain.

Just as the temperature conditions differ very greatly in Britain and in the Alps, so there is also a considerable difference in other conditions. Speaking generally, British uplands lie wholly within the range of altitudes in which rainfall rises as the height increases. At higher altitudes, however (above about 5,000 ft. in these latitudes), rainfall would diminish with further increases in elevation, and this is the condition obtaining in the Alps and Pyrenees. Further, the lower layers of air are denser as well as more humid. Hence they absorb light strongly, and so higher altitudes receive much larger proportions of the sun's energy, particularly of the ultra-violet and blue rays.

Thus Alpine conditions imply not only lower precipitation of rain or snow, but also a clearer atmosphere and intense insolation. The average summer temperatures and the illumination are much higher in the Alps, but they are accompanied by the possibility of strong radiation at night and by the certainty of great diurnal and seasonal variations of temperature, in great contrast to the small variations of temperature observed on British mountains. It is evidently better to distinguish upland climatic conditions in Britain as montane rather than alpine, and, as we have already noted, there is a great similarity between these montane conditions in summer and the corresponding features of Arctic coastal regions.

RAINFALL

The influence of the high humidity that is characteristic of British hills is not easily assessed. Atmospheric humidity undoubtedly has a considerable direct effect on plant and animal life, so that most biologists would be able to point to facts of distribution, such as the greater abundance of mosses and lichens in the western hills, which can reasonably be attributed to greater air humidity. But climatic humidity expresses itself not only through its direct effects on the distribution of living organisms but indirectly by affecting the character of the soil, and in the British Isles these indirect effects are extremely important. The only climatic data available for examining them on a sufficiently extensive scale are the rainfall data, and these we must now consider to see how far it is possible to use them in defining climatic limits. In doing this it will be necessary to adopt the following rather rough method of analysing climatic effects.

In the southern part of the Pennines, and probably generally among their eastern foothills, the average annual loss of water by evaporation is equivalent to a rainfall of about 18 in. This figure has been obtained partly as the estimate of the average amount of water lost by evaporation from a 6-ft. Standard tank, and the figures given in Table 4 are actually monthly estimates of the average losses so obtained (as inches of rain). But a similar annual figure (about 18 in.) can be obtained by comparing the rainfall over a given river basin with the " run-off " down the river, and access to much unpublished data has shown that this figure is fairly representative for the eastern Pennines. The difference between rainfall and run-off (assuming no loss into the ground or taking an average over many years) gives the net amount lost by evaporation, and we shall assume it to be distributed seasonally as in the figures given. It may be noted in passing that the problem of estimating evaporation losses may be considerably more complex than this. Empirical formulae have been worked out for estimating these losses in which it is usually assumed that they increase with increasing rainfall as well as with rising temperature.

Table 4 gives, in addition to the monthly figures for evaporation, the average monthly rainfall, also in inches, for two adjacent stations. One of them, Doncaster, lying in the Plain of York and at an altitude of 25 ft., represents a typical lowland station in Eastern England, with an average rainfall of about 25 in. per annum. The other, Woodhead, lies among the high Pennines and is surrounded by " cotton-grass " moors. It therefore represents fairly well the climate of these high moorlands, with an annual average rainfall of about 50 in. The actual figure on the hills is probably more, rather than less, than this, say 55 in.

Table 4

MONTHLY EVAPORATION
AND RAINFALL IN INCHES AT DONCASTER
AND WOODHEAD

						MONTH						
	1.	2.	3.	4.	5.	6.	7.	8.	9.	10.	11.	12.
Evaporation	0·1	0·4	0·9	1·8	2·8	3·3	2·9	2·2	1·8	0·9	0·3	0·2
Rainfall Doncaster	1·8	1·6	1·6	*1·9*	2·7	*2·3*	2·7	3·1	*1·8*	3·6	2·0	2·9
Woodhead	4·1	3·5	3·7	3·1	3·4	3·7	4·2	4·4	4·6	5·8	5·1	4·6

The figures show very plainly that there is *no* month in the year when the average rainfall at Woodhead does not exceed the evaporation. In contrast, at Doncaster, there are five months when evaporation approximately equals or exceeds rainfall (the rainfall figures in Table 4 are italicised when this is the case). Consider the implication of these facts, and particularly their effects on soil conditions. During the summer, at a station like Doncaster, the soil gradually dries out.

This means that the water in the soil interspaces is replaced by air. The drains cease to run until the autumn, when rainfall once more exceeds evaporation and the water-level begins to rise in the soil.

At a station like Woodhead, on the other hand, the same filling of the soil interspaces will take place in winter, but the soils will have no opportunity of recovering and of drying out in summer, for any evaporation will be balanced by the higher rainfall. It follows, therefore, that as a whole, soils will usually be waterlogged in a rainfall of the Woodhead type and only those on considerable slopes will have a chance of becoming drained and well aerated. We may thus recognise that in a rainfall of this type and magnitude there will be a strong tendency towards *bog-formation*, and it may perhaps be useful to note that in Britain a rainfall of 50 to 55 in. (that is, about three times the evaporation figures) will apparently suffice to give conditions favourable to bog-formation. This is a useful measure, even if a rough one, of the effective humidity of an upland climate.

The influence of high rainfall is exerted in another manner also. When rain falls on soil and percolates through it, the water naturally carries away in solution and into the drainage system any soluble mineral salts present in the soil. These will include most of the substances valuable as plant food as well as the lime which prevents a soil from becoming sour. The process is called *leaching*, and the rate of leaching will obviously depend very largely on the rainfall. When this only just equals the evaporation losses there will be little or no leaching, but the higher the rainfall becomes in comparison with evaporation, the more rapid leaching will be. Very roughly, then, we shall expect little or no leaching when the rainfall is about 18 in. per annum, but where the annual rainfall is 54 in. we may expect leaching to proceed at about twice the rate expected under a rainfall of 36 in. It will be realised that these rough comparisons as to leaching apply only to porous soils through which water can freely percolate and there is obviously no need to stress the numerical comparison, although it serves to emphasise the high rate of leaching found in upland areas, where a rainfall exceeding 54 in. per annum is common.

The analysis carried out in the preceding paragraphs gives us one method of obtaining a significant boundary of humidity which must have pronounced biological effects. It is perhaps worth noting that a similar figure, an annual rainfall of about 55 in., has been obtained by noting the rainfall at upland sites where reclamation of moorland has proved just possible or has failed. If allowance is made for the nature and porosity of the underlying rock, this is roughly the altitude at which habitation ceases, and in the northern Pennines and eastern Cumberland it is stated to lie very near to the point at which rainfall exceeds 55 in. Of course, this is an extremely indirect method of approaching such a problem, for the result must be greatly affected by the nature of the prevailing occupations in the district examined; nevertheless in this particular instance the relation is clearly one which operates through soil effects, so that it agrees with the conclusion already reached in suggesting that the rainfall indicated is one of distinct biological significance.

The examples already quoted indicate that high rainfall and high altitudes are associated in a general manner, much depending on slopes and topography. No hard-and-fast rule can be given as to the increase of rainfall in relation to altitude, but it is useful to note what is commonly observed in different parts of upland Britain. Along the western margins an annual rainfall of 35 in. is generally found near sea-level, while one of 55 in. would occur at 500 ft. or even less. Where the slopes rise fairly uniformly, as on the west of the Bowland Forest area, the rainfall rises steadily as the height increases, as shown in Fig. 11. The curve given in the figure is contrasted with similar data for the eastern Pennines, showing the much lower rainfall at corresponding heights in the east. The gradient of increase in rain-

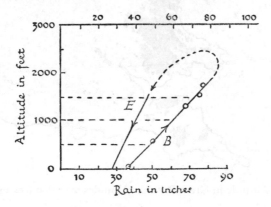

FIG. 11.—Rainfall and altitude on a western slope, B (Bowland Forest), and on the corresponding eastern slope of the Pennines, E.

FIG. 12.—Altitude in Great Britain. Altitudes over 800 feet shown in black.

fall with altitude rises much more steeply elsewhere, however. Thus, for example, an average rainfall of 150 in. per annum may be assumed at 2,800 to 3,000 ft. in the Central Lake District, in Western Wales and in parts of Western Scotland. In contrast, the rapid decline in the rainfall on the eastern slopes of mountainous Britain is equally striking, for there a rainfall of 55 in. would not be found much below 2,500 ft., and indeed so high a figure is often not reached. A rainfall of 35 in. is not often found below about 700 ft. There is thus a marked difference between the westerly and easterly aspects of British uplands, a point worthy of emphasis because the change-over in the effective climatic conditions often takes place very rapidly in passing in an easterly direction from a watershed.

Moreover, there are indeed large areas in the eastern uplands where a maximum rainfall of between 45 and 50 in. is reached at about 1,500 ft. and no greater rainfall is observed at higher levels. For practical purposes, then, we may say that the western uplands above 500 ft. lie almost wholly above the rainfall limits of the bog-forming climate, while a large proportion of the eastern uplands is below these limits.

The general truth of this statement can be illustrated by a comparison of the maps in Figs. 12 and 14, which show that the zone of high rainfall by no means corresponds with any particular altitude. Further, if the map (Fig. 13) showing moorland and waste lands be compared with that of rainfall, it will be found that a considerable part of the eastern moorlands lies outside the zone possessing a " bog " climate. The distinction is particularly clear in the Scottish Highlands. The importance of this type of relation has hardly received the emphasis it deserves, perhaps because the climatic index is not one it is easy to employ in the field. Indeed, average annual rainfall alone cannot be a reliable guide to the distribution of this type of climate, for the essential feature is the normal absence of soil-drying in summer, and this must depend on evaporation rate and hence on other factors such as mean temperatures, cloudiness and air humidity as well as on local topography. But the field ecologist learns to recognise the certain signs of the existence of local variations in rainfall, of which the most valuable is usually the local distribution of cloud. Some areas are persistently under cloud, while others not far away may be as frequently cloud-free. Generally, rain-showers show a similar distribution, and these are both things which can be noted even in a brief visit.

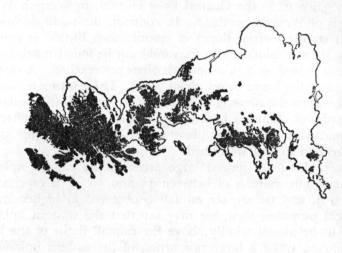

Right, Fig. 13b.—Distribution of Rainfall. Areas with over 50 inches of rainfall per annum shown in black.

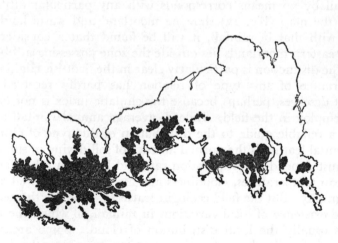

Left, Fig. 13a.—Moorlands in the British Isles.

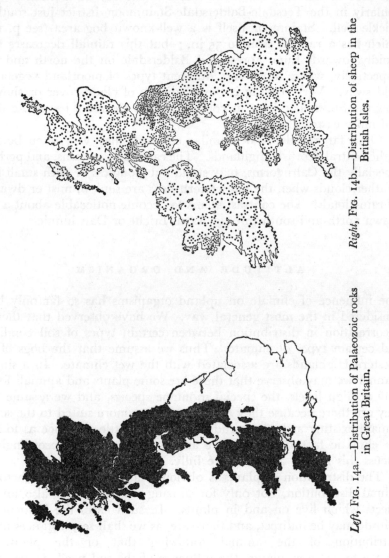

Right, Fig. 14b.—Distribution of sheep in the British Isles.

Left, Fig. 14a.—Distribution of Palaeozoic rocks in Great Britain.

Very good examples of considerable local variations in climate which can thus be detected are to be found in the eastern Pennines—particularly in the Teesdale-Baldersdale-Stainmoor district just south of Mickle Fell. Stainmoor itself is a well-known bog area (see p. 150) which has a rainfall near to 55 in. ; but this rainfall decreases very rapidly towards Lune Forest and Baldersdale on the north and east respectively, where other very different types of moorland vegetation hold sway. Very striking is the frequency of cloud-cover or showers over the Stainmoor bogs in contrast to the clearer skies of the drier and more easterly areas.

On a far grander scale, similar contrasts may very often be seen in the central Scottish Highlands. The eastern mountains, and perhaps especially the Cairngorms, may stand out cloudless or with small fair-weather clouds when the big western Bens are sunk in mist or dwarfed by rain-clouds. The contrast seems to become noticeable about a line drawn north and south through Loch Ericht or Dalwhinnie.

ALTITUDE AND ORGANISM

The influence of climate on upland organisms has so far only been considered in the most general way. We have observed that there is a correlation in distribution between certain types of soil condition and certain types of climate. Thus we assume that the bogs of the Western Highlands are associated with the wet climate. In a similar manner we may observe that there are some plants and animals found only at high levels, the special montane species, and we assume that they are there because they are in some way more suited to the severe climate existing at high altitudes. We have little evidence as to how the climatic factors are effective and it will be useful accordingly to discuss this matter a little more fully.

The distribution of plants is obviously a very important factor in animal distribution, not only for grazing mammals but also for the insects which live on and in plants. In such cases the influence of altitude may be indirect, and there are, as we shall see, instances of the distribution of the animal following that of the plant. If we are to consider plants, the influence of the soil needs to be taken into account, and we have already seen reason to believe that the wet climate may be effective through its influence on soil conditions. But climatic humidity varies greatly in different parts of the country—being high in the west and lower in the east. If this were the effective montane influence then we should expect to find a richer montane fauna and flora in the west. It is well known that on the whole there are on the eastern mountains more of the species restricted to high mountain life ; so that in one aspect at least humidity cannot determine the altitudinal zonation. However, the fauna and flora of upland country as a whole is very different from that of the lowlands, in proportionate representation if not always in the individual species, and a large part of this upland fauna and flora is associated with the ill-drained and wet soils. What humidity does do is to give great areas dominated by a limited fauna and flora of this type, which is upland rather than montane and which is evidently related to the soil conditions induced by humidity.

The more common view and one which has been referred to and used already in this chapter, is that temperature largely controls the altitudinal zonation, and we may look at this problem as something which would repay attention from naturalists and as a subject which requires little in the way of special equipment.

The principal biological effect of temperature is that it greatly affects the rate of biological processes. Thus a lowering of temperature such as would be experienced at a higher level would retard growth and development so that there would be less likelihood of a given developmental process being completed within the shorter period available in a montane summer. Some upland organisms do in fact appear to take longer over a given process of development. A well-known case is that of a moth, the northern eggar (*Lasiocampa callunae*), which spends two years in the larval stage instead of the one characteristic of the original woodland race, the oak eggar (*L. quercus*). It is unlikely, however, that the difference is due to the lower temperature of the upland habitat. To double the period of development, or to halve the rate of development, would require a reduction of temperature of about 7·5° C. or 14° F., equivalent to an increase in altitude of about 4,500 ft. ! The lengthened larval period may be just too long to fit into one growing season, but it seems more likely that the change in the length of the life cycle is either genetical or mainly due to nutritional differences imposed by the moorland habitat.

There are, of course, other ways in which lower temperatures may affect distribution. Where two organisms are dependent on one another for success, but possess life-cycles of different duration, an alteration in temperature may put the two life-cycles " out of step " with one another, as it were. A case which might involve something of this nature is one in which an insect mined or fed on a plant organ at some particular stage in development, as in an example discussed later in this chapter.

Lastly, of course, alterations in temperature may produce qualitative effects on plant and animal metabolism (in the widest sense), and it is perhaps in this direction that we have to seek an explanation of the tendency of certain insects to be represented by short-winged races at higher altitudes (see p. 226). In plants, the effects of temperatures approaching the freezing point are often to induce the conversion of insoluble food-reserves like starch to soluble sugars. To this type of change has been ascribed the immunity of some evergreen plants from frost injury, which is attributed to the difficulty of freezing cells containing a high sugar-concentration. Undoubtedly the presence of these sugar solutions does confer on plant tissues a certain immunity from frost injury and the effect may easily help to account for the over-wintering of arctic and montane plants, just as it would undoubtedly be advantageous in helping to promote the rapid growth and early flowering observed in arctic climates. Dr. Scott Russell has verified the existence of high sugar-concentrations in spring in arctic plants collected on Jan Mayen Island and in the Karakorum mountains.

The only clear effect of this general type I know of in animal tissues is the very characteristic production of orange-coloured and fat-soluble pigments in certain aquatic copepods during the winter months and commonly also in cold, high-level tarns.

When one goes on to consider the ecological effects of these factors in nature, it is generally difficult to dissociate the effects of temperature and humidity. Thus the presence on mountain-tops of certain spiders usually found in damp cellars might plausibly be attributed either to high humidity or low temperature. A clearer example of the influence of temperature on animal distribution is that of the alpine flatworm, *Planaria alpina*, for this lives in water and is not therefore subject to the great variations in humidity which may effect mountain-top habitats. *Planaria alpina* is a small creature about a quarter of an inch long, resembling a somewhat flattened grey slug. It is a carrion feeder, living under stones in the margins of streams and in mountain

PLATE VII

The Blaven ridge, Skye, from the east: gabbro with basalt dykes underlying the depressions

PLATE VIII

Atmosphere, Glen Einich, Cairngorms

runnels. In this country, these little water-courses usually contain a second, much darker species of flatworm, *Polycelis nigra*. The two species are always distributed in the same way, *P. alpina* at the higher levels, certainly at least to 2,000 ft., and *P. nigra* in the lower reaches of the water-course. This distribution is mainly a matter of temperature. Numerous observations in Britain and on the Continent have shown that *P. alpina* is *never* found in nature where the temperature exceeds 14° C., while *P. nigra* may be found where the water reaches as much as 20° C. Further, prolonged observations on the animals under controlled conditions by Mr. R. S. A. Beauchamp have shown that *P. alpina* cannot long survive temperatures exceeding 12° C. Thus in nature it occupies the high-level runnels and cold springs, occurring at high levels in mountain districts. There are reasons for believing that other animals confined to high-level streams and soils owe their distribution to similar effects, particularly perhaps certain insect larvae.

It is less easy to point to instances in which similar effects are produced on plant distribution, though they doubtless exist. Plants are not able to change their positions readily, and most of the high-level species are perennials, which means that the effects of the environment if not immediately lethal are likely to be the integration of the prolonged effects of the given habitat factor or factors. In some cases, perhaps especially in grasses, a given species is represented in the montane zone by separate races, often it may be not very distinct in form, but possessing some ability to live under the especial montane conditions. The common upland grass, the sheep's fescue (*Festuca ovina*) is thus represented in the montane zone by an allied highland species (*F. vivipara*) which has the ability to produce young plants in place of the floral structures. This feature is much accelerated by, if not wholly dependent on, the existence of humid conditions, and this is probably the reason why the viviparous form of this plant is found at low altitudes along the seaward margins of Western Britain.

It seems that in order to get some idea of how climatic factors affected upland plants one would have to consider the influence of whole seasons upon the growth of a chosen plant. After making observations upon a number of plants it became clear that there were good practical reasons for using a relatively common plant like the moor-rush (*Juncus squarrosus*) as material for estimating these effects of altitude. This plant has certain practical advantages for work of this type. It occurs at almost every altitude in Britain and it prefers the wet and base-deficient peaty soils which predominate in the uplands.

The plant consists of a rosette of rather fibrous leaves just above ground level with a long flower-stalk bearing an upper group of brownish flowers or fruits (Pl. IX, p. 52). The latter contain numerous small seeds. At ground level there is a woody stem having numerous roots. The flower-stalks are numerous, they are tough and so can be collected rapidly and transported for subsequent measurement. The fruits, small brown capsules about a sixth of an inch long, are also tough and numerous enough to give suitable numerical measurements. The inflorescence is laid down as part of a bud in summer. It develops the following year, and its length may be taken as a partial expression of the conditions favourable to growth in the preceding summer and

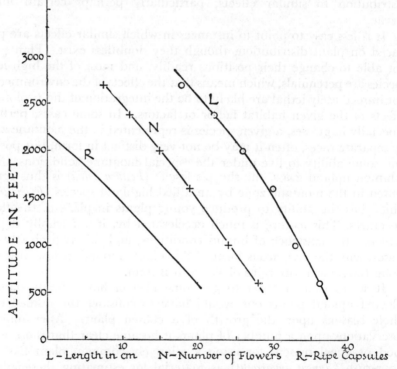

FIG. 15.—Effect of altitude on moor-rush, *Juncus squarrosus* : L, Length of flower-stalk ; N, Number of flowers produced ; R, Number of mature capsules.

also in the summer in which it has developed. These conditions affect reproduction in addition by controlling the number of flowers and, later, of fruits and seeds. The only method by which the plant is distributed is by the numerous small seeds.

If one studies the performance of such a common moorland plant at different altitudes, it is apparent that the amount of growth and the production of flowers, or better still, of fruits and seeds, both diminish as the altitude increases (see Fig. 15). But fruit production is affected far more than growth in length, so that a point is reached, generally about an altitude of 2,500 ft. to 2,700 ft., above which fertile fruits are not usually produced, although the plants may form inflorescences of considerable size and in other ways be capable of making satisfactory vegetative growth.

This effect is evidently due mainly to the retardation of the development of the flowers and fruits. Thus in the Lake District in 1942, flowering was completed during June at 700 ft., but it had not begun at the end of July at 2,000 ft., and, at 2,500 ft. to 3,000 ft., it was not complete by the end of August. Thus at these highest levels there was little or no chance of most of the fruits becoming mature and they did not in fact do so. Again, in late September, 1943, only one mature capsule per 20 plants was found on the summit of Ingleborough (2,373 ft.). These and similar facts thus suggest that viable seeds are not usually formed above about 2,500 ft. to 2,700 ft., although large and healthy plants can be found up to at least a thousand feet higher. Until 1947, viable seeds had not been collected from above 2,700 ft., but the exceptionally long and warm summer of that year led to very abundant seed production—so much so that viable seeds were obtained from 3,400 ft., on Ben Wyvis.

In view of the infrequency with which such seeds are formed at high levels, the presence of moor-rush plants at 2,700 ft. and upwards is interesting. They are certainly very long-lived (twenty years or more) and possibly originally due mainly to transported seeds. It is noticeable on some mountains that the plants are not only sporadic but also are often collected in colonies, suggesting a group of individuals centred round a parent plant which has fruited only at rare intervals. The fruits are, perhaps, distributed in the wet wool of sheep, for, as far as is known, no mammals eat the inflorescences although snow-buntings habitually eat the dry fruits in winter and so may help to disperse seeds. The rush is commonest on sheep-infested mountains, and although it occurs to at least 3,700 ft., I have looked for it in vain on the high and grassy Scotch summits where deer habitually graze.

However, it seems certain that the effects of altitude are differential, affecting the seed-production most, flower-production less and vegetative growth least. The analysis of these effects shows that they vary little as between districts receiving great differences in rainfall, and they can thus be attributed mainly to the diminution of mean temperature with increasing altitude. Thus temperature, though it actually operates by controlling the relative rates of development, affects the distribution mechanism.

It is interesting to carry this problem a little further by considering how these things affect a little rush-moth, *Coleophora caespititiella* (see Pl. 30, p. 245), that lives in association with the moor-rush and also with the common rush. Its life-history is not very well known, but moths are mature and the eggs are apparently laid in June-July, on or near the flowers of the rush. The larvae then feed on the growing seeds inside the developing fruit. By about the end of August, the infection of a fruit capsule becomes noticeable because of the presence of the larval case, a small cylindrical and white papery object in which the larva may live (see Pl. XI, p. 60). The larvae, possibly usually with the case, leave the rush-heads in late autumn and hide in the surrounding vegetation until the following summer. With certain obvious precautions, the presence or absence of the white larval cases can be used to study in an approximate way the extent to which the population of heath-rush is infected by the moth. The data also give a picture of the altitudinal distribution of the moth. This is much more restricted than is that of the rush on which it lives. In the central Lake District, in 1942, the frequency of the larvae decreased rapidly from a maximum infection of about 40 per cent of the capsules at 700 ft. and no signs of the moth were seen above 1,800 ft., although in that district the moor-rush goes up to 3,000 ft. Now at first it was thought that the larval cases might become more frequent at a higher level later in the year. In fact larval cases were never seen above this level except in the abnormal summer of 1947, when some were found at 2,000 ft. on the south-facing slopes of Saddleback.

It seemed obvious at first that at higher altitudes the lower temperatures would retard the development both of rush-flowers and of the moth growth-cycle, for both last a year. When no infection was

PLATE IX

R. Brinsden

b. Larval cases of the rush-moth,
Coleophora caespititiella

R. Brinsden

a. The moor-rush, Juncus squarrosus

PLATE X

C. H. Wood

Aerial view of the central Pennines as a dissected plateau: Ingleborough in the distance and the junction of Wharfedale and Park Gill Beck in the left centre. The nearest summit is that of Great Whernside. The flanks and valley sides show extensive and recent erosion, characteristic of many upland peat-covered areas found above 1,800 ft. it was thought that the lower average temperatures might so retard the development of the larvae from the egg to the case stages, that the cases were not produced at higher levels even although there was infection. In this case the larvae might fail to overwinter or the whole growth-cycle might take two seasons. However, no evidence of a later infection at higher levels could be found.

A possible alternative explanation was that, as suggested earlier, the whole growth-cycle of the moth might get " out of step " with that of the rush, so that mature moths and " infectable " rush-flowers (i.e. in the young stage when they are infected) might not coincide in time.

This does, in fact, happen, though not quite in the manner expected. It was found, in samples from the higher levels, that only the early maturing fruits were infected by *Coleophora*. It followed that there was normally no infection above 1,800 ft. because no rush-flowers were normally open in July above that altitude (1944 and 1945). Even in the abnormal summer of 1947, no sign of infection was seen above 2,000 ft. (and this on a south slope) in the Lake District, and in the Eastern Highlands (Ben Wyvis and Rothiemurchus district) none was noted above 1,400 ft. On the whole, then, it seems as though the main population of mature *Coleophora* individuals comes out at one time, about June-July. It may then infect any rush-flowers which are then open. This severely limits its altitudinal range, for as we have already seen, the high-level flowers are not mature at these early dates. One difficulty about these findings is that there seems no reason why the cycle of development of the moth should not be retarded somewhat at the higher levels just as that of the rush-flowers is. If this were the case, a small number of late-maturing individuals should appear at higher levels. No individuals of this type have been seen, nor has it been possible to find signs of rushes which might have been infected in this manner. It seems to be only possible to explain this apparent absence of the mature moths at higher levels by assuming also a temperature bar to their development such as we have already encountered in the flatworm *Planaria alpina*.

There are many further observations that could usefully be made on this matter. It appears that *Coleophora* is generally confined to lower altitudes on the Eastern Highlands as compared with the Lake District, and, at first, it seemed that lower mean temperatures might explain this. However, I have not seen this. moth at all in the Western Highlands or Islands—perhaps because I have generally been too early or too late for the moth and too early for the larval cases. Certainly the creature seems to be much less common in this area of high rainfall, a result that could not be easily explained on the grounds of temperature alone.

The brief summary of upland climates and the analysis of their possible effects on animals and plants suggests that temperature has much to do with the zonation of plants and animals we observe on ascending a mountain. It controls the distribution of some organisms because they are not able to live in the higher average temperatures of the lowlands. In other cases, it seems that the low montane temperatures so lengthen the life-cycle that it cannot be completed in the short mountain summer. Perhaps more often low temperature retards some part of the developmental cycle, so that we get short-winged insects (see pp. 226-28), or plants unable to produce flowers and fruit. For these reasons, some zonation of organisms is inevitable as altitude rises and temperature falls.

In practice, the most widespread influence of altitude is the change in the character of the prevailing plant communities, with all that it implies in its effect on animal habitats. Most noticeable is the disappearance of woodlands and trees with their varied faunas and ground floras. As this commonly takes place at about 2,000 ft. and as the restricted montane species appear above that level, we may take it as a convenient altitudinal separation of *montane* and *sub-montane* zones.

Within the limits thus defined by temperature other factors must play their part. Every naturalist knows that shelter from wind is often vitally important, so that here and there among the mountains there are oases in which the frequency of plant and animal life is altogether different from that found on the exposed and wind-swept faces. Within the limits imposed by temperature, humidity also exerts its restrictions, not only by presenting a range of habitats running from pool or rivulet to desiccated rock, but by influencing the character of the soil. It is to the consideration of these soil conditions that we must now turn.

CHAPTER 4

SOILS

T H E second important group of factors in upland habitats is the nature of the soil covering—or perhaps more strictly, of the surfaces available for plant growth. Geologically, as we have seen, these surfaces may be classified either as *stable* or *unstable*, depending on whether they are still subject to active erosion or not. As habitats for plants there is a more profound difference between these two classes. Most of the unstable surfaces are rocky or are covered by rock fragments in various stages of disintegration, and even their physical properties differ greatly from those of fertile lowland soils. They are, in fact, soils in the making, and it is one characteristic of upland areas that they exhibit in profusion all the varied stages of soil-formation. We see the native rock breaking down under the action of frost and other weathering agents to rock fragments, which become progressively finer as the process is longer continued, ultimately to yield the small mineral particles which form the basal material of most soils. The weathered material may remain *in situ*, covering the original rock surface, or it may be removed by erosion and redeposited elsewhere by streams and rivers as banks of silt or alluvial plains, by solifluction or rain-wash, or formerly in Britain by widespread glacial movements.

The raw mineral material is, however, comparatively sterile. It is converted into what we call a soil partly by chemical modifications resulting from the presence of water, often charged with carbon dioxide or humic acid, and partly resulting from the gradual accumulation of organic materials derived from plant remains. This latter material is called *humus*, and is particularly important because it forms a medium upon which can grow various micro-organisms, mainly bacteria, moulds and protozoa. With the accumulation of humus and the gradual colonisation of the material by these organisms comes a final stage, when it is usual to imagine that the original particles of mineral substance have become covered by a jelly-like mass of colloidal material—in part gelatinised minerals but also including humus—on and in which the population of soil micro-organisms lives.

It will be evident from this brief summary that upland soils can usefully be considered as belonging to a developmental series. But it is true of any soil that one of its outstanding characteristics is its capacity for change. Soils are inherently dynamic systems even when they are developed in physically stable situations, and to a far greater extent is this true of mountain soils, most of which are of geologically recent origin, even if not physically unstable.

Five types of environmental factor control the development of a soil mantle. First comes the nature of the rock or other *parent material*, from which soil is formed by physical and chemical weathering. *Climate* also exerts a marked effect on the weathering process, affecting both its physical and chemical parts, and, in particular, determining the amount of rain-water percolating through the soil in any season, a process known as leaching, which is responsible for the removal of soluble substances, bases like lime as well as plant nutrients like nitrates. *Relief* influences the lateral movement of percolating water down a slope, the degree of drainage and the stability, and thus affects the degree of leaching. But none of these effects is instantaneous and so there is a *time-factor* to be considered. Lastly, there are the obvious biological factors, of which the action of *vegetation* is most significant. Vegetation derives part of its sustenance from the soil and so incorporates a portion of the soil material which is returned to the soil on the decay of the plant tissues. The fertility of a soil is the result of this cyclic exchange. An efficient type of plant which draws heavily on the soil nutrients keeps them in a form of biological circulation which mitigates the losses due to leaching. Thus there is a natural mechanism for maintaining soil fertility, which, by drawing on the deep layers of the soil, is capable even of increasing the fertility of the surface layers provided the leaching factor is not too intense. Further, in any environment where the climatic factors have remained reasonably stable for a long time, it is possible for the soil-vegetation system to achieve a measure of temporary stability. In upland Britain, however, the soils are generally in dynamic states moving along definite trends of soil development. The trends due to a severe climate are particularly marked, and they operate during the different stages of soil development in the following manner.

SKELETAL AND IMMATURE SOILS

The initial stages of soil development in which rock fragments predominate are what we can only call *skeletal* soils. They are found principally where the surface is unstable or where further development is retarded by hard rocks or low temperatures. Of these factors, the low temperatures have also distinct qualitative effects, because while they greatly retard chemical modifications, the associated physical disintegrations caused by frost and solifluction are especially vigorous. There may thus be much physical commination of rock fragments with little chemical change. Thus the soils, even if finely divided, are *immature* in the developmental sense because of the deficiencies in their chemical and biological equipment. Soils of this general type occur on mountain-tops, where they are found under the mountain-top detritus except, perhaps, where it is especially coarse and deep. Generally, however, the detritus seems to be a superficial layer of stones extruded from below during the frost-caused or solifluction movements of the materials. Beneath the stones there is commonly a sandy loam, generally brown in colour and little leached. When vegetation is present this merges at the top into the almost black humus that collects among the surface detritus. The depth of the soil varies with the nature of the rock and the degree of erosion, but it is usually between one and three feet, and then comes disintegrating rock.

Parallel to these summit soils in general quality may be the scree-slopes of finely-divided material which occur lower down a mountain, often approaching stability but still subject to soil-wash and soil-creep, and so often distinguished as *creep-soils*. These show great variability in detail, but, like the mountain-top detritus, they often show coarse material at the surface and finer below. As they approach stability, they merge into the woodland soils described below, but in the earlier " gravel-slide " stages, a vertical section usually reveals a sequence of more or less alternating sandy or stony layers parallel to the slope (see Fig. 8). All soils of these types are alike in possessing a high base-status because they consist mainly of rock particles as yet not greatly modified by chemical change.

In all upland habitats there are in addition the overall trends caused by continual washing by rain, and as a result every exposed and porous surface will be more or less leached. Wherever leaching has taken place there must be corresponding areas that receive the products of leaching. The water that carries away lime or other bases from the higher upland surfaces must produce elsewhere lime-rich or base-rich habitats. Areas of this latter type may be distinguished as *flushed* or enriched habitats to distinguish them from the *leached* or impoverished ones.

FLUSHED SOILS

In general, of course, leaching will preponderate in upland regions and enriched soils will be commoner in lowland regions. Nevertheless enriched soils are always to be found occupying characteristic localities in mountain areas. Thus there is a flushed area around every spring-head and around every rivulet. However, the water need not emerge as a separate spring but may perfuse the surface soil—a type of flush that can be recognised by a zone of greener vegetation. The various types of " damp flush " may be associated with a soil of almost any physical category. Enrichment by water from a higher level is greatest when such water has penetrated into the rock by means of structural fissures, and permeated the rock strata on its way down ; a mere receiving area for surface run-off from acid upland soils is often as severely leached and as acid as the upland soil itself.

Parallel with enrichment by water (" damp flushes "), there is enrichment by presence of freshly-weathered rock particles, and areas of this type might be called " dry flushes." The lower part of any steep slope is constantly enriched by such particles washed down from above. Screes and gravel-slides, in which the breakdown of new rock by weathering continually yields a supply of bases, could thus be considered among the enriched or flushed habitats. In this category also comes any unstable surface, crag, gullies and the like, where new rock surfaces are being exposed by erosion.

It will be observed that the flushed habitats are determined by a diversity of factors producing enrichment and have thus few physical characteristics in common. They tend to fall technically into four categories :

   a. Bare rock or oversteepened slopes with soil particles washed away or present only in narrow fissures. Enrichment by continual weathering of freshly exposed rock surfaces.

   b. Block scree in which leaching tends to preponderate over weathering, although the latter nevertheless does continually refurnish some of the bases lost, especially in the case of more rapidly weathering and base-rich rocks.

   c. Unstable scree-slopes and solifluction areas with movement and accumulation of weathered soil particles, often below the surface layer of coarse detritus ; enrichment both by weathering and particle accumulation.

d. Accumulation areas—nearly always showing fine and deep soils, with enrichment mainly by accumulation from above.

Upwelling of base-rich waters may occur in conjunction with any of the four categories above, although it is rarest in *a* and commonest in *c* and *d*. In both *c* and *d* the total " flush " effects normally counteract losses by leaching unless the soils are deriving from base-poor rocks.

LEACHED SOILS

On the whole, the unstable surfaces are areas of enrichment, and as such show distinctive types of vegetation. When they become stable enough to permit a complete vegetation cover, they inevitably tend to become leached—a tendency that is in some slight measure accelerated or retarded according to the nature of the plant cover. Because heavy rainfall is the rule and because plant remains tend to accumulate on the soil surface, it is characteristic of upland soils, once soil-creep and the forces of erosion are sufficiently arrested, that they rapidly develop the stratification or " profile " indicative of the more advanced (or " mature ") stages of soil development.

The extreme form of stratification found is that of the soil type known as a *podsol,* in which, under a surface layer of peaty humus and of humus-stained soil, there is a grey soil-layer from which almost all of the available bases (especially lime and iron) have been removed by leaching. With them also have gone the finest particles of clay and the humus colloids. These accumulate at a lower level, commonly two or three feet below the surface, as a dark-brown layer of " humus pan," while immediately below this can usually be seen a red- or orange-brown precipitate of iron compounds (" iron pan "). Still lower is the little altered parent material. Thus these highly leached soils show a characteristic *soil profile,* with the following layers :

      A.   *a* Surface peaty humus and " litter "
           b peat-stained inorganic soil
           c leached grey   ,,   ,,
      B.   *d* humus accumulation zone (" pan ")
           e iron   ,,   ,, (" pan ")
      C.   *f* little altered parent material

In continental areas, podsols characterise the cold temperate climates on stable and porous substrata receiving moderate rainfall. They are there associated with the northern evergreen forests of coniferous trees (firs) and with an abundance of small shrubs like the heathers.

In the British uplands, podsols are most characteristic of the eastern regions where the annual rainfall is relatively low (say about 35-40 in.) and the parent material is often sandy or gravelly morainic material. They are often now associated with heather-moor and pine forest, and originally this association may have been still more widespread. In the wetter western areas, although podsolic features in the soils are frequent, good examples of podsols are infrequent. Often this is because of great irregularity or diversity in the composition of the parent material. In particular, the deposits of iron or of peaty colloidal matter which suggest the appearance of a podsol are often due to *lateral* seepage from higher up the slope and are not necessarily derived from the soil-layers immediately and vertically above them. Varying porosity, in particular, leads to very irregular local accumulations of the humus and iron colloidal layers, which may appear in blotches along the lines of seepage and at a varying distance below the surface. But it is probable that most of what were once free-draining forest soils have now been transformed to bog (see below and Chap. 10), and that those which are left are but transitional stages.

Between the extreme podsols and the young or slightly leached soils, there is a range of soil profiles usually classified together as "brown earths" from their ochreous brown colour, and in the lowlands characteristic of forests of deciduous trees, oak, beech and the like. The surface layers have been somewhat leached of bases but retain a brown colour along with a base-status sufficient to give a moderate fertility. This is the characteristic soil-type of lowland Britain. In the uplands, however, this condition can only be long maintained, where the original rock fragments are base-rich, where flushing of some sort maintains the base-supply, or where the vegetation is such as to renew the base-supply in the surface layers. The latter condition would be favoured, for example, by oak woodlands rather than by a covering of birch or of pine, for the lime contents of the leaves of these trees differ considerably: that of oak approaches 3 per cent, while those of birch and of pine are only about 1·5 and 1·0 per cent respectively. Thus by absorbing more lime from the lower layers of soil and returning it to the surface, oaks would maintain the base

PLATE XI

a. Stone stripes on a solifluction area, Blaven

b. Solifluction slope showing terracing, Ingleborough

PLATE XII

C. H. Wood

Aerial view of the summit of Ingleborough, showing the instability of the western face. On the right are the crags of Yoredale limestone on which typical montane organisms occur. In the centre is a zone of pits or sink-holes due to drainage into the limestones, and the left part of the upper face shows great instability due to the collapse of shales below the summit cap of millstone grit supply of the surface soil-layers for a longer time and so would tend to retard the effect of leaching.

The upland soils of brown earth type are usually recently stabilised " creep soils," flushed glacial drifts, or soils derived from base-rich rocks. Almost always they were until recently under woodland, normally of oak though often with much ash. Now they are almost always cleared of trees and are covered by grasslands of various types. The removal of the original tree-cover was often followed by destruction of the surface humus through its oxidation and by the removal of the surface layers by rain-wash. Thus many upland soils of this general type, like the " frydd " soils in Wales, have been considered now to show " truncated profiles," the top strata having been removed, often by erosion. In some cases, however, it is also probable that the profiles are immature and that the soils owe to this their comparatively high base-status.

It is quite clear that generally in the uplands the process of leaching can only be retarded and not completely stayed. The high summer rainfall in particular ensues that leaching will continue under the most favourable conditions of temperature. In lowland climates, in contrast, there is in summer an excess of evaporation and drying in the surface layers of soil so that base-rich water ascends from below by capillarity. This opportunity for replenishment is lacking even in a well-drained upland soil so that the soils as a whole must tend towards the leached condition.

Thus it seems inevitable that any porous soil, once stabilised, must ultimately develop towards a podsolic stage. In the majority of cases it seems that the process has not ceased at this stage. The downward movement of fine particles of clay and humus which characterises podsol development leads to the formation of impermeable pan-layers which impede drainage. Thus under conditions of high rainfall the upper layers of soil become waterlogged, seasonally if not permanently. This leads to peat accumulation, which in turn accentuates both leaching and poor drainage. Thus in mountainous Britain, podsols have almost always tended to become peat-covered bog soils, such as are described below, and it seems probable that the characteristic podsolic profile becomes modified when this change takes place, and ultimately disappears.

These trends of soil development favourable to bog formation are undoubtedly much accentuated by the topographic relations of the mountain soils. Once bog conditions have been established at any point on a hillside—a process which in most cases clearly must have taken place at an early stage in the physiographic history of the area —there must inevitably be a tendency for bog seepage to extend downward and to produce a general degeneration in the soils below it. The greater the area of peat accumulation in the upper bog zone, the more rapidly would this influence extend downwards. Moreover, because a mountain is a gathering ground with a considerable excess of rainfall over evaporation, it seems likely that the lowest slopes will often also show a marked trend towards the establishment of bog, the degree to which this happens being controlled by the geological structure of the mountain and the amount of mineral bases (lime, potash and so on) the mountain yields to the seeping water. So soon as the mountain-side becomes stable enough to show signs of leaching these trends are strongly in favour of it passing over to bog. Thus the upland soil problems are very complex, affected not only by the immediate characters of the soil but by lateral movements, by adjacent relief, rock and vegetation.

CHEMICAL STAGES IN LEACHING

The chemical stages which can be distinguished during the leaching process can now be outlined. In the first instance, most British soils are principally calcium soils, or, putting it in another way, they have lime as their principal base, and are lime-saturated. Agriculturally and ecologically, soils of this type possess high fertility. As leaching goes on, most of the lime and other bases are removed, being replaced by hydrogen, so that the soil finally becomes acid and sour (e.g. to the taste). For ecological purposes there are, however, two intermediate stages in this process which can usefully be distinguished : a state of partial lime-deficiency and one of higher lime-deficiency. Most British soils also contain a good deal of iron oxide—to which their colour is largely due—and under conditions of good aeration this is removed much more slowly than lime. The following four types of soil can conveniently be recognised as stages in the leaching process :

a   Lime-saturated ;
b   Lime-deficient ;

    c Base-deficient, iron oxide becoming mobile and relatively
        more important than lime ;
    d Acid, with podsolic profiles in stable soils, often masked by
        peat accumulation.

Of these *b* and *c* represent the stages usually referred to as brown
earths. The ecological value of this series lies in the fact that very
decided transitions in vegetation occur at a point between *b* and *c*
(which is also approximately half-way between *a* and *d*)—that is, a
point of half-saturation with bases.

The technical methods of distinguishing these soil-types depend on
the methods of measuring the percentage of base-saturation, which
decreases from *a* to *d*, or of measuring the increasing acidity. The
latter is perhaps a mode of expression more familiar to biologists.
Estimates are made of the hydrogen-ion concentration and expressed
in the following way. Concentrations, varying, for example, as 1/100,
1/1000 or 1/10,000 gm. per litre of hydrogen ions can be written either
$1/10^2$, $1/10^3$ or $1/10^4$, or 1×10^{-2}, 1×10^{-3} or 1×10^{-4} g/l, and *for convenience*
these are termed pH 2, 3 or 4 respectively. The notation extends over
a range of 1 to 14. In terms of this notation, pure water has a pH
value of approximately pH 7, lime-saturated soils have a somewhat
similar pH value, of above 6, while natural soils which are about half-
saturated with bases have a pH value of approximately 5. The
characteristic acid soils in the ecological sense lie below pH 3·8.

These soil types can, however, often be distinguished by their
appearance and biological characters. The grey and leached zone
in a well-developed podsol is likely to be mainly a hydrogen soil, as
is the humus-stained layer on the surface. In many upland soils, the
leached but still brown layer of inorganic materials below the surface
humus has a characteristic orange-brown colour—not grey as in a
proper podsol. This condition is associated with the removal of
most of the lime and the mobilisation of iron, at first perhaps dissolved from the soil minerals near the surface by humus compounds,
but then reoxidised on the surface of the soil particles in a state which
accounts for the characteristic colour. This type of soil is probably
very definitely associated with periods of waterlogging, such as are
frequent in upland areas, and it normally has a lower base-status
than the more typical soils of brown-earth type.

In these and in other ways, therefore, the characteristic appearances of soil profiles give a good deal of information about the base-status of the soils. It is perhaps worth emphasising also at this stage that two factors in particular are especially effective in removing iron and other bases during the final stages of the leaching process.

One of these is the increased acidity and especially the effects of acids derived from plants like oxalic and citric acids, in which iron salts are especially soluble. The second is the establishment or development of waterlogging, which, by eliminating the oxidising effects of air or oxygen, permits the reduction of iron to the ferrous state, in which it is very much more easily soluble, as well as more readily replaced by the process known as base-exchange. In aerated soils, however, waterlogging can only be temporary even though it must be frequent in winter in all upland soils. When it occurs permanently the soil commonly acquires a blue-grey appearance (see below) which we associate with the presence of ferrous iron compounds, and this contrasts very noticeably with the reds and browns of the ferric salts in air-containing soils.

Of course, where there are extensive areas of waterlogged soil and especially where peat is abundant, large amounts of ferrous salts may be present in solution in the soil-water. Wherever this becomes exposed to air it becomes oxidised either to metallic iron or to ferric salts and so considerable amounts of ferric substances may be precipitated. The orange-brown or metallic films due to this process are familiar objects round any peaty spring, and, long continued on a large scale, it has in the past been responsible for the production of deposits of bog iron ore. The same process continues in any peaty flush soil which receives drainage from waterlogged surfaces and into which air can, at times, penetrate. To the ecologist, the colours due to iron compounds are of great importance as visual evidence of the existence and progress of leaching or accumulation and also as useful clues to the presence or absence of aerated conditions in the soil. There are, of course, many chemical tests which can be used to confirm and extend these visible signs.

WATERLOGGED SOILS AND PEATS

What has just been said about waterlogged soils serves as a useful preface to the further consideration of this subject. These soils are distinct in being *anaerobic* or devoid of oxygen, and this is reflected in

PLATE 9

John Markham

Ground moraines in Upper Ribblesdale, Yorkshire: the limestone in the foreground is masked in the middle distance by glacial moraines of non-calcareous material bearing moorland vegetation. November

PLATE 10

John Markham

Llyn Padarn, Caernarvonshire; morning mist. Truncated spurs are shown in the background. April their " sad " appearance and in the characteristic blue-grey colours of the mineral matter due to ferrous iron salts. Such mineral soils are usually called *gley* soils, and, in the British uplands, they almost always possess another characteristic. The absence of oxygen prevents the decay of the organic matter derived from the plants growing on the surface. Consequently, upland waterlogged soils are also normally covered by layers of peat, and these are deep wherever waterlogging has been long continued, while they are usually shallower where this condition is of more recent origin. As a result of these accumulations of peat, the mineral soil below may be stained and mottled by peaty material.

The waterlogged peats are of two main types : (i) bog-peats and (ii) flush-peats. The bog-peats are widespread, covering the majority of stable upland soils and characteristic of those of slight slope (cf. Pls. 22a, p. 144, and 24, p. 161). They fall into two topographic types: those found on concave lowland forms, valley bottoms or lake basins, which have sometimes been distinguished as *basin-peats*, and, in contrast, those on long slopes and gentle ridges, for which Dr. H. Godwin coined the name *blanket-bog*, a term expressive of the way in which the peat covers all stable features of the original surface. Strictly speaking, basin peats are part of the blanket-bog in the uplands and it is only useful to separate them because they have, at times, a somewhat different and longer history as well as differences in present vegetation.

Flush-peats are also topographically conditioned, occurring only where water from a higher level impinges on the bog surface and brings to it a distinctive supply of minerals in solution. The three main types of dissolved materials (see p. 62) give rise to the flush types : (*a*) lime-rich, (*b*) iron-rich, (*c*) peaty, but the first of these types is not nowadays common in our uplands, except where the bed-rock includes limestone. It is usually marked by the presence of certain mosses, and of gasteropod shells, elsewhere absent from the upland zone. Iron-rich flushes are, however, frequent, not only in the upper woodlands, but also around the bog margins. They are usually indicated by the presence of ferric-iron deposits, either on or in the surface layers of soil or peat. Moreover, if this peat is exposed to air-drying, the red-brown colour frequently becomes widespread. Certain types of vegetation (see p. 107) are characteristic of these iron flushes. Peaty flushes are topographically distinct within the bog area but generally only show variants of the general bog vegetation.

While the properties of the soil in wet flushes are determined largely by the inflowing water in bog soils, certain other properties commonly exist to which attention may now be directed. The development of a peat-covering not only marks a stage in the soil development but it also modifies subsequent development by acting as a blanket which insulates, as it were, the mineral soil from the plants growing on the peat surface. At first these plants are rooted and are drawing mineral matter from the soil, but they get less and less dependent on it as time goes on and the peat gets deeper, and the soil water becomes more and more that derived from rain. As a general rule, then, the vegetation might be expected to show a transition in its mineral salt requirements from *eutrophic*, with high demands, to *oligotrophic*, with low salt requirements. Two things result from this : first, a succession of vegetation types, and secondly, a resultant succession of peat types. We shall see later that these facts help us in the analysis both of moorland vegetation and of the history of moorland areas. For the moment, however, we are more simply concerned with its effect on the properties of the soils. There will clearly be a change in composition throughout the peat profile, and the amount of mineral matter present in the peat will decrease as the level rises above the mineral base. This is apparently a general rule in upland peats, though, locally, flush effects may disturb the normal sequence. It should be noted, however, that it does not usually apply to the actual surface peats. Moor-burning is an almost universal practice nowadays, and its effect is to destroy the existing vegetation, leaving the mineral matter it contains to enrich the surface peat. Similarly, any form of oxidation of the surface peat, due, for example, to drainage, must have a similar effect, for the oxidation products of the organic matter are mainly carbon-dioxide and ash—the former of which escapes to the air, leaving the ash to increase the amount of mineral matter in the residual peat. Thus the surface peat, where moor-burning is practised, commonly contains more ash than the layers below it. The table opposite gives illustrative figures from peat-profiles in different British areas.

There are, of course, other effects which appear to be associated with this distribution of ash. Thus the acidity of the peat almost always increases from the lowest levels upwards—showing a general correlation with the decreasing ash content.

It will be seen from Table 5, and it follows from the arguments used above, that typical upland peats are remarkable for the small

Table 5

ASH CONTENTS (AS PER CENT OF THE DRY WEIGHT)
OF PEAT SAMPLES AT DIFFERENT DEPTHS

Depth below surface in cm.	*Lake District* (Stonesty Pike)	*Bowland Forest* (Clougha)	*Perthshire* (Rannoch Moor)	*Connemara* (Maam Cross)
10	3·0	7·3	4·7	4·9
30	1·4	2·3	2·2	3·0
50	4·4	4·8	3·0	2·4
80	6·3	5·3	3·1	6·4
100	15·2*	21·0*	5·6	19·3*
130			9·1	
160			13·2*	

* about 5-10 cm. above the mineral soil.

amount of ash they contain, and when we seek to define the term *bog*, it is usual to regard it as referring to peat of this type supporting an extremely oligotrophic vegetation. In this use of the term a bog is mainly dependent on atmospheric water (i.e. rain) and uninfluenced by ground-water. The term bog contrasts in usage with the term *fen* —derived from the extensive peat deposits in East Anglia. In terms of this usage, fen-peat is characterised by its high mineral content and hence by its dependence on ground water. It usually shows signs of an abundance of lime and is always lime-saturated peat with a luxuriant and eutrophic vegetation of tall reeds and small trees, willows and alders. Peats of this type are almost non-existent in the British uplands to-day, although long ago they existed in some of the hollows where lime-rich waters accumulated in small ponds and lakes. These now often show their former character by an underlying bed of marl. Almost all these areas are now deeply buried beneath bog-peat, and only small areas of flush peat remain round the bog margins to illustrate the effects of this type of peat on the vegetation. Where the basal peats were originally calcareous the succession of peat types above usually shows a much more gradual decrease in mineral content, and the sequence of vegetation types was often different.

Finally, where a peat-profile generally shows signs of differences in botanical composition at different levels, it also usually shows differences in physical structure. The changes are due partly to alterations in the composition of the vegetation from which the peat was formed, and sometimes they may be due to changes in the conditions (of humidity or temperature or drainage perhaps) under which the peat was formed. As a general rule, however, the most important progressive change in the peat must be associated with its decomposition as it gets older. Two sorts of change are possible : partial oxidation, which occurs particularly in the surface layers, and the slower changes which can ensue in water-saturated peat from which oxygen is absent. We assume that these are mainly hydrolytic—that is, caused by the slow action of water on the organic materials present. These are the changes which are generally implied when we say that a peat is *humified* or that it is undergoing *humification*. They are thought to result in the plant-remains gradually becoming gelatinous, so that, although the peat appears to retain visible structure, it escapes as a jelly through the fingers when squeezed in the hand. In contrast, the more recent peats usually retain a firm and fibrous structure. Even when a peat bed appears, on first opening it up, to consist of more or less uniform material, the bottom layers will normally differ in the degree of humification from those at the top. One result of this is that if such a bed is cut and a profile exposed to the air, it will soon appear to consist of two different types of peat. The fibres quickly become prominent and some are exposed by weathering, while the upper layers which contain them are often more quickly oxidised and so may become darker in colour. The lower layers, however, remain as a damp gelatinous mass and show less alteration on exposure. After a period of exposure they may thus appear to be of quite different composition, although the apparent difference is really one mainly of different physical and chemical condition.

THE BIOLOGICAL CHARACTERS OF SOILS

The peaty nature of upland soils is one of their most easily observed attributes. It is by no means confined to waterlogged areas, but it is equally noticeable on leached podsolic soils and even in the early stages of soil-formation on mountain-top detritus. This clearly indicates that the climatic effects characteristic of these three extreme types of habitat—waterlogging, leaching and low temperatures—are alike in leading to humus or peat accumulation in the soils affected. They do so in a generally similar way by reducing the activity of the soil micro-organisms.

Their effects differ in some respects and it will therefore be convenient to consider them separately, although actually they overlap in nature to a considerable degree. The effects produced on and by the soil organisms in their turn affect the vegetation of larger plants, and hence, as later chapters will show, have much effect on the larger animals.

Numerically, the soil flora mainly consists of vast numbers of bacteria and fungi. These are colourless plants, mostly of microscopic size in the soil, that obtain their nutriment by chemically changing the remains of dead plants and animals. They are responsible for what we usually call decay, although the chemical processes involved are analogous to and, indeed, often identical with, the processes of food digestion and utilisation in animals. The breakdown of plant organic matter in soil is, however, very generally initiated by small invertebrate animals, sometimes by the larvae of flies but particularly, as Charles Darwin showed, by earthworms. These break down the cellular structure of plant-remains and partly transform it, making it suitable for further transformation by fungi and bacteria. Most soils also contain single-celled animals, protozoa, which browse on the fungi and probably serve to keep them in check. There are also insects, such as springtails and fly larvae, whose role in soil economy is usually less well known.

This large soil-population requires air, or rather oxygen from the air, for breathing and it is consequently said to be *aerobic* in character.

In a normal soil the chemical materials produced during these transformations by the soil organisms are substances containing oxygen, carbon dioxide, which escapes to the air, nitrates, which contain the nitrogen which was present in the animal and plant proteins, and other substances such as sulphates and phosphates. Of these, nitrates are generally regarded as most important because they are quantitatively the materials a normal plant requires from the soil in largest amounts. Thus the fertility of a soil is usually determined very largely by the rate at which it can produce nitrates, i.e. the rate at which the nitrogen locked up in the decaying organic materials can be released in a form available to plants. In actual fact, plants can also use ammonia, but the amounts of ammonia in a natural soil are normally small. This substance is the first simple substance to be formed by bacteria and fungi during the soil decompositions. It is converted by other soil organisms, the *nitrifying* bacteria, into nitrate. These processes of ammonia production and nitrate formation seem to be particularly sensitive to adverse soil conditions. So also are the parallel processes of *nitrogen fixation* by which a fertile soil is usually able to increase its nitrogen content (to an extent which balances leaching losses) by fixing the gaseous nitrogen present in the air. This process is brought about in most soils by bacteria, as well as by the nodule-forming organisms which are found living in the root-nodules of leguminous plants like peas, beans and clover. Adverse soil conditions almost always produce their effects by retarding these processes as well as the numerous other processes, e.g. of decomposition, going on in the soil. Special effects are produced by the different adverse factors.

AEROBIC AND ANAEROBIC—OXIDISING AND REDUCING SOILS

The principal result of a soil becoming saturated with water is that the amount of oxygen in the soil is reduced to vanishing point. Consequently as most of the soil organisms are *aerobic*, requiring oxygen, the soil population is reduced to the minimum, and there can remain active only a few *anaerobic* organisms with specialised methods of maintaining their existence without oxygen. The products of the decompositions going on in the soil also change in character. Instead of the formation of carbon dioxide, nitrates, sulphates and phosphates, all containing oxygen, there may be produced instead marsh-gas (or methane, CH_4), ammonia (NH_3), sulphuretted hydrogen (H_2S) or other sulphides, and sometimes phosphine (PH_3), a series of compounds devoid of oxygen. All of these products are associated with the activities of anaerobic types of moulds or bacteria, the latter usually being most abundant. The microflora of waterlogged soils is thus specialised in character as well as poor in numbers, while the products of anaerobic composition include substances, in addition to those mentioned above, which may be toxic to the larger rooted plants. Some of the products are also responsible for other manifestations peculiar to boggy soils, such as the " will o' the wisp " and " corpse-light," these being attributed to the burning of the highly inflammable marsh and phosphine gases.

In effect, in contrasting waterlogged and aerated soils in this way, we are contrasting two sorts of micro-biological activity—*oxidising* and *reducing*—depending on whether the organisms can form chemically oxidised products like carbon dioxide and nitrates or chemically reduced substances like marsh-gas and ammonia.

The particular value of being able to recognise these possibilities is because they give us information as to the effect of the soil conditions on the action of living organisms, and we may infer that the conditions which affect the soil flora will also affect its fauna (see p. 212) as well as the larger plants. Moreover, the level of oxygen content which produces these biological effects is low and it is not one which can be detected in the field with any certainty, if at all, by measurements of soil oxygen. For our present purpose, therefore, it is useful to think of upland soils as belonging to the two types named above.

oxidising soils *contain*	*reducing soils* *contain*
nitrate	ammonia
carbon dioxide	marsh-gas (methane)
sulphate	sulphides
phosphate	phosphine
ferric-iron	ferrous-iron

It is useful also to realise that a large proportion of wet soils may be oxidising in drier periods and reducing in wet.

MULL AND MOR

In some respects the quantitative effects of leaching are similar to those produced by saturation with water—namely, a great reduction in the activity of the soil organisms. The qualitative effects of leaching on the soil micro-flora are, however, even more pronounced, and so much so that it is customary to give a special name, *mor*, to the peaty humus formed in leached soils, in order to distinguish it from the more fertile leaf-mould (or *mull*) typically associated with fertile forest soils. While *mor* is chemically different, as we shall see later, its most notice-able distinguishing features are biological and are easily recognised. There is a vegetation dominated by plants such as heathers, bilberry and wavy hair-grass (*Deschampsia flexuosa*), and normally an absence of earthworms. Usually, too, no tree seedlings are to be found except those of pine and birch. Moreover, leguminous plants such as clover are absent, while suitable tests show that the soil lacks nitrogen-fixing bacteria or, at least, effective strains of this type. Finally, the mor soil has a high and characteristic degree of acidity (p. 63), normally marked by a pH value below 3·8. It yields low proportions of ammonia, while nitrates are absent. It is evident, indeed, that in *mor* the rate and extent of nitrogen transformation is greatly reduced, presumably by the reduction in the numbers of suitable bacteria. It is in fact usually considered that the micro-flora of this type of humus contains few bacteria and is mainly one of moulds and of other fungi like actino-mycetes and basidiomycetes, but the evidence is far from conclusive owing to the difficulties of identifying these microscopic organisms in a dark-coloured peaty soil. Moulds and other fungi are generally more tolerant of acidity than are many soil bacteria, which fail to develop either in acid or in lime-deficient maedia.

It may be useful to add here a note on the soil animals which are more characteristic of *mor* soils. They include certain mites, the larval stages of two-winged flies (*Diptera*), click-beetles (*Elaterideae*), and often centipedes and predatory beetles. In contrast, earthworms, snails and millipedes are particularly characteristic of good forest leaf-moulds.

Mor soils in the strict sense in Britain are confined to the acid types of soil (normally with a podsol profile) distinguished in an earlier section. Characteristic *mull* soils are found on lime-deficient as well as on lime-saturated soils. More strongly base-deficient soils generally have humus of this type which produces nitrates (for example) rather slowly and may, at times, be somewhat intermediate in other respects.

The third factor which must profoundly affect the properties of the soil organic matter is the low temperature of many upland habitats. There can be no doubt that the soil organisms, like other forms of life, have their activity greatly reduced by low temperature. Hence the rate of decomposition of soil organic matter declines very rapidly in cold climates and peat accumulates, for the rate at which higher and larger plants *form* organic matter is less affected by low temperature, depending rather on the carbon-dioxide content of the air and on light. So far as I am aware, little or no investigation of the characters of this peaty material has been attempted, and the matter would probably be most easily examined by studying the rather peaty humus that accumulates on and among the mountain-top detritus. This is usually a black and easily crumbling peat generally containing a good deal of sand. It differs very markedly from a typical *mor*, such as that from below heather, for example, which is generally red-brown in colour, closer in texture and more acid. On the other hand, both soil-types have certain features in common such as some resemblance in fauna, e.g. scarcity of worms and frequency of dipterous larvae. There is also a good deal of evidence, though it is mainly derived from studies in arctic regions, that the bacterial processes affecting the accumulation of nitrogen (by fixation) and its liberation in forms suitable for plant food are especially curtailed by low temperature. As a result, there is certainly a notable scarcity of soluble forms of nitrogen in mountain-top habitats, though the limited available evidence suggests that this scarcity is not as severe as is the case in either bog-peat or acid *mor*. In my own observations, about half the tested soils have given traces of nitrates in late summer, and higher proportions might possibly be observed at other times. The interesting feature of the samples of humus from among mountain-top detritus has been their high proportion of nitrogen, usually 4 per cent of the total humus content. This does in fact suggest that there has been a rather slow decomposition of nitrogenous materials, though this is not the only possible explanation. The following short table summaries a few values for the nitrogen proportions of characteristic humus types.

Table 6

NITROGEN CONTENT OF DIFFERENT SOIL TYPES
AS PER CENT OF THEIR HUMUS CONTENTS

Soil	Vegetation	Percentage
Mountain-top detritus (2800-3000 ft.)	Moss-lichen grassland (see p. 85)	3·6-4·0
Mor over podsol (700-1000 ft.)	Heather-moor	1·0-2·0
Upland bog peat (1200-1500 ft.)	Mixed-bog with bog-moss (p. 147-152)	1·7-2·4
Flushed brown earth with *mull*	Oak-wood with soft-grass	3·1-3·5*

* Nitrates normally present.

This table brings out the low nitrogen content of the upland bog-peats and *mor* when contrasted with the *mull* humus of an oak-wood. Still more evident would this contrast be if we included the humus of lowland woods or of agricultural soils. The well-decomposed humus of a fertile arable soil, such as a wheat field, has commonly a nitrogen content of between 4·5 and 5 per cent, a value which seems to be a characteristic of soils in the lowland north temperate climate.

SIGNIFICANCE OF NITROGEN CONTENT OF HUMUS

The lower nitrogen content which is characteristic of upland peats and humus is due partly to the slow breakdown of the original plant materials. These, as a general rule, are rich in carbon and poor in nitrogen, though these proportions vary with the plant species. Consequently undecayed plant remains reflect principally the low nitrogen content of the original material. On the other hand, the ultimate nature of the humus produced depends also on the relative rates of breakdown and removal of the two main components—which are the carbonaceous and nitrogenous compounds. In many peats the soil bacteria are unable to attack cellulose, one of the principal materials containing carbon—a substance which makes up the bulk of plant cell-walls and skeletal structures. Slow though the breakdown of nitrogenous matters may be, therefore, it still is often more rapid than that of the chief carbon compounds, so that the latter gradually become more abundant and the percentage of nitrogen remaining in the humus becomes less. This condition has a further harmful effect on the activity of the soil fungi and bacteria, for most of these organisms prefer a growth medium containing a low C/N ratio. Thus in order to facilitate the breakdown of dead leaves in a rubbish-heap, gardeners often mix with it nitrogenous manurial materials, a treatment that results in a greatly accelerated rate of bacterial decomposition of the plant remains.

As a general rule, then, soil humus containing a high proportion of nitrogen normally indicates a soil which contains an active micro-biological population and a more rapid turnover of the nutrient substances (like nitrogen and phosphorus) which are present in the soil humus. We can, indeed, use this as a useful index of soil fertility.

In the table, for example, the humus of the montane oak-woods is clearly producing a heavier crop of vegetation than that of the heather-moor, which is comparable as a site of somewhat similar humidity. Similarly, while upland bog peats as a class have a very low nitrogen content (1·7 to 2·4 per cent), " flushed " areas in the same localities have humus with a higher nitrogen content (usually 2·5-3·0 per cent). Dr. G. K. Frazer, who first drew attention to this fact, observed that certain coniferous trees would grow on the flushed peats, though not on the nitrogen-poor ones, a fact which is, in part at least, associated with the higher rate of nutrient turnover in the flushed habitats. Thus there are grounds for associating higher proportions of soil nitrogen with higher fertility, even though the method of basing the arguments wholly on the size of the vegetation cannot always be safely applied, particularly in upland areas where exposure, soil instability and human interference may often have as much effect on the vegetation as the soil properties.

The high nitrogen content of " flush " peats is a feature which is equally evident in other flush areas—when they are compared with their leached surroundings. Not only is this due to the fact that flushes of all sorts are accumulation areas, into which soluble forms of nitrogen are carried—as well as lime and potash—but there is also the probability that the higher base-status due to the latter greatly favours the fixation of nitrogen and so enhances the accumulation effects. At any rate, the high nitrogen content of the humus from flushed soils, whether dry or wet, is a striking and invariable feature of upland areas.

It is, therefore, interesting to note again (Table 6) the high nitrogen content of the humus of mountain-top detritus which supports the assumption that this type of surface may be regarded as a type of dry flush, a conclusion made earlier on purely physical and topographic grounds. There is, however, no reason to believe that the deeper peats which may finally accumulate on a mountain-top differ in any material respect from those of the " bog " and " mor " types already described.

THE SOIL HABITATS AS A WHOLE

This survey of upland soil properties will perhaps serve to emphasise the value of the method of looking at soils both as dynamic and also as biological systems—views which are, of necessity, very closely related.

It will be profitable now to consider more fully the inter-relations of the factors operating in the soil habitat, excluding at this stage the mountain-top types as mostly those showing retarded development. Upland soils clearly range from lime-saturated to highly acid and from comparatively dry to permanently waterlogged. In order to show their inter-relations it is necessary to have scales both of acidity or lime-saturation and of humidity. For the former we can use the terms suggested earlier (p. 62): lime-saturated, lime-deficient, base-deficient and acid. For degrees of soil humidity it is convenient to use the water/humus ratio. It was shown many years ago by Mr. W. B. Crump that the relative humidity of a peaty soil depends on its humus content and that the most convenient way of expressing this humidity was to take the ratio of water to humus. In the present instance we can use the humidity of a well-drained sandstone oak-wood or a dry heather-moor to represent a normal value, with relative humidity between 2 and 3 in summer. As a second limit we might take another convenient biological one : the degree of humidity at which trees fail to grow. This is commonly at a relative humidity just above 7 in summer, for samples taken at 4-6 in. below the surface. (Isolated bushes of water-tolerating species like willows may occur in more humid conditions.) The last limit would logically be to separate soils which are permanently waterlogged—*reducing* soils—from those that may have a period of aeration and oxidation in summer. It must be admitted that it is almost impossible to define this condition in terms of water content, as this quantity varies enormously in wet peats, depending on their texture, whether fibrous or gelatinous, for example. A peat with a summer water/humus ratio of 14 or 15 is probably always waterlogged and reducing. Some peats of this type have summer relative humidities as low as 10 or 11. Nevertheless for the purpose of description we have :

1 normal soils, relatively humidity (R.H.) 2 to 3
2 damp soils, R.H. 3 to 7
3 wet soils, but periodically oxidising, R.H. to 10
4 waterlogged and permanently reducing soils

Another thing makes it hard to compare the very wet and the dry soils. The levels of acidity are very different. So far as is known, peats which have been permanently waterlogged are never very acid, their pH values do not seem to fall below 5 and are often well above this limit. The reasons for this are not fully known but one effect may easily be appreciated. If one part of the same peaty material contains, in one example, 2 parts of water, and in another, when waterlogged, 20 parts, it is probable that the acidity will be reduced in the latter example to approximately one-tenth of the former value. This would in effect increase the pH value by one, e.g. from 4 to 5. However, the differences in acidity between dry and waterlogged peats of similar origin are often much greater than this, and there is reason to believe that the highly acid peaty soils owe a good deal of their acidity to oxidation processes, probably those brought about by micro-organisms in the soil when air is allowed to penetrate. The practical effect of this is, however, that soils of " normal " humidity have a range of acidity about twice as great as that of waterlogged soils.

Moreover, in waterlogged soils ferrous iron is present, and this leaches out or becomes " available " for plants as readily as does lime. Thus there are commonly three biological types of waterlogged soils, (a) lime-saturated soils, (b) flush soils, often base-deficient, through which iron is being transported, (c) strongly base-deficient soils when peaty ; (a) and (c) are " fen " and " bog " peats.

If we try to present all these features together it is necessary to represent them graphically—in some such way as is indicated in Fig. 16.

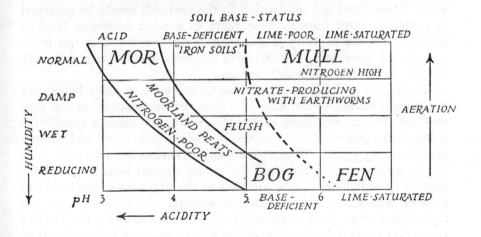

FIG. 16.—Summary of upland soil relations, somewhat idealised. Wet reducing and acid soils are normally without woodlands.

This diagram should not be interpreted too literally, but it is useful as a way of thinking about the upland soils.

The diagram may perhaps help us to visualise the moorland soils as a range of peats extending from the bog type to the acid mor. They vary greatly in acidity as well as in aeration and water content. Though they show diversity in all these respects, they possess two chemical characters in common : a great deficiency in mineral bases and a humus containing very low proportions of nitrogen. The latter feature indicates one of their biological characteristics, a low rate of decay ; and this coincides with a second biological attribute, the absence or inactivity of the nitrogen-fixing and nitrefying bacteria, shown also by the absence of nitrates. A third biological feature that is easily ascertained, the absence of earthworms, seems to be generally similar in distribution.

The diagram may be equally useful if the attempt is made to define the characters of upland soils as a class and in contrast to those of the lowlands. They fall naturally into the left-hand half of the diagram, the classes of acid and base-deficient soils. Most of the peats are in the class of acid soils.

As a rule, only the flushed soils and those which have more recently become stable belong to the category of base-deficient soils, while the upland soils which we could call only lime-poor occupy a negligible area. These latter are soils which in the lowlands would be regarded as requiring extra lime to raise them to a good economic level of fertility. Yet the majority of upland soils lie far below even this level, and, as we have seen, the trend of soil-development is continually tending to increase these deficiencies.

Correlated with this marked scarcity of lime and other bases goes the transformation of the humus. It is rich in nitrogen in the *mull* soils (at the top and right of the diagram), diminishing steadily as either the degree of aeration or the base-status gets lower and the soil becomes more peaty. Thus upland soils as a class are relatively poor in nitrogenous matter, although the actual amount locked up in peat may be considerable. These changes in the character of the soils run parallel with major changes in soil fertility. In both natural and agricultural types of vegetation, fertility, as measured by the bulk of vegetation produced annually, diminishes in response to the trends in soil development that are produced by leaching and waterlogging.

CHAPTER 5

MOUNTAIN VEGETATION

T H E vegetation of the uplands consists of two main types. At the highest levels and on the more mountainous types of surface are *montane* types of vegetation which are usually most prominent at altitudes of 2,000 ft. and upwards ; below this level there are various types of *submontane* vegetation, readily distinguished by the form and mode of life of the principal plants as well as by their relation to the main topographic features, and hence to the trends of surface and soil. Thus on the steeper slopes and better drainage there are grasslands and woodlands. Wherever the slopes are gentle and comparable with those of the lowlands, lowly vegetation of the *moorland* and *bog* type occupies the leached and waterlogged surfaces. It will be convenient to consider the types of upland vegetation in this order, montane vegetation being dealt with in the present chapter, and submontane in Chapters 6-8.

Technically this is not a wholly logical arrangement, since presumably bogs may occur at any level. In practice, however, the extensive areas of bog are mostly submontane, and those at higher levels show comparatively unimportant differences from those at lower levels, about which very little is known.

In considering British montane vegetation, it is perhaps especially necessary by way of introduction to ask first, what is to be looked for, secondly, where it is to be found, and lastly, why it is there. This is because to unpractised eyes at least much of our high-level vegetation is somewhat undistinguished in appearance—and, in particular, lacks the striking flowers which one may meet in profusion among mountains such as the Alps and Pyrenees. The commonest form of montane vegetation in Britain is some sort of poor and stunted grassland, and further description of these grasslands may be conveniently left to a later stage (p. 86). It must be remarked now, however, that they show what we might call the average condition in the montane zone, representing the sum of the effects of an inclement climate, a rain-washed and base-deficient soil and, also no doubt, the uniformity which has resulted from almost continuous cropping by sheep or deer. For our present purpose much more interest is to be found in looking at the extremes of the mountain vegetation types, for these contain most of the special mountain plants. We can obtain a clue as to what to look for by recalling from the preceding chapter that the especially characteristic physical features of a mountain are its topographic instability and the presence of " immature " soils. One group of very important vegetation types will thus include vegetation *colonising* bare areas, these being usually disintegrating rock-waste. At the other end of the scale there will be areas (usually those of gentle slope) which have long been stable and which have become quite leached by rain-washing so that they now support peat or heath vegetation. The salts washed from these leached areas must emerge somewhere, so that finally there will be a series of enriched or " flushed " soils bearing what we may call *flush* vegetation. We can thus arrange the sections of this chapter in the following way : (*a*) colonising communities, (*b*) grasslands, (*c*) vegetation on leached soils, (*d*) flush vegetation.

COLONISING VEGETATION

The bare montane areas which are in process of being colonised by montane vegetation show a wide variation in physical condition. They range in stability, for example, from bare rock-faces to constantly shifting gravel-slides on the steeper and most unstable scree-slopes. The former of these habitats supports only a colonising vegetation of mosses, and as these appear only where some moisture is constantly coming from above, their consideration falls more conveniently under the heading of " bryophyte flushes " (p. 94). On unstable gravel-slides, in contrast, large size seems to be a chief requisite for success as a plant colonist, for the successful ones are never mosses, which cannot keep pace with the moving gravel, but robust plants like the tufted hair-grass (*Deschampsia caespitosa*), followed by other flowering plants as the surface becomes partly stabilised.

The commonest montane types of bare area, however, are the two we can call block-scree and mountain-top detritus, found respectively on the mountain's flank and crest. Given fairly normal exposure, both of these are alike in being first colonised by the woolly hair-moss (*Rhacomitrium lanuginosum*), but after this the resemblance ceases. The large rocks of which a block-scree is usually composed offer a good deal of shelter, so that flowering plants and ferns establish themselves at an early stage. On mountain-top detritus, however, most of the

PLATE II

B. A. Crouch

a. View from Grassmoor to Scafell Pike: mountain-top detritus and sub-alpine grasslands. September

B. A. Crouch

b. The Pillar mountain from the Haystacks: a rock mountain and a wet summit September

ENGLISH LAKE DISTRICT

PLATE 12

John Markham

Cairngorms, Inverness-shire: *Rhacomitrium*-heath at 3,800 ft. with mountain-top
detritus exposed. June

early vegetation is composed of mosses and lichens, flowering plants being much less prominent. Another noticeable feature of block-scree is the way in which the colonising plants vary in response to diversity in the nature of the rock, a feature that may, perhaps, best be illustrated by a few examples. On millstone grit or sandstone in the Pennines, or on granite in the Scottish Highlands, one would expect to find only colonists such as the lichens already mentioned, the woolly hair-moss and the rock-moss (*Andreaea rupestris*). The first flowering plants to appear are bilberry (*Vaccinium myrtillus*), cowberry (*V. vitis-idaea*) and crowberry (*Empetrum nigrum*), usually with the fir club-moss (*Lycopodium selago*)—species, on the whole, characteristic of leached soils and raw humus.

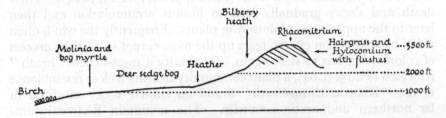

FIG. 17.—The southern ridge of Ben Wyvis, showing effects of slope and rock-dip. Rainfall 45 inches. Vertical scale x 2.

On block-spree in the Lake District, where the rocks are slaty and modified volcanic ashes, these plants are likely to be accompanied in the hollows by other species, particularly by the parsley fern (*Cryptogramma crispa*), the mountain fern (*Thelypteris limbosperma*), the least willow (*Salix herbacea*) and alpine lady's mantle (*Alchemilla alpina*). On block-scree from mica-schists, these might be further augmented by the mountain lady-fern (*Athyrium distentifolium*), the brittle bladder-fern (*Cystopteris fragilis*) and beech-fern (*Thelypteris phegopteris*). On strongly basic plutonic rocks in Skye and Rhum, isolated flowering plants may appear even before the hair-moss. The earliest arrivals are often the rock-cress (*Arabis petraea*) and stone-bramble (*Rubus saxatilis*), closely followed by the alpine saw-wort (*Saussurea alpina*) and alpine meadow-rue (*Thalictrum alpinum*).

Enough has been said to illustrate the great influence the under-lying rock has on the colonising flora in this type of habitat. Equally marked is the way in which the proportion of ferns increases when the slope has a northerly aspect.

Rhacomitrium-heath.   The most striking of the strictly montane types of vegetation and among the most extensive are those colonising the stony wastes of mountain-top detritus.   The surface instability of this material is such that it is often very difficult for plants to establish themselves on it and consequently, even where vegetation is most extensive, it usually does not completely hide the substratum.   In the first instance, the rock-waste is colonised by the woolly hair-moss (*Rhacomitrium lanuginosum*), accompanied by a number of lichens.   The deep, greenish-grey carpets of the moss develop from between the stones, and are held among them (Pls. 12, p. 81, and 13, p. 84).   Their death and decay gradually lead to humus accumulation and then later to the appearance of flowering plants.   Frequently the wind, often aided by solifluction effects, tears up the moss carpet so that the process of colonisation has to start again.   Gradually a moss-lichen " heath " is formed (Pl. 13, p. 84), a plant community bearing a close resemblance to the " Rhacomitrium-heath " found on similar rocky substrata in far northern and arctic countries.   The mountain Rhacomitrium-heath appears in various aspects.   Sometimes it may consist of little except a soft and deep carpet of the moss.   Very often the mountain sedge (*Carex bigelowii*) may be present as almost the only associate. Next may appear either the sheep's fescue (*Festuca ovina*) or the wavy hair-grass (*Deschampsia flexuosa*), the former more frequently in the west, the latter more often in the drier east, though much depends on local conditions.   Wherever the moss carpet is not continuous there are other mosses and numerous lichens, of which the most abundant are lichens, (*Cornicularia aculeata* and *Cetraria islandica*), Cladonias (including *C. rangiferina*, the reindeer moss, and *C. arbuscula*, Pl. 13), and the coral-like *Sphaerophorus fragilis*. Other common associates among the larger plants include another grass, the bent (*Agrostis tenuis*), heath bedstraw (*Galium saxatile*) and the dwarf shoots of bilberry. There may be present also the least willow (*Salix herbacea*) and two club-mosses, the fir (*Lycopodium selago*) and the alpine (*L. alpinum*). The runners and rhizomes of all these plants are usually buried beneath the moss carpet and the tips of their shoots emerge through it. With the plants already mentioned, these make up the normal species which are likely to be present on most mountain summits, though in varying proportions.

It should be emphasised that the simple moss-lichen carpet is characteristic of areas which are still unstable through frost-heaving and other soil-moving agencies. In this condition, the lichens play an especially significant part in the process of soil development, for, by fixing nitrogen from the air, they build up the nitrogenous reserves of the soil to levels at which the soil bacteria and the flowering plants normally operate. They have, of course, a similar role on the coarser scree slopes or on any other mainly inorganic and newly-colonised area. On the mountain-top, the moss carpet next tends to develop into some form of grassland, and later into summit heath or bog. These changes depend partly on the degree to which the mountain-top detritus becomes stabilised, partly on the nature of the underlying rock and partly on the topography.

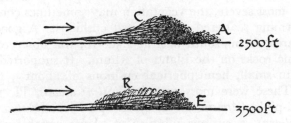

FIG. 18.—Wavelike plant development on high wind-exposed slopes : A, Bearberry ; C, Heather ; E, Crowberry ; R, Hair-moss.

Wind Exposure. Before we go on to consider these changes, however, it may be of interest to refer to other features of plant colonisation in this habitat. Every naturalist knows how profoundly shelter and exposure affect plant and animal distribution in mountain areas. Nowhere is this more clearly shown than on the mountain-top detritus, where exposure and insolation may be extreme. The Rhacomitrium-carpet is especially liable to be torn up by strong winds, and probably for this reason it is often absent on exposed westerly or north-westerly slopes. It is also almost always absent from areas showing marked solifluction effects of the polygon or stone-stripe type.

It was remarked by C. B. Crampton in Caithness and Sutherland, where exposure to north-westerly winds is especially severe, that heathy vegetation often gradually establishes itself in a wave-like form, and Dr. A. S. Watt has recently described the development of these waves in detail as it occurs in the Cairngorms (see Fig. 18). The essential feature is the presence of small shrubs like heather (*Calluna*)*, bearberry (*Arctostaphylos*) and crowberry (*Empetrum*), which, once established, grow horizontally with their leaves and branches towards the more sheltered direction. Thus there is gradually built up a sheltered zone in which the mosses and lichens can develop and in which new individuals of the shrubby plants can start. At lower altitudes (say 2,500 ft.) this often gives a " wave " of bearberry and heather, the former growing in the shelter of heather but being suppressed by the heather growing over it. At levels above 3,000 ft. crowberry is more usually the " holdfast," with Rhacomitrium and lichens growing among its older and leafless branches, often with such species as bilberry and three-leaved rush (*Juncus trifidus*).

Elsewhere, however, colonisation may follow quite a different pattern. On some exposed areas of detritus, perhaps those on which insolation is most severe, the vegetation may sometimes consist wholly of plants forming scattered and isolated cushions. A good example of such an area, facing south-west at 2,500 ft., was observed on ultra-basic plutonic rocks on the island of Rhum. It supported only four species, all in small, hemispherical cushions of about 3 to 4 in. in diameter. These were moss campion (*Silene acaulis*, Pl. 14, p. 85), thrift (or sea-pink) (*Armeria maritima*), sheep's fescue (*Festuca ovina*) and heather (*Calluna*), a curious mixture of plants capable of living in widely different localities and apparently alike only in their ability to form small cushions.

Elsewhere, and possibly where there is some flushing by underground water, the open sand or gravel of solifluction areas may show a sprinkling of slender plants such as three-leaved rush and mountain woodrush (*Luzula spicata*). An area of this type is shown from the Cairngorms in Plate 25, p. 208. Dr. A. S. Watt has observed that these areas also are more typical of exposed west-facing slopes in the Cairngorms, while the eastern slopes are more often moss or grass-covered. Fig. 19 illustrates another flush effect, recorded by C. B. Crampton from Caithness.

On areas showing stone-stripes or polygons, vegetation usually starts first in the lines of stones, presumably because seeds are caught

---

*Throughout this book the English name " heather " is used to denote *Calluna vulgaris*, also known as ling.

PLATE 13

John Markham

Rhacomitrium-heath at 3,600 ft.: mainly woolly hair-moss, mountain sedge and
Cladonia sylvatica

PLATE 14

John Markham

a. A dry flush with *Silene acaulis*, 4,000 ft. Cairngorms, Inverness-shire, June

J. S. Barlee

b. Saxifraga oppositifolia on base-rich rock, *c.* 2,500 ft. Cwm Glas, Snowdon
Caernarvonshire, April

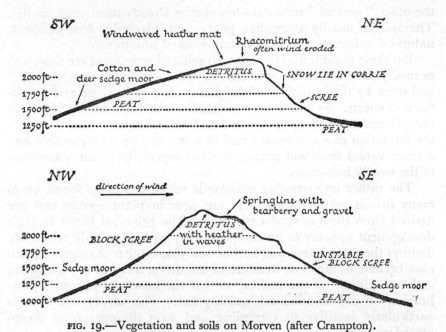

FIG. 19.—Vegetation and soils on Morven (after Crampton).

in the gaps between the stones. There appear to be no constantly present colonists in such places ; almost anything producing seeds in the near vicinity may be represented, even the peat-loving cotton-sedge (*Eriophorum vaginatum*), but woolly hair-moss is curiously infrequent.

MONTANE GRASSLANDS

It has already been pointed out that the commonest form of mountain vegetation is some form of grassland. This is a natural development from the Rhacomitrium-heath. As humus accumulates in the cracks of the mountain-top detritus, grasses become increasingly numerous and finally almost entirely replace the moss. When complete, this change is also associated with another development: that of a continuous vegetation and humus cover, the underlying stones being now no longer visible. The chief plants in the grassland are viviparous sheep's fescue (*Festuca vivipara*) and wavy hair-grass along with the other " normal " mountain-top species already mentioned (p. 82). The soil is usually somewhat peaty and markedly base-deficient, natural developments in heavily rain-washed situations.

But these natural developments in soil and vegetation are slow, and normally they are much retarded by the continual " frost-heaving " and often by the instability of the surface due to its slope and to soli-fluction effects. So long as the winter frosts are continually lifting up the soil-surface, puffing up the soil and extruding stones, so long will the formation of a continuous turf of a few species be impossible and a more varied flora will persist, marked especially by an abundance of the woolly hair-moss.

The rather uninteresting grasslands which are to be found on so many British mountain summits are poor in plant species and are derived from these normal conditions. The principal factor in their development appears to be sheep-grazing, which not only selectively destroys the more interesting herbaceous plants other than grasses, but also, because of the close treading of the sheep, leads to the trampling and " puddling " of the surface, so that the beneficial effects of frost-heaving on soil aeration are quickly lost. The woolly hair-moss is particularly sensitive to trampling and soon disappears on sheep-grazed summits.

In contrast, some mountains possess grasslands with a much greater variety of plant species present than is normally the case. In these " rich grasslands " the small flowering plants of the less common mountain species are as numerous as the grasses, and a considerable proportion of hair-moss always persists.

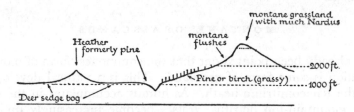

FIG. 20.—Meall Buidhe (Perthshire), showing subnatural vegetation and slope. Rainfall 70 inches. Vertical scale x 2.

This type of grassland is particularly characteristic of the friable mica-schists of the Central Scottish Highlands, such as are found on

Ben Lawers. The list following is taken from the long ridges of Meall Buidhe (2,813 ft.) and Ben Chreachain (3,540 ft.) in Western Perthshire. In addition to what we may regard as the " normal " mountain-top species of the Rhacomitrium-heath already mentioned, there were the following, while the alpine lady's mantle and heath bedstraw were markedly abundant.

> *Carex pilulifera*, pill-headed sedge
> *Deschampsia caespitosa*, tufted hair-grass (mountain forms)
> *Euphrasia spp.* (e.g. *E. frigida*), eyebright
> *Gnaphalium supinum*, dwarf cudweed
> *Juncus trifidus*, three-leaved rush
> *Luzula spicata*, mountain woodrush
> *Oxyria digyna*, mountain sorrel
> *Polygonum viviparum*, alpine bistort
> *Potentilla erecta*, tormentil
> *Rumex acetosa*, sorrel
> *Saxifraga stellaris*, starry saxifrage
> *Sibbaldia procumbens*, sibbaldia
> *Solidago cambrica*, mountain golden-rod
> *Thymus serpyllum*, thyme

There were also additional mosses of which *Rhytidiadelphus loreus, Pleurozium schreberi, Olichotrichum hernicynicum* and *Polytrichum alpinum* were most frequent. The presence of numerous montane or arctic plants, which is the most noteworthy feature of these rich grasslands, is associated with two features : one, already mentioned, being the presence of an underlying rock which readily weathers to maintain the supply of mineral salts (bases), and the second being the presence of open spaces in which the mountain plants can establish themselves. Plate 12, p. 81, shows clearly the rather open type of vegetation in which these plants are found. It is evident that topographic features may also be important in producing these open and rich grasslands. Even on rich or friable rocks such as mica-schist, the " rich " grasslands are confined mainly to the steeper, better-drained and less stable slopes above 2,000 ft., and especially to the narrower ridges, where the surface undergoes some erosion and consequently shows " dryflush " effects (Fig. 20). On the more extensive mountain summits, even on the rocks richer in lime, the slopes are more gradual and the grasslands generally are poorer in species, except where solifluction effects or weathering maintain surface instability and flush conditions.

On such mountains, the summit vegetation often shows very definite zonations, which are well shown on Ben Alder (see Fig. 21). Commonly the mountain-top detritus in the highest zone is that most recently colonised, and it is covered by a deep mat of Rhacomitrium with little else but the mountain sedge, though lower down this gradually changes to a belt of poor grassland. On more westerly mountains (e.g. Ben Alder) this contains viviparous fescue and mountain sedge in addition to the moss; in the east (e.g. Ben Wyvis), wavy hair-grass often replaces the fescue.

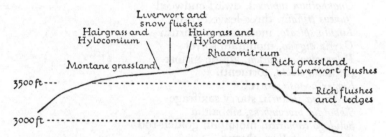

FIG. 21.—Ben Alder : Mountain " grasslands " and flushes. Rainfall 80 inches. Vertical scale x 2.

Still lower, the water draining from these higher zones comes near the surface, carrying with it the salts leached from above. The grassland will now be dominated by small alpine forms of tufted hair-grass (*Deschampsia caespitosa*), such as the variety *brevifolia*, characteristically associated with the mosses *Rhytidiadelphus squarrosus* and *Rhytidiadelphus loreus* and often also with *Hypnum splendens* and *Pleurozium schreberi*. This grassland of tufted hair-grass and *Rhytidiadelphus* is the most widespread and characteristic damp-flush community of the montane grasslands, always occurring on a brown soil of rather higher base and nitrogen status, in contrast to the more strongly leached soils of the summit Rhacomitrium-heath.

On all these modifications on the gentler and more stable summit slopes, however, the vegetation cover is usually more complete and individuals of the less common mountain species are correspondingly less frequent, though they at once appear where the gentler summit slopes fall more steeply into crag and scree. This point is shown clearly in Plate 12, as well as in Figs. 20 and 21.

In the Lake District and in Wales, the summit grasslands are generally poorer in species, even though the rocks are often fairly rich in bases and the topography is apparently suitable. To some extent this may be due to the hardness of the rocks and the slowness with which they weather. Partly also it is due to the geographical factors which cause some of the species to be absent. There seems to be no obvious reason, for example, why the alpine lady's mantle and yellow mountain saxifrage (*Saxifraga aizoides*) should be common in the Lake District but absent from Snowdonia. Similar differences in flora exist between these areas and the Scottish Highlands, where generally the arctic and montane plants as a whole are commoner. Both the Welsh and the Lake District grasslands have, however, also suffered very greatly from heavy sheep-grazing, which eliminates the herbaceous plants, leaving the grasses and sedges predominant.

The high-level or sub-alpine grasslands thus described are probably the only wholly natural form of grassland in this country. On the one hand and at lower levels, they merge into the extensive Festuca-Agrostis grasslands described later (p. 101) which cover so much of the lower slopes of our mountains, but which are for the most part derived from former woodland or scrub. On the other hand, the sub-alpine grasslands can be traced into the more open vegetation of scree and gravel-slide, where physical instability prevents a complete vegetation cover, and at the same time the combined effects of this factor and perhaps of wind exposure or solifluction seem to prevent the formation of a continuous moss-carpet.

SUMMIT-HEATH VEGETATION

The mountain-top detritus is a porous material which must be continuously losing salts by leaching. It therefore shows a marked tendency to give rise to poor and rain-washed soils. The poorer grasslands correspond to a phase in this development when the soils are base-deficient and poor in plant nutrients such as available sources of nitrogen. The process proceeds, however, to a still more extreme condition in which even poorer and more acid soils are produced. These support a vegetation in which small heath-like shrubs of low nutrient requirements are prominent. The actual plants vary with humidity and drainage, but they normally include five species in particular—namely, cowberry (*Vaccinium vitis-idaea*), bilberry (*V.*

myrtillus), crowberry (*Empetrum nigrum*), bearberry (*Arctostaphylos uva-ursi*), and the wavy hair-grass. In the drier eastern Highlands in particular, cowberry is often the most noticeable plant, and the mountain azalea (*Loiseleuria procumbens*) may also be abundant, as it is on Lochnagar. There is a variant of this heath on the southern ridge of Ben Wyvis (Fig. 17), which also has much alpine lady's mantle (*Alchemilla alpina*), the dip of the rock causing the development of a dry, leached surface, although it is not quite stable. In the western Highlands, crowberry is usually much more prominent. In Caithness, C. B. Crampton observed that the bearberry and its alpine counterpart (*A. alpina*) became dominant where acid flush waters drained from the summit detritus (see Fig. 19).

A somewhat closely related form of vegetation occurs on many of the lower and flatter summits where a deeper bog peat covers the original detritus. The most abundant plant in addition to the heath species is likely to be sheathed cotton-sedge (*Eriophorum vaginatum*), but the peculiar feature of the vegetation is often the presence of such plants as cloudberry (*Rubus chamaemorus*), mountain blaeberry (*Vaccinium uliginosum*) and mountain forms of the creeping willow (*Salix repens*). That northern curiosity, the dwarf birch (*Betula nana*), occurs with these at times but only at lower altitudes.

These summit-heaths and bogs are particularly characteristic of areas which are becoming topographically stable and of mountains composed of hard rocks poor in lime, such as granites or hard sandstones. But summit-heath is also present, often in a ragged form, on the many flatter summits which were formerly peat-covered, and from which most of the peat has now been eroded. In such places there is an inheritance of acid peat between the stones, while remnants either of the original deposit or of redistributed peat are common. The colonisation of these areas resembles that of the original raw-rock detritus, but the presence of such species as the two cotton-sedges (*Eriophorum angustifolium* and *E. vaginatum*), the moor mat-grass (*Nardus stricta*) and moor-rush (*Juncus squarrosus*), all of which may be more or less abundant, is indicative of the difference in origin.

The normal trend of vegetational development on the mountain-top detritus with increasing stability of surface thus follows the sequence : Rhacomitrium-heath→|summit-grassland——→|summit-heath (dry or wet), and it is associated with the leaching of the humus which follows the stabilisation of the surface.

FLUSH VEGETATION

There are many places on a mountain that support flush vegetation simply because there are many channels for the constant downward movement of soil and of drainage water from above. The most easily defined habitats are those that surround emerging springs, that lie above the crumbling sides of little water-courses, or that occupy ledges on rock-faces which receive soil or downward-draining water. These are all lines of active erosion or deposition, exposing new soils or accumulating material from above. There are, of course, innumerable other places where there is some measure of soil-creep or the occasional percolation of flush water.

The vegetation of these places is as infinitely variable as their slope, aspect and drainage. Its common feature is that it includes the numerous montane plants which are not normally found at lower altitudes or are much less frequent there. Some of these have already been met with in dealing with the summit and scree vegetation, others are more restricted in distribution and are confined to the moister flushes. The majority are indeed not much affected by the humidity of the soil, but a limited number possibly show a preference for drier rock-ledges and soil-flushes. They include such forms as the mountain avens (*Dryas octopetala*), northern bedstraw (*Galium boreale*), alpine cinquefoil (*Potentilla crantzii*), mountain saxifrage (*Saxifraga oppositifolia*) and spring sandwort (*Minuartia verna*). All occur on occasion on dry limestone rocks. The wet flushes are far more abundant and characteristic and they can roughly be separated into two extreme forms, those around spring-heads and those on rock-ledges, but many of the same species occur in both. These places differ mainly in that the rocky ledges are generally inaccessible to grazing animals and as a consequence their vegetation includes many broad-leaved and woody species which cannot survive where grazing animals can feed. In contrast, the wet flushes away from the rock-faces are more commonly saturated with water. Partly for this reason and perhaps partly because they are open to grazing, their vegetation is more lowly and usually has a large proportion of rushes and sedges.

Damp Ledges. The vegetation of the flushed ledges is extremely variable, but it usually follows a logical pattern. Almost all the montane flush species may at first be present, and the yellow mountain saxifrage (*S. aizoides*), roseroot (*Sedum rosea*) and mountain sorrel (*Oxyria*) are usually prominent. The sea-campion (*Silene maritima*) is not infrequent, a somewhat unexpected plant to find at high altitudes. More local in their distribution are the mountain species of Poa (*P. alpina, P. glauca*), the alpine hawkweed (*Hieracium alpinum*), the alpine meadow-rue (*Thalictrum alpinum*) and alpine saw-wort (*Saussurea alpina*). After an initial stage of colonisation, there is usually a considerable accumulation of humus, and as time goes on the montane colonists are augmented by shrubby and large-leaved forms. Commonly the mountain willows (e.g. *S. phylicifolia, S. myrsinites* and *S. lapponum*) become very prominent and they frequently project outwards to form a sort of gradually extending platform on which still more humus accumulates. Large, damp-flush plants like the globe-flower (*Trollius europaeus*), mountain cranesbill (*Geranium sylvaticum*), water avens (*Geum rivale*) and great woodrush (*Luzula sylvatica*) then tend to crowd out the more strictly montane species. After heavy rain, the whole system may collapse and then the process starts again, but often humus accumulation continues long enough to allow the upper layers to become more and more base-deficient. The vegetation then comes to include a considerable proportion of heath and bog plants growing in the poorer surface layers of humus, as well as the true flush species rooted in the lower layers of soil or those nearest the rock. When this is the case the vegetation is generally shrubby, with the mountain blaeberry particularly characteristic, growing among a carpet of crowberry and bilberry. The dwarf cornel (*Chamaepericlymenum suecicum*) is often present, and, very commonly, sheets of bog-mosses (*Sphagnum cymbifolium, S. girgensohnii* and *S. rubellum*). Of the flush flora in such places, the least and the downy willows, the mountain bistort, alpine meadow-rue, and fir and alpine club-mosses, usually persist longest.

While the ledges show every conceivable gradation, there is a general tendency for the heathy or boggy ledges to be commoner on buttresses as well as on the harder and chemically poor rocks which are more resistant to weathering or are poor in lime. Ledges in gullies more often remain flushed, and while they are noteworthy for the luxuriance of their flora, they finally tend to support closed masses of vegetation which, except at the margins, offer little scope for the restricted mountain flora. Otherwise, the noteworthy features of the ledge flora are the presence of shrubby species and the scarcity of

PLATE 15

John Markham

Liverwort flush above 3,000 ft., mainly *Scapania* sp., and golden saxifrage. June

PLATE 16

b. Dryas octopetala, " one of the most striking of alpine plants"

a. A damp flush including *Saxifraga hypnoides* and mosses grasses, the latter being remarkable when the abundance of these plants on most mountains is considered. The luxuriance of the vegetation is particularly noticeable when the area of mountain-side drained by the flush is extensive or when this area is a favoured grazing place of sheep or deer. In the latter case, the manurial effects of animal droppings may fertilise the drainage waters and hence affect the ledge vegetation for a long distance below. Two species in particular with an especially high nitrogen requirement, nettle (*Urtica dioica*) and herb robert (*Geranium robertianum*), often become abundant. More frequently this type of flush effect is associated with a greater prominence of the great woodrush (*Luzula sylvatica*) and of the tufted hair-grass, which is then represented by its large lowland form. C. B. Crampton noticed that both these species were very luxuriant below eagle's eyries in northern Scotland, where there is also, no doubt, an abundance of nitrogenous refuse.

Wet and Open Flushes. These differ in that they always support a luxuriant vegetation of bryophytes—that is, of mosses and liverworts. Marginal and very characteristic are usually silver-green carpets of the moss *Philonotis fontana*, while immersed in the water there are likely to be reddish-black beds of liverworts, *Scapania* spp. Other mosses often present include the golden *Hypnum commutatum* (indicative of a limey flush water), the pale-green *Dicranella palustris* and *Bryum alpinum*, another species of red-black coloration.

The flowering plants are usually somewhat scattered, not crowded as on ledges, and gravel with or without mosses commonly occupies the intervening spaces. The flowering plants usually occur on the mixture of humus and sandy silt which has accumulated in pockets among the brophyte flora.

The flush flora is likely to include certain species present at almost all levels with others which are commoner in the montane region (i.e. above 2,000 ft.).

In the former group belong water blinks (*Montia fontana*), small sedges like *Carex lepidocarpa* and *C. flacca*, small forms of jointed rush (*Juncus articulatus*), cathartic flax (*Linum catharticum*), eyebright (*Euphrasia* spp.), lousewort (*Pedicularis palustris*), butterwort (*Pinguicula vulgaris*) and *Selaginella selaginoides*. All are small. The typical montane species of the wet-flushed areas are commonly slightly larger. They may include three saxifrages: mountain, mossy and starry (*Saxifraga oppositifolia, S. hypnoides* and *S. stellaris*), the northern yellow-rattle (*Rhinanthus borealis*), the mountain willowherb (*Epilobium anagalli-difolium*) and mountain bistort (*Polygonum viviparum*). Here are to be found also other mountain rushes and sedges with a more restricted distribution, such as the three-flowered rush (*Juncus triglumis*), the chestnut rush (*J. castaneus*) and, along the drier margins, the three-leaved rush (*J. trifidus*). The montane sedge most commonly encountered is *Carex saxatilis* (the russet sedge). Here again, however, one normally finds also the species of both the drier and the flushed ledges side by side, and it is evident that the important factor is often the presence of the nutritional conditions implied by an adequate supply of lime and mineral nutrients, the water content being relatively unimportant.

The flora of these wet flushes may be extremely varied, but the large number of species often found need not be expected even in every flush on the same mountain. Towards the summit, the characteristic flushes are of a very different type. The two bryophytes, the moss *Philonotis* and the liverwort *Scapania*, are still likely to be very prominent, and other species of bryophytes can also be expected, of which, at altitudes above 2,000 ft., the liverwort *Gymnomitrium* (generally *G. concinnatum*) is the most striking. This is dark green or red-brown when thoroughly wet, but is very often silvery in appearance owing to the retention of small air-bubbles between the closely-fitting leaves. Another moss which is commonly found at high altitudes and in stony and intermittent flushes is *Andraea alpina*, which also possesses the prevalent red-brown or red-black tinge. This colour is characteristic of such habitats and it is probably very significant, for, when present, it is apparently associated with a deficiency in available nitrogenous foods. It is particularly marked in the high flushes (see Pl. 15, p. 92) which also show another characteristic: that they generally possess only a few flowering plants. The starry saxifrage is almost always present, the alpine willowherb is not infrequent, and common in northern England is the water blinks, *Montia fontana*. Because of this scarcity of flowering plants we may perhaps distinguish the high flushes as "bryophyte flushes" (Pl. 15, p. 92 and Pl. XIII, p. 100).

As a rule the bryophyte flushes are of small size, but on some of the larger mountains they may be represented by stony zones, which in some cases run for as much as 200 yards along the flanks of the summit detritus and are from 10 to 20 yards in breadth. Even in such a case the number of additional flowering plants is small, the most noteworthy being the viviparous *Deschampsia alpina*.

Still another type of bryophyte flush, the so-called snow-flush, seems to be especially characteristic of high and broad mountain summits on which considerable snow-fields may accumulate. On gentle slopes, the melting of the snow often leads to a series of modest erosion furrows in the surrounding grassland, below which a stretch of darker surface shows where humus and flakes of mica or gneiss have accumulated. The noteworthy plant on these snow-flushes is a liverwort, *Anthelia* (either *A. julacea* or *A. juratzkana*), and generally associated with it the mosses *Polytrichum alpinum* and *P. norvegicum* and, at the highest altitudes, the orange and green lichen, *Solorina crocea*. The few occasional flowering plants are drawn from the surrounding grassland—namely, the mountain sedge, dwarf cudweed, viviparous fescue and eyebright (e.g. *Euphrasia scotica*).

It is easy to see that the greater richness in species of the lower flushes would give us a logical basis on which to study or to classify the montane and flush floras. The types of flush evidently depend on whether the water is richer or less rich in lime, and on whether they contain adequate supplies of available nitrogen or not; a sufficiency of this element might be assumed if the flush drained a considerable area of soil. We have seen that the reddish-coloured forms are probably associated with nitrogen scarcity. Other species like *Cratoneurum commutatum*, *Scorpidium scorpioides* and *Ctenidium molluscum* are indicative of lime-rich flushes and are generally associated with a varied flora of flowering plants. Iron flushes include *Drepanocladus revolvens* and flushes from peat contain *Acrocladium stramineum*, while bog-mosses (*Sphagnum* spp.) of the *cuspidatum* group are usually near-by. These last types of flush show few of the montane flowering plants. The liverworts as a class seem to be more strictly montane than many of these mosses.

The comparative poverty in species of the high flushes on a typical mountain, in contrast to the richness of these lower down, is a good example of the fact that the rarer montane plants are usually not to be sought for at the highest levels; they are more likely to be found a considerable distance below the summit (see Fig. 21). The reason for this is plainly that the water emerging in springs lower down the mountain has had a greater opportunity of dissolving lime and other minerals from the rock as well as of acquiring plant foods, such as nitrates, from the decay of humus. In contrast, the water supply of the high flushes must be very little different from rain-water.

THE MONTANE FLORA

In describing these habitats in which the mountain plants are found, it is difficult to avoid giving an entirely erroneous impression of the mountain vegetation and flora as a whole. It seems desirable at this stage, therefore, to reiterate that the montane flora includes two groups of plants—many like the grasses and some of the heath plants with wide altitudinal distribution that are able to exist in poor soils and in unfavourable conditions. These make up the bulk of the mountain vegetation ; they form what the plant ecologist calls " closed communities "—types of vegetation like montane grasslands, for example, in which a comparatively few species completely cover the ground. Much of what we see on a British mountain consists of vegetation of this general type.

In addition, however, there are the special montane plants, rarely or never found at low altitudes, which make mountains places of especial interest to field botanists. These appear during the colonisation of bare areas, on block scree and mountain-top detritus, as well as on the ledges of rock-faces and wherever erosion and deposition are exposing or laying down new surfaces. It is evidently one characteristic of these plants that they cannot withstand competition to any great extent.

Many of these montane plants grow also in arctic regions, and Dr. N. Polunin, from his extensive knowledge of arctic vegetation, has drawn up a list of the 62 British species with a wide distribution in high arctic latitudes, which includes most of the montane plants mentioned in these pages as well as others which are very rare in Britain. It includes also five species which are almost always found on peat nowadays in Britain—namely, cloudberry, crowberry, cotton-sedge (*E. angustifolium*), dwarf birch and mountain blaeberry, as well as a few (16) which are plants of other habitats such as lake margins and sea-shores.

We may note that in Britain two maritime species, thrift (*Armeria maritima*) and sea-campion (*Silene maritima*) are not infrequent as montane plants.

Of these 62 British plants which reach high latitudes, no fewer than 47 (75·8 per cent) are plants predominantly of open soils or rock crevices in which competition is scarce, while another eight are fre-

PLATE 17

John Markham

Ingleborough, Yorkshire: the western face

PLATE 18

John Markham

Rothiemurchus, Inverness-shire: pine-forest on the River Beanaidh quently found in such places, making a total of 88·7 per cent of the flora growing in that type of habitat. The arctic element in our montane flora grows therefore in open habitats in the arctic, even as it does in this country, and it evidently owes its survival in this country to the persistence of such habitats in mountainous regions.

These places are, however, not only spaces open to colonisation, they are immature soils, presumably poor in available nitrogen (see p. 57) and also places which have either not yet lost their lime and other mineral salts and bases by leaching, or else those that are receiving these substances by flushing from above. In a few cases, those of the montane species growing now on peat in Britain, it may be that scarcity of nitrogen is a principle feature of the habitat, but for most of the montane species a sufficient supply of mineral salts is at least as important.

Apart from these examples which have already been given, it is comparatively easy to illustrate the dependence of the rarer alpine plants upon a sufficiency of lime. In the Pennines, particularly on Ingleborough and Penyghent, the typical montane plants are confined almost entirely to the thin belts of limestone which interrupt the prevailing grits and sandstones. These are clearly shown in the illustration of the western face of Ingleborough, where the limestone outcrops high up (Pl. 17, p. 96). Here are found such montane species as the saxifrages (*S. oppositifolia*, *S. aizoides* and *S. hypnoides*) and alpine poa, as well as hoary rock-cress (*Draba incana*), the green spleenwort (*Asplenium viride*) and a number of uncommon mosses. On the more gradual eastern slope of the mountain these limestone bands are so buried beneath talus and peat as to exert little influence on the vegetation.

Similarly in Snowdonia, the key to the distribution of the most interesting mountain species lies in the presence of beds of Ordovician Limestone, either capping the mountains or more often outcropping high up on them. The long ridge of the Glyders is particularly interesting in this respect, for three stages can be distinguished in it. Much of it is composed of " acid " lavas with thin Rhacomitrium-heath on the summits and grey or heath-covered hillsides. But the west side of the big Glyder is dolerite, containing a larger proportion of lime and capped by mountain grassland. More striking still is the outcrop of calcareous lava towards Llyn Idwal, a few hundred feet above the lake. This is a station for many species with a very restricted distribution in Wales, especially for the mountain avens (*Dryas octopetala*), one of the most striking of mountain plants (Pl. 16b, p. 93). Here occur also moss campion (*Silene acaulis*) and purple saxifrage (*Saxifraga oppositifolia*) as well as other mountain species. The richness of the montane flora on these rocks is in marked contrast with its poverty elsewhere on the cliffs of the Glyders or on Tryfan.

Mr. Price Evans has shown that equally striking contrasts of a similar type are to be found on the main Snowdon massif as well as on Cader Idris, while almost every field botanist has learnt that the high limestones and the whin-sill of Teesdale and elsewhere, and the strongly basic plutonic rocks of Skye and Rhum, are the home of many rare mountain plants, particularly those of drier habitats.

In the Scottish Highlands, many of the richest areas for montane species lie on the mica-schist, a rock of adequate lime-content which breaks down very readily to give a loamy, lime-rich soil. It is probable that in the case of Ben Lawers, one of the Scottish mountains with the most varied montane flora, its position also contributes something towards its wealth of species. Lying towards the eastern margin of the Highlands, Ben Lawers has a rainfall considerably less than that of the Western Highlands, and this not only reduces the leaching effects but at the same time is less favourable to peat accumulation. In the Western Highlands, peat usually smothers all but the steepest slopes, greatly reducing the area available for montane species.

In the Lake District it is less easy to distinguish limited areas with a mountain flora of marked richness, though most of the species present are confined to the volcanic rocks of the Borrowdale series, and they are practically absent from the acid western granite, for example. But on the whole the Lake District rocks are hard and they break down so slowly that areas of dry lime-rich soil are uncommon. In such a case, the mountain species present are mostly those of the wet flushes and damp ledges.

Thus the montane flora is evidently one which depends on an adequate supply of lime and other bases, and its restriction to newly exposed and open sites must be partly because they offer new soils with an adequate supply of the necessary minerals as well as an opportunity for colonisation. From the point of view thus emphasised, the montane plants in Britain must be the remains of a vanishing flora, for on account of the humidity of the British mountain climate, leaching and peat accumulation must both be continually reducing to a minimum the possible sites for montane species. Further, the restriction of many of these species to rock-ledges and other inaccessible places is an indication that their range has been greatly diminished by the great extension of sheep-grazing. Particularly is this the case in the southern uplands of Scotland and among the English and Welsh mountains, and no better evidence of the influence of sheep can be obtained than by comparing the conditions of the vegetation of some particular flush in the early summer and in late September, when almost every vestige of a herbaceous plant will be found to be nibbled to the ground.

The montane flora has still other peculiarities. It consists almost entirely of perennial plants, usually provided with an underground rhizome or root which enables the plants to over-winter. Sir Edward Salisbury has pointed out also that the montane plants must usually be species which can be independent of insect pollinators. They rely, in case of need, on vegetative methods of propagation, on wind-pollination or on self-fertilisation or apogamous methods of seed-setting, for which no extraneous pollen is required. We know very little about the biology of seed-production in these plants, which belong to such varied families that generalisation hardly seems possible. Few of them have special methods of vegetative propagation. The grasses, however, are often an exception to this statement as several of them are viviparous, such as the alpine poa (*Poa alpina*), alpine tufted hair-grass (*Deschampsia alpina*), and viviparous sheep's fescue (*Festuca vivipara*), producing new shoots instead of seeds. So, too, does the mountain bistort (*Polygonum viviparum*), while the fir club-moss produces small readily detachable plantlets in the axils of the leaves. However, these species form a small proportion of the whole.

In addition to these features, the other important biological property of the mountain flora must be that they are " tuned," as it were, to existence at lower temperatures than lowland plants. On the whole, then, their biological character is very similar to that of the true arctic plants they include, which have been described as " usually perennial dwarfs which can propagate vegetatively or flower and ripen seed in the short cool summer obtaining north of 75°." We may add to this their preference for open habitats and usually for soils adequately supplied with lime.

The conditions of life required by arctic plants must have been prevalent all over Britain at the time of the recession of the ice-sheets, and the arctic and montane plants must have been equally wide-spread. Those we see remaining on the high mountains to-day are thus the survivors of a vanishing flora—interesting not only because of its peculiar habitat requirements, but also because it was the precursor of the more familiar types of vegetation in Britain to-day.

PLATE XIII

The Wells of Dee, Braeriach, Cairngorms (about 3,800 ft.): a large bryophyte flush

PLATE XIV

R. Brinsden

Matgrass, *Nardus stricta*, invading overgrazed montane grassland, Stonesty Pike,
Lake District

CHAPTER 6

THE LOWER GRASSLANDS

W H E N we leave the montane regions and turn to the lower slopes and their submontane vegetation, we can still make out contrasted types which, on the whole, are those either of flushed habitats or of leached ones. Generally, as we have seen, the high-level (or montane) grasslands represent flushed areas, and, on the whole, this is true also of the lower grasslands into which the montane types descend. On the leached slopes, in contrast, there are various types of moorland, generally distinguished by the presence of heathers or of strongly tufted plants, such as cotton-sedge and deer-sedge, which gradually become predominant wherever the drainage deteriorates. There is, however, little doubt that all the existing upland grasslands and much of the moorland, if not all, has been derived from woodland, and, indeed, in most mountain areas fragments of woodland still remain, hanging on here and there, often showing signs of degeneration, but enabling us to build up a picture of what the primitive woodlands were like and of the factors which led to their decline.

The convenient manner of treating the vegetation is clearly, therefore, to consider the grasslands first, next (Chapter 7) to consider the woodlands from which they have been derived, and lastly, and in contrast (Chapter 8), to consider the moorlands and bogs and what they show.

FESCUE GRASSLANDS

The most characteristic form of upland grassland in Britain is that dominated by sheep's fescue (*Festuca ovina*) and the bents (*Agrostis tenuis* and *A. stolonifera*), and so generally termed Festuca-Agrostis grassland. It occurs characteristically on brown earth soils—generally more or less base-deficient and somewhat acid—but usually on the steeper and better-drained slopes (Pl. XV, p. 108). Besides the predominant grasses, there are present with great constancy such species as the tormentil (*Potentilla erecta*) and heath bedstraw (*Galium saxatile*), and often also the sweet-scented vernal grass (*Anthoxanthum odoratum*) and dogstail (*Cynosurus cristatus*). Almost equally constant is the moss,

Rhytidiadelphus squarrosus, and frequent are *Pleurozium schreberi* and *Hypnum cupressiforme.* The grass sward is very complete, covering 65-75 per cent of the whole ground, so that associates are not numerous, though they actually include many species. Of these some are rather uniformly scattered, like the sheep's sorrel (*Rumex acetosella*), milkwort (*Polygala serpyllifolia*) and speedwell (*Veronica officinalis*). Others like the white clover (*Trifolium repens*) and the mountain violet (*Viola lutea*) are, like the fescue itself when very abundant, useful as indicating a larger lime supply in the soil, although it still remains lime-deficient. The presence of other species indicates acid humus. Such include the heath-grass (*Sieglingia decumbens*), the heath woodrush (*Luzula multiflora*), the wavy hair-grass (*D. flexuosa*), as well as the almost ubiquitous bilberry. Lastly there are plants associated with former cultivation or treatment. These, though most common at low levels (say below 1,000 ft.), occur also at surprisingly high ones on occasion. They include the ribwort plantain (*Plantago lanceolata*), the creeping buttercup (*Ranunculus repens*), cat's ear (*Hypochaeris radicata*) and self-heal (*Prunella vulgaris*).

The Festuca-Agrostis grassland deserves a great deal more attention than we shall be able to give it because it is the mainstay of all grazing animals on British mountains. It is said to support more stock per unit area than any other common form of mountain pasture, but there must be great variations in its fertility. At one end of the habitat range it merges into the sheep's fescue grassland of the limestones and basalts— one of the best sheep pastures available and certainly a favourite feeding ground of both deer and sheep—while at the other end of the scale it approaches equally closely to the unpalatable *Nardus-Juncus squarrosus* grasslands of the more peaty and base-deficient soils. The great range of possible variation is evidently very much affected by the lime content and friability of the underlying rocks. The grasses also appear to prefer a soil of uniform and open texture, and so rocks which easily weather, such as basalt and mica-schist, commonly support good grasslands. Finally, the composition of a grassland is always much affected by the amount of grazing it receives and the season at which it is grazed. On the one hand, grazing causes a certain amount of stimulation, both through treading, which increases the tillering of the grasses, and through the marked manurial effects of animal droppings. Thus a certain amount of grazing is always an important feature of hill grassland improvement. On the other hand grazing is always selective in that some species are eaten while others are not.

As a general rule, grasses are least affected by grazing, but plants with exposed growing points (e.g. flowering herbs, heather and shrubs such as bilberry) are much damaged. Further, selective grazing means that species which are least palatable tend to persist at the expense of the more palatable. Thus heavy grazing of Festuca-Agrostis grassland by sheep seems to lead first to the spread of the bents and then to extension of the mat-grass (*Nardus*), a species which is hardly, if ever, eaten. One of the commonest signs of over-grazed upland pasture is thus an abundance of this grass and of its associate, the moor-rush, *Juncus squarrosus*, even though the latter affords a welcome " bite " in seasons of scarcity.

BRACKEN

As a general rule, the Festuca-Agrostis grasslands cover the brown earth and creep-soils of the steeper upland slopes. Where these soils are deep enough, more than nine inches or a foot in depth, they are likely to have on them also the bracken (*Pteridium aquilinum*). Consequently almost all the lower grasslands are to-day bracken-covered (Pl. 20b, p. 113). The tall and frequent fronds overshade the grasses in summer, and smother them in winter and spring beneath a litter of dead leaves, through which grasses cannot penetrate. Thus by the elimination of grass, the grazing value of bracken-covered slopes quickly becomes negligible.

There is no doubt that bracken has spread enormously over the hill pastures in the last one hundred years or so, particularly in those areas among the foothills where pockets of glacial drift often provide a deeper soil. The spread of bracken has probably been hastened by two things : the general replacement of cattle by sheep on hill grazings and the greater cost of labour. Cattle eat young bracken and, moreover, they break down and trample more than they eat. Thus it normally fails to establish itself in cattle grazings. Elsewhere it maintains itself, once established, and spreads by means of branched and cable-like underground stems, in which considerable reserves of food are stored. In order to eliminate an established colony, the underground stems must be removed or their food reserves used up. The latter is rather simple, given sufficient time and labour. The fronds are cut off in spring as soon as they appear, and the process repeated later in the year whenever new growth develops. Thus the food reserves are used up in producing new growth and no new stores can be laid down if the leaves are cut off as soon as they develop. Three or four mowings usually suffice to eliminate the plant, but the time-consuming nature of the treatment has led to the attempt to devise machines capable of uprooting the underground stems. Bracken remains, however, one of the biggest problems in the utilisation of hill country, especially as it invades the better grasslands and, by shading out the grasses, renders them almost useless as pasture.

NARDUS GRASSLAND

On grassy mountains three zones can often be distinguished : the lowest one in which bracken is abundant, a middle one above 1,000 ft., in which the mat-grass (*Nardus stricta*) is prominent, and finally the highest zone containing the montane species, which starts about 2,000 ft. There is, in short, a zone in which Nardus is most characteristic, and this corresponds roughly with the region of higher rainfall and thoroughly leached soils.

Apart from the moor-rush (*Juncus squarrosus*), this type of grassland contains few constant associates. In the drier parts, the wavy hair-grass (*Deschampsia flexuosa*) largely replaces the moor-rush. Otherwise the most usual associates are bilberry, and, though somewhat more scattered, the heath bedstraw (*Galium saxatile*) and tormentil (*Potentilla erecta*).

The characteristic sites of Nardus grassland are the long dip-slopes (see Figs. 4 and 20), and on this type of slope the Nardus may remain dominant up to 3,000 ft. It is equally common on the gentler and more stable slopes below rocky knolls or ancient screes (see Pl. XV, p. 108). Because it indicates areas which are less thoroughly drained than most of the mountain grassland, the bleached and whitish Nardus-covered grassland is generally a very useful aid in estimating slope from a distance during the winter months. But in some districts it marks out areas which have been plastered over by impermeable glacial drifts, while many years ago W. G. Smith pointed out that it was equally characteristic of areas of *redistributed* peat (see Fig. 30), so that it often surrounds high-level peat-masses that are undergoing degradation. Like its common associate, the moor-rush, it is not often common on deep, undisturbed peat, however, and both plants seem to require some contact with mineral soil, even if this is a very poor one.

On the whole, the soils under Nardus grassland are almost always peaty ; they are base-deficient and acid, always oxidising in summer, and, though often somewhat damper, strongly resemble those found beneath a heather-moor. On the other hand, Nardus grassland also occurs on the poor and well-washed sandy alluvia beside mountain streams.

It has already been suggested that Nardus grassland may result from over-grazing under conditions favourable to leaching. In Wales it is said that Nardus has spread much, because fewer old wethers or hill ponies now graze the hill pastures. Both these types of animal graze on mat-grass to a limited extent. Over-frequent burning also leads to extension of Nardus rather than heather under grazing pressure, on the damper soils of heather-moor—for the young heather is greedily eaten by sheep.

On heavily grazed turf, the greater size of the ungrazed Nardus leads to its extension (Pl. XIV, p. 101), while its tufted habit makes it difficult to eradicate once established. It has, however, no capacity for withstanding shade and so does not colonise woodlands. Nor can it compete with large grasses like Molinia. Almost always, then, it has colonised poor ground or succeeded old and grazed-down Fescue grasslands. It is a form of vegetation typical of sites which were cleared of woodland at an early stage and which have since been grazed and leached to a moorland state. This is often very noticeable from the sea along the western seaboard, where the sites of old settlements can be picked out by the presence of Nardus on the hills above.

MOLINIA GRASSLAND

Purple moor-grass (*Molinia coerulea*) is one of the half-dozen or so moorland plants that cover an enormous area of country. Along the western margins, from Cape Wrath to mid-Wales and from Donegal to Kerry, it is without doubt one of the most widespread plant species. Unfortunately it is not easy to describe briefly its habits or its associates, for both are extremely varied. It is a species living chiefly on peat and one preferring habitats that are at least damp if not wet for part of the year. It is also a peat-forming plant and for the two latter reasons its preference for peaty soils is understandable.

Molinia is a grass, and so any plant community in which it is a dominant partner should logically be called a grassland. Nevertheless, as its habitats suggest, its affinities are with the peat plants, the species of bogs and moors, and it finds its true place as a plant which marks the transition from fen to bog or from damp woodland to bog. On bog habitats it is small and non-tufted, but on aerated soils it develops large tussocks some 3 ft. or more across. In its bog forms it is usually associated with bog-moss and with bog-myrtle (*Myrica gale*), as is described later, or with deer-sedge (*Scirpus caespitosus*).

Molinia grassland is found in the Pennines, Wales and the Southern Uplands only along the lower margins of the peat-mosses, where there is good drainage in summer and flushing by peaty water. But in the Western Highlands and islands some form of Molinia grassland is extremely widespread up to 1,500 ft. In many moorland areas it provides a most valuable form of pasture.

Molinia grassland in British uplands is curiously irregular in its distribution. In some areas it is practically absent, while elsewhere it is frequent. The origin of these irregularities is probably to be sought in two factors, of which an important one is the susceptibility of Molinia to grazing. It is a favourite spring feed for stock, both sheep and cattle, but seems also to be extremely sensitive to grazing and quickly disappears when regularly and heavily grazed. Curiously enough, it is often not so greatly affected by burning. The second factor of importance is that most upland Molinia grassland seems to be associated in its distribution with the type of bog in which Molinia is common along with the bog-myrtle (*Myrica gale*) and the bog-moss *Sphagnum*. Molinia grassland is, therefore, more common where this type of bog occurs—which is mainly on the western margins of Britain and particularly where much recent modification of the bogs by human activities has taken place. On the other hand, where human influence has long been active, or where the Molinia-Sphagnum bogs have always been scarce, Molinia grassland is restricted to scraps occurring along a narrow zone just below the main peat-masses.

Many of the peculiarities of the Molinia distribution are, however, associated with the fact that it occurs on peat of higher ash-content than most moorland plants require. Rather surprisingly the plant has a very low lime-requirement, as is shown by the analysis in Table 9. The fact is that it is one of a curious class of plants that tolerate or perhaps require a high iron supply and which, as a result, are found in iron flushes (see p. 65). They include such plants as the carnation-sedge (*Carex panicea*), and in woodland margins the rush *Juncus acutiflorus*. Molinia thus grows on damp base-deficient soils in which lime is scarce and iron is being mobilised. These soils include the characteristic type of transitional podsol found in wet climates (see p. 60).

GRASS-HEATHS, FLUSHES AND ALLUVIAL PASTURES

Many other forms of grassland are to be found in upland country, though either they occupy small areas or else the composition of their vegetation is inconstant and not easily described. Among these is a type on dry and strongly leached soils that may merge into Festuca-Agrostis or Nardus grassland to give what has sometimes been called a *grass-heath*. The distinguishing feature is an abundance of the wavy hair-grass (*Deschampsia flexuosa*), a plant indicative of acid *mor* soil. This is a characteristic type on steep slopes in the Pennines or, indeed, wherever the underlying rocks are poor in lime and the rainfall is relatively low.

Festuca-Agrostis grassland is itself a vegetation type belonging to soils which are at least slightly flushed (brown earth and " creep " soils), and in its commonest forms it shows few of the *mor* species such as hair-grass. But there are also still more clearly defined flushes wherever there is emergent water containing dissolved salts, and these are generally recognisable not only by their greener colour but also by the presence of broad-leaved species of grass in much larger proportions. Similar effects are produced around dwellings where lime has been added as a manure. Finally, along the streams there are often strips of alluvial pasture belonging to the same type of flushed grassland. All of these areas yield heavier crops of grass and owe their superior fertility mainly to the higher lime or base-status of the soil. They may vary greatly in the composition of the sward owing to the diversity of their water relations, and they possess the common character of a predominance of larger and broad-leaved grasses, usually also with clover, which readily distinguishes them from the short and wiry turf of the hill pastures. At times the grasses include various " lowland " species like rye-grass (*Lolium perenne*)—interlopers brought in by man or by grazing animals so that it is not easy to give an average composition. But significant plants are Yorkshire fog (*Holcus lanatus*), one of the earliest indicators of flush effects, the tufted hair-grass (*Deschampsia caespitosa*), a very definite indicator of a higher base-status (in the uplands, that is), and cocksfoot (*Dactylis glomerata*), an indicator of high available nitrogen which, with clover, suggests a reasonably fertile soil.

The largest areas of flushed grasslands are the alluvial pastures, themselves almost infinitely variable. They range from Nardus grassland, on leached and coarse high-level alluvia, while at lower levels, in addition to the grasses just mentioned, they may include meadow-grasses (*Poa trivialis* and *Poa pratensis*) and meadow fescue (*Festuca pratensis*). Often, if much grazed or used as hay meadows, they include great numbers of root parasites, like eyebright (*Euphrasia* spp.) and yellow-rattle (*Rhinanthus minor*). But so soon as one passes away from the sandy or gravelly stream margins, the soil becomes peaty and the moor-grass becomes increasingly common. Where these alluvia are in agricultural use they are usually riddled with drains in the attempt to keep down the ever-encroaching moss. Their natural fate in a wet climate is to turn into Molinia grassland and Molinia-Myrica swamp. At their best they are the equivalent for grazing purposes of the poorer lowland pastures.

NUTRITIVE LEVELS

The grasslands are important biologically because they are the source from which most upland animals ultimately derive their food. It is thus worth giving some attention to their relative nutritive values as well as to the comparison of these values with those of other types of moorland vegetation. We may take as representative three important grassland types—alluvial pastures (as a strongly flushed type), Festuca-Agrostis and Nardus grasslands ; Table 7 gives analyses showing the most important mineral elements in these three types.

The value of the grasslands to grazing animals depends partly on the needs of the animals for calcium and phosphate which they require in building up their skeletons. It will be seen from these figures that the lime (calcium oxide) content of Festuca-Agrostis grassland ranks very low as compared with alluvial pasture, but even so it is still 50 per cent higher than that of Nardus grassland. The difference between

PLATE XV

R. Brinsden

Nardus grassland in the foreground: fescue grassland above on steeper slope. Lake District

PLATE XVI

Robert Adam

Upland oakwood in spring, Creag nan Caorruirin, Glen Falloch (Grampians), showing the open character and shallow soils typical of these high-level woods

Table 7

PERCENTAGE OF MINERAL ELEMENTS
IN DRY MATTER FROM LEAVES

	Lime (CaO)	*Phosphorus* (P)	*Nitrogen* (N)
1. Alluvial pasture	1·10	0·20	3·0
2. Festuca-Agrostis grassland	0·44	0·15	2·1
3. Nardus grassland	0·29	0·07	1·6

the two latter grasslands is still more marked in regard to the phosphorus content.

Thus the preference of stock for flushed grasslands is simply a reflection of their physiological needs. As a measure of these needs we may note that most cattle are unable to make growth on the higher pastures, though they usually can do so on those of the flushed types in the valleys. Mature cattle, however, can be maintained on Festuca-Agrostis or Molinia grassland.

The question of palatability to stock is, probably, affected not only by these factors but also by the softness of the leaves. If a transverse section of the leaf of a grass is examined under a microscope (see Fig. 22) it will be found to show two sorts of cells or tissues. There are some which are green, and these are the active living cells which are rich in protein and hence of high nutritive value. But there are also some cells which are colourless and which have thick walls composed of modified cellulose. These are fibres, running longitudinally down the leaf, and imparting to it a great deal of its rigidity. They serve as " roughage " to grazing animals and they are not digested easily, if at all. If we examine a section of the grass leaf microscopically we can roughly estimate the value of the plant as a pasture grass by finding out the proportion of green living cells to fibre ; and the comparison may be made, for example, between the grasses shown in Fig. 22. It will be seen that Nardus has a very high proportion of fibre which, indeed, its stiff and rather brittle leaves would lead us to suspect.

Of course, the comparison of different pasture plants in respect of nutritive value is usually made in other ways. One of these is to estimate the proportion of nitrogen in the leaf material, because this proportion is a measure of the valuable protein constituents in the tissue. These proteins contain about 16 per cent of nitrogen, so that

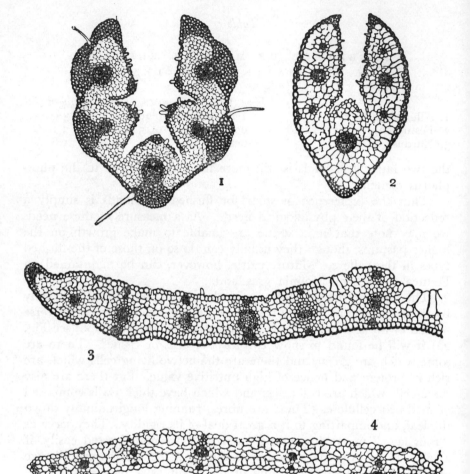

FIG. 22.—Transverse sections of grassleaves to show fibrous tissues (with heavy black walls) and active, thin-walled living cells. 1, Matgrass (*Nardus*) ; 2, Sheep's Fescue (*Festuca ovina*) ; 3, Heath-grass (*Sieglingia decumbens*) ; 4, Annual Poa (*Poa annua*).

(Figures reduced from Burr and Turner.)

" Nitrogen × 6·25 " is a rough measure of protein content. The " fibre," which is as resistant to chemical treatment as it is to digestive action, can also be estimated roughly as a residue by removing all the soluble materials from the leaf, estimating the ash and nitrogen content, and regarding the insoluble residue as fibre. For the three sorts of pasture we have been comparing we should get figures like these for " fibre " and nitrogen estimates as percentages of the dry matter.

Table 8

	Alluvial pasture	Festuca-Agrostis grassland	Nardus grassland
" Fibre "	21·5	24·6	31·2
N × 6·25 = " protein "	18·75	13·12	10

From these figures we can see that the ratio of " fibre " or roughage to valuable food-material in the three examples increases almost in the proportions 1 : 2 : 3.

Because an animal requires these proteins to build up its own flesh, the supply of this form of nitrogen in the herbage is usually more important in fixing the nutritive value than any other constituent, for it determines the quantity of living animal material that can be made. As a matter of fact, it often happens in the uplands that the supply of the three important substances—lime, phosphorus and nitrogen—rises and falls in a roughly parallel manner, as it does in the three types of grassland just considered. Thus a flushed soil, such as that of the alluvial pasture, commonly contains adequate supplies of each

Table 9

ANALYSES OF COMMON GRASSLAND AND MOORLAND PLANTS
(Figures as per cent of dry weight)

	Nitrogen	Phosphorus	Ash	Lime (CaO)
Moor-grass (*Molinia*)	2·4	0·27	9·4	0·17
Deer-sedge (*Scirpus caespitosus*)	1·7	—	3·7	—
Cotton-sedge (*Eriophorum vaginatum*	1·6	0·30	3·3	Below 0·01
Moor-rush (*Juncus squarrosus*)	1·35	0·13	3·3	0·14
Heather (*Calluna vulgaris*)	1·4	0·12	3·8	0·78
Bilberry (*Vaccinium myrtillus*)	2·0	0·23	4·3	1·20
Festuca-Agrostis grassland	2·1	0·15	—	0·44

of these constituents, while leached ones are normally deficient in both lime and nitrogen if not in available phosphorus also.

On comparing the vegetation of grasslands with that of moorlands in the strict sense, we shall find that the greater nitrogen—and lime— deficiencies of moorland soils are generally reflected in the compositions of the moorland plants. Typical analyses are given in Table 9. Nearly always, however, peculiar features are shown by the plants growing on acid, peaty soils. Thus Molinia shows a fairly high nitrogen and phosphorus status but is deficient in lime. Both the two sedges are poor in nitrogen, and the cotton-sedge, though it is, like Molinia, rich in phosphorus, is still poorer in lime, being almost without this base.

Of the plants analysed, the moor-rush is the poorest in nitrogen and is also lime-poor, so that it is perhaps understandable that for most animals this is a last resort for winter grazing. In contrast, heather, though generally poor in mineral matter, shows a marked capacity for accumulating lime, which is shared by bilberry.

Thus if we take the Festuca-Agrostis grassland as the standard upland vegetation type, we have to class as nitrogen-deficient : deer-sedge, cotton-sedge, moor-rush, heather and mat-grass (*Nardus*). On the other hand, the following are lime-deficient : moor-grass, mat-grass, cotton-sedge, moor-rush and perhaps also deer-sedge, for which information is lacking. Curiously enough, of the plants mentioned in the tables, only Nardus is very poor in phosphorus.

Of course, if we were to compare these figures for moorland plants with corresponding analyses for normal woodland vegetation or for lowland pastures of even low fertility (for which the data for alluvial pastures included in Table 7 might well be taken as representative), we should then have to rate the Festuca-Agrostis grassland as possessing a low nutritive level while the deficiencies shown by the moorland plants would then become still more marked. The sequences of soil types :

flushed——→leached——→peaty and acid

are thus accompanied by changes in the nutritive levels of the associated plants. In a broad manner, the nutritive levels fall in the sequence :

woodland or	montane and	moorlands
flushed grassland ——→	submontane ——→	and bogs
	grasslands	

PLATE 19

John Markham

Cairngorms, Inverness-shire: heather moor and alpine grasslands, Sghoran Dubh. June

PLATE 20

B. A. Crouch

a. Carn Spout Crag and Scafell Pike, English Lake District: cotton-grass in foreground on slight slope, *Nardus* on steeper slope to right, fescue grassland above
September

B. A. Crouch

b. The lower grasslands, Cwm Henog, Central Wales. July

MOUNTAIN GRASSLANDS

These features seem to be sufficient to account for the observed grazing preferences of upland animals.

But before we leave this subject, its ecological aspects should also receive consideration. Grazing animals take away from the grasslands nitrogenous substances, calcium and phosphate, which are essential for plant growth. Every animal carcase and its wool or hide represents, therefore, a considerable reduction in upland fertility. It is thus easy to see that grazing has the same biological effects as leaching by rain ; it accelerates the naturally rapid trend towards the production of acid soils and *mor* or bog peats. It is thus to be expected, for example, that vegetation forms of low nutritive value such as Nardus grassland will result from long-continued grazing of Festuca-Agrostis grassland. Furthermore, it looks as though grazing may not be a suitable method of exploiting upland country because it accelerates the natural processes leading to soil degeneration.

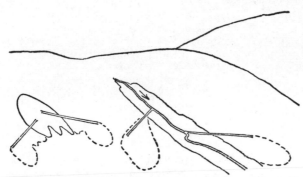

FIG. 23.—Methods of extending flushes on mountain grasslands.

At any rate, if it is to be used, much attention needs to be given to the question of the maintenance of soil status. There are three ways in which this can be done. An obvious way is the artificial one of adding at sufficiently frequent intervals manures containing the requisite lime, nitrogen or phosphorus. In practice, lime alone generally suffices, for phosphate is least often deficient and, if the lime status is raised sufficiently, nitrogen-fixing bacteria and leguminous plants like clover will raise the nitrogen content by fixing this gas from the air.

There are, however, natural ways of bringing about soil improvement. One which has been widely used in some parts of the uplands

M.M. I

is the method of distributing flush water over a wider area by cutting small runners obliquely across a hillside as shown in Fig. 23. Lastly, there is the possible method of using deep-rooted plants to draw on the deeper layers of soil—often, as we have seen, freshly decomposing rock. So far as I know, the majority of our native grassland species, however, seem to be rather shallow-rooted, so that in order to bring about this type of replenishment we should probably have to use trees and shrubs. It seems, therefore, that one natural way of maintaining soil status may be to keep the soil under forest.

CHAPTER 7

WOODLANDS

THERE is no question that in this country woodland formerly extended upwards to altitudes of as much as 2,000 ft. Consequently, much of what is now grassland and moorland was probably once woodland, certainly so at the lower altitudes and on the steeper slopes, and also wherever the underlying rocks are comparatively rich in lime. The fragments of these woodlands that still remain fall into six main categories—four of them composed of almost pure stands of a single tree—either oak or alder or birch or pine—and a fifth type in which there is present a greater variety of trees and shrubs. Finally, we must here include the new State forests, for the most part composed of exotic species of coniferous tree.

The two most distinct types are the oak-woods and pine-woods, the former surviving here and there on the steeper slopes of most British mountain areas. Natural pine-woods, however, are nowadays only found in the Highlands of Scotland. A third form of high woodland, that of stands of birch, accompanies both oak and pine-woods and, indeed, often forms a fringe round them. There is little doubt that these birch-woods generally mark the sites of more extensive former woodlands of oak or of pine.

MIXED WOODS ON FLUSH SOILS

On the whole, these first four types of woodland are characteristic of the more stable and more or less leached soils, while the type which we may now consider in detail is found on unstable or *flushed* soils and is therefore especially characteristic of montane areas. It differs also in being composed of several or many species of tree in association. Because leached soils are the rule in upland country, these mixed woods are confined to very distinctive habitats, places where weathering and erosion are active and, consequently, where new surfaces are continually being exposed. The characteristic sites are thus often the broken sides of gorges and gullies, and these form one fairly distinct topographic type.

A second is often seen where small cliffs of easily weathered rock exist, on and below which woodland has established itself. Here the trees are rooted on the crumbling edges and the new scree below. An essential feature is that there shall be a continuous supply of soil bases, such as lime and potash, as a result of weathering. Consequently this type of woodland rarely if ever establishes itself on block scree, except where this is composed of a calcareous rock like limestone. The two types of topography, gully and unstable scree, are alike in presenting new and unleached surfaces for woodland colonisation, and it is this feature which results in the special characters of the vegetation. Hence similar fragments of colonising woodland can often be seen on such materials as quarry waste-heaps.

In all these places, the trees are for the most part species with wind-borne or bird-sown seeds and fruits. There may be and usually is a considerable proportion of ash (*Fraxinus excelsior*) and of birch (usually *Betula pubescens*) and often, in the damper parts, of the wych elm (*Ulmus glabra*) and sallow (*Salix atrocinerea*). Two other species, a willow (*Salix phylicifolia*) and the aspen (*Populus tremula*), are especially characteristic of higher sites, though more sporadic in their distribution. Of bird-sown species, the yew (*Taxus baccata*), bird-cherry (*Prunus padus*) and rowan (*Sorbus aucuparia*) are the most usually seen, juniper (*Juniperus communis*) being more local. Finally, hazel (*Corylus avellana*) and dur-mast oak (*Quercus petraea*) are both likely to be present where old-established woodlands are or have been near at hand. With the exception of birch and rowan, most of these species avoid base-deficient soils and peats.

A mixed collection of trees and shrubs such as this is generally regarded as characteristic of a colonising phase of vegetation, and the distribution of this type of woodland on unstable and weathering surfaces is in agreement with this point of view. In other respects, the group of plants in these woodlands varies greatly, owing to the great diversity that may exist in the nearness and nature of any supply of tree seeds. Equally varied are the conditions of humidity which range from those of the exposed rock-face to the shelter and shade of deep ravines. It is this factor, together with the amount of light penetrating between the canopy of trees, that largely determines the nature of the ground-flora, though in extreme cases the character of the underlying rock, whether calcareous and friable or hard and siliceous, may be of great importance.

The richest ground-flora is associated with the deep " gills " on

PLATE XVII

R. Brinsden

Oakwoods and grasslands, Langdale Valley, Lake District

PLATE XVIII

John Markham

High-level ashwood (1,100 ft.), Colt Park Wood, West Yorkshire the Carboniferous limestones, but almost always these colonising woods are the home of interesting moisture- and shade-requiring " flush " species which are elsewhere rare in mountain districts. On unstable slopes the false brome-grass (*Brachypodium sylvaticum*) is often noticeable and with it, in rock crevices, the melic-grass (*Melica nutans*). The high rainfall ensures that species of rather damp habitats, as well as of flushed ones, are well represented. Especially characteristic, even if they are not numerous, are plants like the wood cranesbill (*Geranium sylvaticum*), marsh hawksbeard (*Crepis paludosa*), stone bramble (*Rubus saxatilis*), water avens (*Geum rivale*), great hairy woodrush (*Luzula sylvatica*), northern bugle (*Ajuga pyramidalis*), globe-flower (*Trollius europaeus*) and the large wood fescue (*Festuca sylvatica*). Of the ferns, shield-fern (*Polystichum aculeatum*) and brittle bladder-fern (*Cystopteris fragilis*) are characteristic, often with beech-fern (*Thelypteris phegopteris*) and oak-fern (*Gymnocarpium dryopteris*). On the drier ledges, the mountain vetchling (*Lathyrus montanus*), the golden-rod (*Solidago virgaurea*) and the hawkweeds *Hieracium pilosella* and *H. sylvaticum* are likely to be present.

Characteristic of the deep ravines is a great wealth of mosses and liverworts, often accompanied by the filmy fern (*Hymenophyllum wilsonii*), and, it may be, interspersed on the rocks by the orange blotches of the alga, *Trentepohlia aureus*. The mosses vary, depending on whether the flush waters on which they must rely are rich in lime, peaty or soil-derived, but those predominate which have at least a

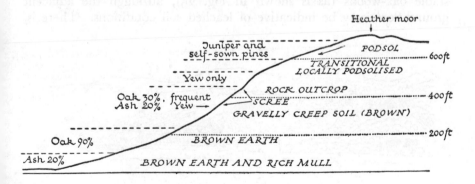

FIG. 24.—Vegetation and soil on Silurian foothills, Southern Lake District. Rain 40-50 inches. True scale.

moderate lime-requirement, species such as *Isothecium myosuroides* (particularly in the west), *E. striatum, Distichum capillaceum* and *Bartramia pomiformis*, and even such indicators of lime as *Cratoneurum commutatum, Ctenidium molluscum* and *Neckera crispa.*

The mixed woods on the upper scree-slopes are less distinctive and have fewer mosses. If they are extensive and long established, they pass into scree-woods of the oak-ash-birch type, of which a few still persist, such as parts of Naddle Forest in Westmorland. The general pattern of these woods becomes a mosaic of bits of more leached soils on the buttresses and knolls, bearing oak-wood, alternating with more flushed " ash-streaks." Towards the upper part of the screes, and particularly on decaying outcrops of rock which represent the remains of former crags, clumps of yew often form, and in some cases these have extended to form local yew-woods (Fig. 24). The frequency of names like Yew-crag, Yew-dale and Yew-barrow (taking just the series common in Northern England) undoubtedly indicates where features of this type were once to be found. Apparently they are absent on non-calcareous sandstones or on granites, though traces or actual examples are to be found in Wales, in Northern England and in Southern Scotland wherever slaty rocks occur, as well as on the " scars " of Carboniferous limestone. These little yew-woods represent communities established under the flushed conditions found in the mixed upland woods and often persisting long after these conditions have vanished. Thus yew communities are often found on knolls in stable oak-woods (as is shown in Fig. 25), although the adjacent ground-flora may be indicative of leached soil conditions. There is,

FIG. 25.—A typical glaciated valley in Silurian foothills—oakwoods, with ash-streaks and yew-knolls, leading down to valley bog with marginal alder and self-sown pine and birch. The cleared areas are fescue-bent grasslands, with Nardus above, bracken below and trees along stream gullies.

of course, normally little or no ground-flora under the shade of the yew trees themselves.

The possible variety of these mixed woods is almost as great as the numbers of examples. Without going into a detail which would be out of place, reference must be made also to two other extreme types which can be found, the " gill-woods " of the Carboniferous limestone and the so-called " vestigial woods " of the western moorlands. In the far west and on the outer islands of the Hebrides, the climate ensures that almost every soil is leached and that most are covered with peat or with bog. Consequently, in a region of predominantly hard rocks, almost the only flushed habitats or new soils (apart from those by the sea) are along the sides of eroding water-courses. Accordingly, here may be found almost the only remaining vestiges of woodland, shelter and often inaccessibility, no doubt adding their influence in allowing trees to develop. In one such place surrounded by moorland, the Allt Volagir in South Uist, which Professor J. W. Heslop Harrison showed me, the chief trees were birch, aspen and hazel, the latter, no doubt, a remnant of former more widely spread oak-woods, like some of the woodland plants found there, honeysuckle (*Lonicera periclymenum*), soft-grass (*Holcus mollis*), bluebell (*Endymion non-scriptus*) and bracken (*Pteridium aquilinum*). But rowan and the two willows, *Salix atrocinerea* and *S. aurita*, were also present, and among the mainly grassy ground-flora were the male fern (*Dryopteris filix-mas*) and the royal fern (*Osmunda regalis*), the moss, *Isothecium myosuroides*, on rocks, and other species indicative of flushed soils such as garlic (*Allium ursinum*), wild strawberry (*Fragaria vesca*), primrose (*Primula vulgaris*), ivy (*Hedera helix*) and the northern bugle (*Ajuga pyramidalis*). The interest of such fragments as evidence of former woodlands in country that is now nothing but bog and moorland is of course considerable. It is of even greater interest to observe that the fragments are quite characteristic samples of the mixed woodland normally to be expected in places of the particular topographical type.

If these isolated fragments represent one extreme, another of widely different character is found in the limestone " gill-woods," perhaps most common in West Yorkshire, but familiar also in the Clyde Valley and in parts of Ireland. A characteristic example of one of them will usually show an astonishingly luxuriant flora in which almost all the species already mentioned may be expected. The vegetation varies with the changing arrangements of slope and with the extent to which they are affected by flush waters. A number of characteristic arrangements is given in Fig. 26. One zonation of the vegetation shown is evidently associated with the structure of the screes, rocky and open above, where nettle (*Urtica dioica*) is abundant, usually with the mosses *Eurhynchium striatum* and *Thamnion alopecurum*. Lower, where the scree is compact with soil and humus, dog's mercury (*Mercurialis perennis*) is dominant, this having constantly associated with it the moss *Eurhynchium praelongum*. On the rather clayey alluvium by the stream there is much garlic, generally accompanied by still another moss, *Atrichum undulatum*. Where there is boulder-clay outside and above the gill, screes are likely to be mixed with or covered with a layer of unstable drift, which is gradually stabilised by two grasses, the false-brome (*Brachypodium sylvaticum*) and tufted hair-grass (*Deschampsia caespitosa*), which may, perhaps, owe their predominance in some cases to sheep grazing away possible competitors. But the false-brome is quite characteristic of such unstable places and it has, moreover, lower water requirements than most of the other woodland species. Thus at times there may be found a series of steps descending as in Fig. 26, where, as a descent into the gill is made, the ledges become covered with species of increasingly high tolerance for wet soils. The lower and wetter ledges show increasingly large amounts of accumulated humus, saturated with lime, on which sanicle (*Sanicula europaea*), woodruff (*Galium odoratum*), marsh hawksbeard (*Crepis paludosa*) and melancholy thistle (*Cirsium heterophyllum*) are characteristic, often also with such nitrate-requiring species as herb-robert (*Geranium robertianum*) and cocksfoot (*Dactylis glomerata*). The lowest ledges often also include an abundance of meadow-sweet (*Filipendula ulmaria*), while the higher and drier ones commonly have much of a grass, the blue Sesleria (*S. varia*), which is limited in its distribution to highly calcareous soils. The astonishingly rich moss-floras of the damp limestone cracks and faces in these gills are well known to every botanist.

The soils in limestone gills are somewhat unusual among upland soils in being almost always lime-saturated and neutral in reaction. Consequently the type of vegetation is directly related to the varying water content rather than to the influence of flush water or the chemical properties of the soil.

The limestone gills widen out into gorges and finally into valleys, while, as erosion continues, the mixed gill-woods gradually change into the valley ash-woods, a well-known type of vegetation which has

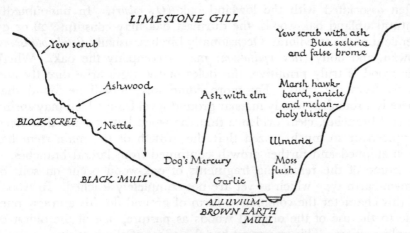

LIMESTONE GILL

Yew scrub

Yew scrub with ash Blue sesleria and false brome

Ashwood

Ash with elm

Marsh hawk-beard, sanicle and melancholy thistle

BLOCK SCREE

Nettle

Ulmaria

Dog's Mercury

Moss flush

BLACK 'MULL'

Garlic

ALLUVIUM—
BROWN EARTH
MULL

FIG. 26.—Section across a typical limestone gill-wood.

often been described. Here we may simply note that they are characteristically scree-woods like that shown in Fig. 26. More frequent in the uplands is the limestone plateau, with its surface of " pavement " as one of the most striking features of high limestone scenery. As Carboniferous limestone is nearly pure calcium carbonate, it is almost entirely dissolved on weathering, leaving behind a negligible amount of soil (Pl. XXII, p. 133). Consequently, unless drifts have been strewn over the surface, there can be little vegetation except that growing on the humus which slowly accumulates in the cracks. Nevertheless in some places, particularly around drift pockets, scrub or woodland had formerly established itself, for the remains, in which either ash or hazel is the more abundant tree, can still be found here and there, as is shown in Plates 4 and XVIII, pp. 17 and 117. Under present conditions, the further development of woodland is usually prevented by the numerous rabbits, which eat off at the rock-level any vegetation which emerges from the cracks.

OAK-WOODS

The high-level oak-woods which still remain are almost always composed of the durmast oak (*Quercus petraea*), a species which in Britain is a plant of shallow and acid soils, though even in mountain valleys often associated with the lowland oak (*Q. robur*). In undoubtedly natural upland oak-woods, the durmast oak may constitute 98 or 99 per cent of the tree flora. Occasionally birches, usually *Betula pubescens*, rowan, and holly (*Ilex aquifolium*) may accompany the oak. Where the wood is truly primitive, the boles of the trees arise directly and singly from the roots. Far more commonly, it will be found that there is a roundish woody mass at ground level from which may spring several branches, clear evidence that the wood has at some time been coppiced or so much grazed that the growth of the main stem has been stopped and further growth continued from lateral branches.

Some of the remaining fragments of oak-wood occur on soils of brown-earth type which as yet are not completely leached. In woods of this character the commonest form of ground-flora is a grassy one, due to the use of the original woods as pasture, one of the oldest of rural practices. This treatment has the effect of eliminating woodland herbs and leading to their replacement by grasses in the following manner : common woodland plants and tree-seedlings are usually species whose growing points are at the apex of the stem and are, consequently, the first part of the plant to be eaten or to be damaged by grazing. The effect of allowing animals to graze in such a plant community is, therefore, to damage seriously and to eliminate gradually these species with exposed growing points and to leave little damaged or undamaged any species with underground or unexposed growing points. Grasses, for example, with the growing points of the leaves at their bases, are little damaged by the removal of the upper and older parts of the leaves. Thus a woodland subject to grazing can usually be distinguished by its development of a grassy ground-flora, as well as by the absence of tree seedlings. When the mature trees die in such a woodland, there will be no successors to replace them, and the woodland will ultimately be replaced wholly by grassland. There is no doubt that this process has been extremely widespread in Britain in the past. It was recognised as a cause of woodland destruction in Leland's day (ca. 1540). It operates so effectively at the present that it is probable that few British woodlands can now regenerate naturally. The evidence for this has been mainly collected by Dr. A. S. Watt in studies of regeneration in lowland woods where mice and rabbits are the chief agents preventing the growth of tree seedlings. But it is possible to obtain equally good evidence for upland woods in which mice and rabbits may be rare, and this can most easily be done by observing the changes which follow the exclusion of the larger grazing animals by a fence of wire-netting. The results of this exclusion are roughly similar whether sheep or deer are the principal grazing types. One of the earliest signs of change in such enclosures is usually the appearance of birch seedlings, for the very numerous wind-sown seeds of birch are usually the first tree seeds to arrive. If pines are present in the neighbourhood, they may follow next, though this may also depend on how near other trees such as fruiting oaks are to the enclosure. The ground-flora will also change, and in particular herbs which have long been absent or unnoticed in the general ground-flora of grass will now appear in great profusion.

A striking instance of this may be cited for some woods in the Highlands, whence sheep were absent and where the grazing pressure was due mainly to roe deer and red deer. In this instance, planted tree seedlings had been surrounded by wire-netting cages, with an area of about nine square yards, some fifteen to twenty years earlier. In the rest of the wood the ground vegetation was that characteristic of grassy woods, being composed mainly of bents (*Agrostis tenuis* and *A. stolonifera*) and vernal grass (*Anthoxanthum odoratum*), though wavy hair-grass and wood soft-grass (*Holcus mollis*) were not infrequent, and the ubiquitous tormentil and heath bedstraw were constantly present.

Inside the cages, though the same species were usually present, the vegetation as a whole was quite different, ferns and the large wood-rush (*Luzula sylvatica*) being predominant, though these were rare outside. The difference was particularly striking in the cases of the sweet-scented mountain-fern (*Thelypteris oreopteris*) and the chickweed wintergreen (*Trientalis europaea*), both of which were abundant in the cages but only to be found with great difficulty outside. Other species at times present in striking abundance on the protected areas were the soft-grass as the principal grass, cow-wheat (*Melampyrum pratense*), golden-rod (*Solidago virgaurea*), sorrel (*Rumex acetosa*) and tree seedlings, particularly those of sycamore (*Acer pseudoplatanus*), aspen, rowan and birch. There was thus striking evidence of the effect of the grazing pressure in this wood, although domestic animals were entirely absent.

Similar effects may be observed in Lake District woodlands, due mainly to deer, although in this region the ubiquitous Herdwick sheep, an animal it is practically impossible to exclude in spring, no doubt contributes to the observed effects also. Dense and shrubby woods haunted by roe-deer generally show a very definitely clear lower storey about three and a half feet high, below which one can look or travel quite easily, although, viewed from the height of the normal eye level, the wood may seem hopelessly dense. The effect, though at a much lower level, is similar to the cattle-line seen in tree-studded pastures and in parkland.

Speaking more generally, the prevalence of the grassy type of ground-flora in flushed high-level woods is not only due to the fact that these woods are almost always subject to grazing. It also indicates that both vegetation and soil have an adequate base status, and hence are attractive to animals. In most cases, it shows also that the woods are doomed to destruction. If we wish to find out what was the original vegetation, we must search for the rare fragments that have long been enclosed, or else visit the islands on lakes or on sea-lochs, from which grazing animals may be absent. Almost all the original woods with soils that were partly flushed have been turned into grasslands. The majority of the surviving woodlands are thus those on leached soils, either too impoverished to yield palatable herbage or too rough or too inaccessible to permit clearing or to encourage grazing. Hence they can hardly be regarded as a fair sample of what the original woods were like.

One standard form still survives in various parts of the Pennines where the underlying grits and sandstones yield a sufficiency of friable soil. On the lower slopes, the familiar flora of the " dry oak-wood " is found, soft-grass predominates, and with it bluebell (*Endymion non-scriptus*) and bracken are commonly present. The latter is a plant which is favoured by the high light intensity which penetrates an oak-wood and by a soil exceeding nine inches in depth. It grows on soils which are not completely base-deficient and so, with its other require-ments of a fair soil depth, its distribution is usually a valuable guide to soil conditions in the uplands. It is for these reasons that it is often also a guide to the former distribution of woodland, for of recent years it has spread greatly, but generally over sites suitable for the growth of trees.

On the upper and more thoroughly leached slopes in the Pennines, however, these dry oak-wood plants are replaced by the wavy hair-grass (*Deschampsia flexuosa*), a species which in this locality forms con-tinuous mats of dark-green tussocks that exclude almost all other plants. It is, moreover, one of the best indicators of the presence of

PLATE XIX

John Markham

Bog-myrtle and moor-grass on the site of former woodlands. Grampians

PLATE XX

John Markham

A bog-moss surface, *Sphagnum papillosum*, showing the untufted character of cotton-sedge in this habitat acid *mor* humus. Still higher up the slopes there may be an abundance of bilberry, on soils which are generally drier as well as completely leached and of podsolic type. Above this, woodland usually gives way to moor, the transition being marked by the increased abundance of heather, which replaces either hair-grass or bilberry where the light intensity is high. Very commonly, however, and wherever there is downward drainage from upland bogs, the purple moor-grass (*Molinia coerulea*) becomes prevalent, forming a characteristic intermediate stage marked by the final disappearance of trees.

Along the western margins of Britain the soils are often shallower and more gravelly than they are in the Pennines, for they are usually derived from harder underlying rocks—slates, ancient grits, schists or granitic types. The rainfall also is usually higher, and when it exceeds 60 in. or so the arrangement of vegetation in the vestigial woodlands is usually quite different. The dry oak-wood vegetation of soft-grass, bluebell and bracken is scarce, its three principal species being mainly confined to pockets of loamy or sandy drift. More common are such plants as wood-sage (*Teucrium scorodonia*), wood-sorrel (*Oxalis acetosella*), honeysuckle (*Lonicera periclymenum*), foxglove (*Digitalis purpurea*), sweet-scented vernal grass, and numerous ferns and mosses. All these occur on soils which, though thin, are of the general brown-earth type. In such woods, however, there are often knolls or projecting ridges from which, during the glacial epoch, all soil was removed by ice action. On these and at higher levels where shallow soils are the rule and leaching is pronounced, a peaty *mor* develops on which mosses become predominant along with scattered plants of hair-grass, heath wood-rush (*Luzula pilosa*) and the hard-fern (*Blechnum spicant*). A great variety of mosses and liverworts may be present in these mossy woods, but usually the mossy carpet is mainly composed of *Dicranum majus* and *Rhytidia-delphus loreus*. Other locally abundant species may include *Pleurozium schreberi*, *Hylocomium splendens*, *Dicranum scoparium*, *Polytrichum formosum*, *Leucobryum glaucum*, and liverworts like *Bazzania trilobata* and *Diplophyllum albicans*. On the trees are likely to be epiphytic plants, including the fern *Polypodium vulgare*, numerous lichens such as *Evernia prunastri* and *Usnea* sp., mosses of the genera *Ulota* and *Orthotrichum* and the liverwort *Frullania tamarisci*.

In addition to the mossy woods there are two other variants of these ground-flora types which are particularly characteristic of the western mountains though by no means confined to them. One very striking variant we may call the fern-sorrel type, in which ferns predominate over all other plants. This is found mainly on north-facing slopes or in narrow and humid gullies. Associated with the shamrock-like leaves of wood-sorrel (*Oxalis acetosella*) is the male fern (*Dryopteris filix-mas*), which is generally common, while the lady fern (*Athyrium filix-femina*) and shield fern (*Polystichum aculeatum*), as well as some smaller species are characteristic of flushed habitats. On the more leached soils with acid humus, *Dryopteris carthusiana* and *D. dilatata* are more abundant, the latter particularly where the soil is moist.

A second striking variant is that dominated by the great hairy woodrush (*Luzula sylvatica*), and this occurs mainly on steep and unstable slopes, and on gully sides, particularly where they are irrigated by flush waters from above. The woodland habitat of the great woodrush resembles its montane one (see p. 93) in the need for flush water containing some source of available nitrogen, and, as we have already seen (p. 92), it is also limited to sites where it is comparatively immune from grazing. Though primarily it occurs as a dominant in regions of high rainfall, it is also very characteristic of some of the narrow valleys in north-east Yorkshire and the Pennines, where suitable irrigation, particularly from banks of clay or from shaley beds, is provided by the dip of the strata.

In all these cases the tree-cover is commonly composed of oak, but on the most highly leached soil *mor* humus develops and a situation is reached where the oaks are unable to regenerate because the surface soil is too acid, though birches and perhaps rowans and pines may still be able to re-establish themselves. The characteristic ground-flora associated with this condition is dominated by bilberry, although the soil conditions under hair-grass or mosses must be closely similar. In the Western Highlands bilberry occupies the better-drained knolls, old stony moraines and the tops of steep rocky banks. It is equally characteristic of wooded islands in lakes and has been noted in that situation in each of the countries along the western margin. Most of these islands are either piles of morainic boulders or else little better than "roches moutonnées," so that in soil conditions they approach quite closely to the glaciated surfaces common in the high woodlands. The dominant bilberry has often associated with it the cowberry (*Vaccinium vitis-idaea*), many of the mosses already mentioned, especially *Hylocomium splendens* and often *Rhytidiadelphus loreus*, the fern *Dryopteris carthusiana* and the cow-wheat (*Melampyrum sylvaticum*).

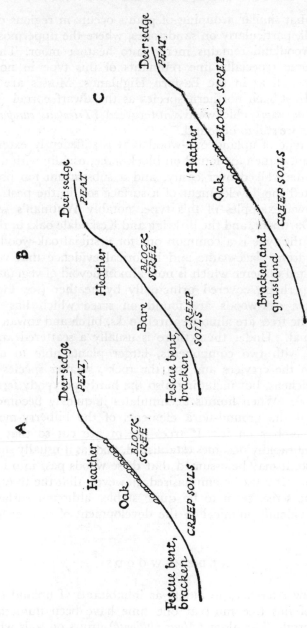

FIG. 27.—Typical arrangements on scree slopes, A and B, granite; C, Silurian grits.

A somewhat similar grouping of plants occurs in regions of much lower rainfall, particularly on sandstones, where the uppermost slopes with their woodland remains merge into heather moor. There are (or were) some especially fine remnants of this type in north-east Yorkshire as well as in the Eastern Highlands. Mosses are usually infrequent. In it such northern species as the dwarf cornel (*Chamaepericlymenum suecicum*), chickweed wintergreen (*Trientalis europaea*) and *Linnea borealis* are still to be found.

The last type of upland oak-wood that is sufficiently extensive to merit comment is the type found on block-scree, usually with a surface too rough to be walked over easily, and a substratum too porous to have permitted the development of a surface soil in the past. There are well-known examples of this type, notably Wistman's wood on the edge of Dartmoor, and the Birkrigg and Keskadale oaks in the Lake District, but the type is a common one for vestigial oak-woods. It is evident also from place-name and historical evidence that woods of this type existed on scree which is now almost devoid of vegetation, or, more often perhaps, covered principally by heather (see Fig. 27c). Most of these oak-woods are found on scree which has become stabilised. The trees are almost entirely oaks, birch and rowan usually being marginal. Under them there is usually a scattered and open ground-flora with two components, larger plants able to establish themselves in the crevices and, on the rocks, smaller species mainly mosses and lichens, but including also the hardy polypody fern (*Polypodium vulgare*). When humus accumulates it quickly becomes lime-deficient, and the ground-flora elements of the bilberry-moss type establish themselves on it. If trees die or are cut so that light is admitted, ling rapidly becomes established, and, as it usually surrounds the wood also, it may be assumed that these woods pass into incipient heather-moor. It must be emphasised, however, that the trees, rooted deeply in the scree, seem to be quite stable, although surface conditions are evidently inimical to the development of oak seedlings.

ALDER-WOODS

There are few references to alders as inhabitants of upland country, yet woods of this tree must at one time have been numerous and almost universal. The alder (*Alnus glutinosa*) grows on soils which are damp in summer and normally oxidising. In upland country, woods of this tree formerly occupied every damp flush and most of the alluvial plains. Three things have contributed to their disappearance. The flush soils they favour are, of course, among the best and most fertile in the uplands and so to-day are almost always valued grasslands. Our Norse ancestors, with their unfailing eye for useful country, drained and cleared the tangles of the valley swamps and alluvia on which the alder formerly grew in profusion. Finally, alder has always been one of the best of British trees for charcoal production. To-day, therefore, upland alder-woods are almost non-existent, though their sites are often indicated by swamps of the woodrush (*Juncus acutiflorus*). There remain a few good examples, in various parts of the Highland zone, often mere scraps near beds of shale, or on the lower slopes of boulder-clay, but more commonly on patches of alluvial sand or silt, made inaccessible by the wanderings of a stream or some other natural feature. The commonest associate trees are ash and birch, the former mainly but by no means only along the stream-sides. The birch, however, comes in where the soil is getting more peaty and base-deficient, and it gradually replaces alder in such places, usually in association with the moor-grass (*Molinia*) and the bog-mosses. The typical alder-wood soil usually has *mull* humus and contains nitrates, but the tree persists until the soils approach the *mor* state. The commonest associates are meadow-sweet (*Filipendula ulmaria*), tufted hair-grass (*Deschampsia caespitosa*), reed canary-grass (*Phalaris arundinacea*) and the moss, *Climacium dendroides*. On bouldery substrata the great woodrush (*Luzula sylvatica*) is also present, while many of the plants of the flushed gill-woods may also be found.

BIRCH-WOODS

It is probable that most of the existing birch-woods at higher altitudes mark the sites of former oak- or pine-woods. Indeed, it is common to find a fringe of birch-wood around the remains of both these types. The common birch in the uplands is *Betula pubescens*, a more erect species with downy twigs lacking the pendulous branches so often seen in the so-called silver birch, *B. verrucosa*. However, the latter is locally present all along the eastern margins of the Highland zone.

The seeds of birch, though produced in great numbers, and capable of germinating freely, do not easily produce viable seedlings in shade. Consequently they are often scarce in closed woodland, as they are also in high bracken or heather. Their opportunity usually comes when there is a gap in the tree canopy on the death of a tree or in long and leggy heather, where suitable openings may develop. Consequently birch frequently establishes itself in clumps in degenerating woodland, and it is more easily able to do this because it can germinate in soils too acid for oak or most other broad-leaved trees.

The trees in upland birch-woods are often misshapen. This is sometimes due to the presence of " witches' brooms," caused by the fungus *Exoascus turgidus*. More often it is due to the breaking down of the upper branches by the weight of heavy accumulations of snow—a feature as characteristic of high Derbyshire birch-woods as of those in far northern Caithness. The damaged trees are particularly liable to develop the fructifications of the bracket fungus, *Polyporus betulinus*.

The ground vegetation of the high birch-woods includes types which are found also beneath pine- and oak-woods. Thus on the glaciated islands in lakes one may see either birch, pine or oak with a ground-flora of bilberry and moss. The higher birch-woods more often have a grassy vegetation in which usually bent is accompanied by much vernal grass (*Anthoxanthum*) and wood-sorrel (*Oxalis*), though at other times blue moor-grass is common. Both these types are found in the western uplands, where often the birch-woods remain as the only vestigial woodlands among the prevailing bogs. In the Pennines, moor-grass or wavy hair-grass are the common ground-flora types with birch. Thus the ground vegetations are those of base-deficient brown-earths, of acid and leached soils with *mor* humus or of these soil types in transition to bog.

The degeneration to bog, of which signs are found almost throughout the Highland zone, is perhaps the natural line of development of the high birch-woods. Otherwise, like degenerating oak-woods, birch-woods tend to develop into bent-fescue grassland where the grazing pressure is heavy, and into heather-moor where leaching effects predominate. There is abundant evidence, however, that the zone between these two types of derivative vegetation is a wide one and that many areas which would naturally give heather-moor can be easily maintained as grassland by grazing, though no doubt they would tend to develop into Nardus grassland in time. When heather-moor develops, it is probable that pine and birch might also become abundant, for both trees have seedlings with a high light-requirement, able to grow on acid *mor* soils. At present, scarcity of seed or, more commonly, moor-burning, prevents the development of pine-birch woodlands in these places. Nevertheless there is evidence that woods of this type formerly existed over considerable areas of moorland in the British Isles.

PINE-WOODS

At present, pine-forests which are undoubtedly natural are confined to a few areas in the central and north-eastern Grampians, where the native Scots "fir" (*Pinus sylvestris* var. *scotica*), a short-leaved, endemic variety of the species, still maintains itself. These pine-woods are the remnants of the upper parts of the ancient Caledonian Forest, now, we believe, largely replaced by heather-moor. Similar woods may once have existed on the uplands of southern Scotland and northern England. They must have been scarce by Roman times and virtually extinct by A.D. 1550.

The best examples of these northern pine-woods, areas such as the Black Wood of Rannoch and Rothiemurchus Forest (see Pls. 5, p. 22, and 18, p. 97), are situated on poor glacial sands and porous morainic materials where the soils are not worth the labour of conversion to agricultural or pastoral uses. A wide survey of the remnants of the ancient Scottish pine-forests suggests, however, that formerly they were also found above the oak-woods on soils which were not always completely leached. Certainly, in many cases, the relics of pine-woods show grassy ground-floras of a type familiar elsewhere under oak and birch, and there are historical records showing that formerly the trees were intermixed in places.

The woodlands themselves are open and the pines are scattered some 10 or 15 yards apart, so that the light intensity near the ground level is high. This is probably necessary to the perpetuation of the woodland, as pine-seedlings have a high light-requirement. The general soil development has reached the podsolic stage with acid-rooting zones and *mor* humus. In the Rothiemurchus Forest, the porous substratum and rather low rainfall apparently make this condition a fairly stable one, representing an altitudinal zone above the oak-woods and brown-earths ; in the west it often appears to represent a sub-permanent stage before woodland gives way to bog as already described, and then pine-woods might also come developmentally between this bog and birch-wood stage and the oak-wood on brown-earth.

Where the ground is undulating, the ridges have a luxuriant vegetation closely resembling the mixture found when a bilberry-moss ground-flora is in transition to open moor. Heather is most abundant, along with bilberry and cowberry and with a great abundance of the moss *Hylocomium splendens*. In the hollows among the morainic material, the blue moor-grass replaces heather, and with it are bog-mosses, particularly *S. rubellum*, *S. girgensohnii* and *S. plumulosum*. Although the soil is much less acid than on the ridges, owing both to flushing and to the high water content, the performance of the pines is poor, and they are evidently able to maintain themselves in these hollows only with great difficulty, presumably owing to seasonal waterlogging.

Thus much of these ancient pine-forests consists of something approaching heather-moor on the drier rocky knolls and ridges, and of incipient *Molinia-Sphagnum* bogs in the intervening hollows. These bogs represent the downward extension of peaty drainage from the moors and the bogs lying at a higher level. Above the pine-woods there is commonly heather-moor where the slopes are essentially similar, or where they are less acute there may be a boggy mixture of heather, deer-grass, moor-grass and bog-moss. This mixture is more common towards the western margins of the Grampians, while there is more heather on the eastern margins of the district, as is shown in the fine photograph of Plate 5, p. 22.

Another striking feature of the remnants of pine-forest is that juniper (*Juniperus communis*), a second of our three native coniferous plants, may also be very abundant. It occurs in a characteristic position particularly along the flushed margins of the damper and the degenerating areas. In northern England and southern Scotland, juniper was at one time equally abundant on what might be called the knoll and hollow type of semi-moorland, where heather crowns the knolls and damp grassland (usually now with bracken) fills the hollows. Here juniper occupies a similar position on the more flushed soils, and the associated species resemble very closely those of the existing Scottish pine-forests (see Fig. 24). From the ease with which self-sown pines are able to establish themselves in such places, it seems that they are ecologically equivalent to the northern pine-forests,

PLATE XXI

Robert Adam

Vestigial birchwoods with *Molinia* and bog-myrtle, Loch an Nostairie, Morar. Rhum in the background

PLATE XXII

W. H. Pearsall

Limestone pavement with Ingleborough behind. Pennines

and they may represent what were once the sites of pine-wood remnants. On the other hand, juniper is, at times, equally abundant along the margins of vestigial grassy woodlands of oak or birch in northern England and southern Scotland, especially those of the damper kind. It grows especially well on north-facing slopes, where on occasion it forms extensive and dense thickets. Though sheep and deer destroy young seedlings, these thickets have sufficient stability to maintain themselves even in the presence of grazing animals, and sometimes, in particular, they may be favourite haunts of roe-deer. Juniper-heather moors are, however, nearly extinct, as both juniper and the other associates are unable to withstand heather-burning.

Juniper establishes itself in open and degenerating woodlands, perhaps owing something to its partial immunity from grazing. It seems initially to be characteristic of soils of a satisfactory base-status and it certainly gives rise to the *mull* type of humus. In virtue of this it persists on the site of the former woodland, whether this changes over to grassland or to moorland. This may suggest that the initial conditions in open woodland were not very different, and that whether moorland or grassland finally prevailed would depend on the amount of grazing or on quite small changes in the balance between leaching and flushing influences. But in either case the juniper remains as a stable component of the vegetation long after the conditions under which it established itself have passed away. Many of the high-level woodlands are in a similar condition. The deeper-rooted oaks seem to be quite stable—although the surface soils have become so leached and acid that oak seedlings can no longer grow in them. It seems clear that the soils must have changed since the original oaks established themselves, and hence we have evidence that leaching is progressive and that it is still continuing.

WOODLAND DEGENERATION

Although the amount of woodland in British mountain areas is now very small, the woodlands are of interest because they represent the units from which much of the existing upland vegetation and fauna has been derived. The wide if rather superficial survey of the vegetation given in the preceding pages suggests that, according to present observations, the upland woodlands are to-day rapidly decreasing in size, principally because of the operation of two groups of factors : those resulting from long-continued leaching and those which are associated with grazing. Some limitation is also due to moor-burning, especially in those types of open pine or birch woodland which are associated with a heather carpet. There is, however, a third type of woodland degeneration which has possibly been of great importance in the past : that associated with the waterlogging of the soil. This is observed to take place at present mainly where there is downward seepage from bogs at a higher level. A characteristic form is, as we have seen, that the woodland plants are replaced by the blue moor-grass, often with the moss *Leucobryum glaucum*, and that the vestigial trees are usually birches. Similarly the failure of the Scottish pine-woods in hollows is associated with the dominance of the moor-grass, usually with abundant bog-mosses, and often also with the bog-myrtle (*Myrica gale*) (Pl. XIX, p. 124). Throughout western Britain, swamps with moor-grass, bog-myrtle and bog-moss are characteristic of that part of the upland zone which has evidently been woodland in recent historical times (see p. 169). In those cases which have been examined, there has always been evidence of former woodland in the peat beneath them. They are found also in the valley bottoms (Fig. 25), wherever old alluvial woodlands are degenerating because they have become cut off from a source of inorganic silt which formerly flushed them, and also in bogs which have developed from the peaty and unsilted parts of lake basins. There is thus good evidence that the conditions of waterlogging which at present suffice to prevent tree-growth are associated with the presence of a plant community in which the moor-grass is dominant, usually associated with both sweet-gale and bog-moss. Throughout its range, this community is marginal to woodland and often associated with woodland degeneration. It is the community associated with the transition of woodland to bog in those cases which have been actually studied.

Armed with these lines of evidence as to the present causes of woodland degeneration, it is interesting to consider the former distribution of upland woodland and the reasons for its disappearance. We can infer that it was far wider than it is to-day simply by examining the present limits of altitude for isolated trees or for the remaining scraps of woodland. Much more complete is the information derived from studying early place-names, as, for example, Dr. T. W. Woodhead pointed out (see p. 198), because they show that tremendous deforestation must have taken place in early historical times. Much of it, we may be sure, was associated with man's activities. A great deal of our present moorland, by these tests, was once woodland. Even Scafell, one of the barest of British mountains, has a name whose derivation (Scofell=Skogafell) is supposed to mean a wooded hill.

Still more striking is the existence of timber buried in the peat, a fact known to every hill-walker. The buried remains often represent trees of very large size, showing the rooting parts apparently *in situ*. It has reasonably been assumed that this buried timber is a sign of former woodland which had been overwhelmed by expanding bogs. Thus, by examining these remains, we can learn something of former woodland distribution, of what the woodlands were like and how they came to be buried, though at the same time it must be remembered that these former woodlands were probably the marginal ones of *mor* soils and of soils of the damper types.

The distribution of buried timber shows that trees were formerly widespread in Britain to at least 2,000 ft. More restricted remains were recorded by F. J. Lewis from as high as 2,400 ft. on Crossfell in northern England, and up to at least 3,000 ft. in the Highlands. These seem, on the whole, to be confined to sheltered places such as corries and the heads of valleys. North of the Great Glen, the upper limits seem to have been lower, for C. B. Crampton records buried timber only to 1,000 ft. in Caithness. Elsewhere, most of the records are at heights below 2,000 ft., and the vast majority of them refer to the preserved remains of birches, which are easily recognised by the grey or white bark. Pine timber also occurs, and though in many places it is rather local, it is as widespread as birch in the Scottish Highlands. On the whole, too, it is often characteristic of higher altitudes. The remains of pine are generally indicative of full-grown trees and suggestive of extensive open woodlands, not dissimilar from those surviving to-day. In contrast, the birch remains are of variable size and suggestive of " scrub," such as might be found in woodland degenerating through excessive acidity or other adverse conditions.

If we pool the timber records of different observers, then we can add to birch and pine the following records of tree species from upland peat : alder, oak, hazel, rowan, aspen and willow. These are usually associated with a good deal of birch, as would be expected under scrub conditions. After birch and pine, alder and oak are the trees most frequently recorded. It is difficult from the records to assess the

relative frequency of these species. The observations seem mainly to
be based on differences noted in the field, where oak is easily recognised either from timber or from acorns. Alder, on the other hand, is
not so distinctive and can usually be identified only after microscopic
examination, though, very rarely, one may see the remains of the
inflorescence. After birch, to which its remains bear considerable
resemblance, it is perhaps the commonest tree in northern England
and southern Scotland, though pine is probably more common in the
Highlands.

On the whole, the evidence which we can most easily obtain from
the records of buried timber agrees with what we know of upland
woodlands to-day. The commonest remains are evidently fragments
of types of woodland or scrub akin to those which at present characterise the more leached soils and those surfaces where peat is accumulating—either because of their leached condition or because of the
downward seepage of bog water. Undoubtedly these conditions
have operated in the past, and it is therefore reasonable to suppose
that they have been responsible for the destruction of the former
woodlands whose remains we see preserved. No doubt, in harmony
with what we see to-day, these changes may have been accelerated
by other factors. Such an effect would almost certainly be produced
by the activities of man and of grazing animals. Equally it might be
accelerated by any effective increase in climatic humidity, such as
might result from a higher summer rainfall or a lower evaporation
rate. Again, on the whole, we might expect that woodland destruction
by man or by grazing animals would be commoner on drier slopes
and would be more often associated with increased leaching. The
effects of climatic change would, in contrast, no doubt, be more pronounced on gentler slopes, where there would be a greater tendency
towards waterlogging.

The birch- and pine-woods described in this chapter represent a
late stage in the effects of these processes on vegetation, a stage of
open woodland with small shrubs and mosses prominent. The oak-
woods generally seem to represent a somewhat earlier stage, when
even though the ground vegetation may be at times that characteristic
of highly-leached soils, the trees still remaining include those (oaks)
which became established before the surface soils had degenerated.

If we were only considering the vegetation changes caused by the
upland climate, this point at which oak is eliminated is undoubtedly

the point at which " moorland " types of vegetation arise. The group of species which is abundant in these woodlands persists in the moorlands, though the balance of frequency may be changed, as we have already seen with reference to the plants and shall later note in regard to many of the animals (p. 218).

REGENERATION—AFFORESTATION AND STATE FORESTS

Much of what has been written about upland woodlands deals with the many signs of degeneration they show. It will be appropriate to turn for a moment to look at the other side of the picture and deal briefly with the attempts being made to regenerate upland forests. In Wales and the Lake District particularly, a certain amount of tree-planting has been going on for the last 200 years, and on the whole this has mainly followed natural lines. In the Highlands of Scotland, any large-scale replacement of trees had to wait until the hill country became popular for game preservation in the mid-Victorian period. There was then a widespread erection of shooting lodges, and this was associated with a good deal of amenity planting which, for the first time, probably, compensated for natural wastage. By the time of the first German war, however, the national need for timber was becoming more and more acute as world demands increased and stocks diminished. Under these circumstances the State has entered the field and has embarked on schemes of large-scale afforestation in upland areas.

As in many of the earlier plantations, the trees used for planting in these State Forests have usually been coniferous or soft-wood types like pine (mainly *Pinus sylvestris*) and spruces. Other species more occasionally used are silver fir (*Abies alba*), Douglas fir (*Pseudotsuga menziesii*) and larch (*Larix europaea*). The latter is rather subject to a disease called " canker " in Britain and is now often replaced by Japanese larch (*Larix kaempferi*), which does not suffer in this way and whose golden-brown young shoots often serve to relieve the monotony of dark-green conifer plantations. There has also been a tendency to replace Norway spruce (*Picea abies*) by a North American tree, Sitka spruce (*Picea sitchensis*). The choice of these is probably based chiefly on the fact that they can be made to give a commercially useful crop in the shortest time, actually about 20 years in favourable conditions. Hardwood trees like oak and beech grow more slowly, and so involve a longer wait before giving any financial return. The coniferous trees are planted closely together to give what is called a " close canopy," so that they produce straight stems with a minimum of branching and a maximum of useful wood. This method of planting has the great biological disadvantage that it entirely suppresses any growth on the forest floor and also any natural regeneration.

The establishment of these planted State Forests of pine and spruce will ultimately change the character of much of our upland scenery. In effect, what is being done is to introduce into this country trees such as spruce, which spread naturally into continental countries in the same latitude, like Norway, but which were not able to pass the water-barrier into the British Isles. Man is thus adding to our woodland types a form of northern coniferous forest for which the climate of British mountainous country is generally very suitable.

Ultimately there is likely to be, then, an introduced coniferous forest which should consist of trees of different soil-requirements. Thus, for example, spruce and Scots pine should form zones, with the pine at higher levels and on poorer soils. Spruce or some other similar tree with higher salt-requirements will occupy the more fertile or flushed soils. It would thus generally be found at a lower level. If you examine the upper limits of many of the existing plantations you can generally see an illustration of these soil preferences. Spruce does much better in the pockets of deposited soil along the small streams or in the flushes and creep soils. Pine generally grows well on the heathery knolls, as we should expect from its British habitats.

Under existing conditions the policy has been to grow the trees in homogeneous blocks which are " clear-felled " at maturity—that is, felled altogether. This is, of course, not in accordance with modern forestry practice, which aims more and more at making such forests self-regenerating and at maintaining continuous cropping. In effect, there should be in the forest, as in a natural woodland, trees of all ages. The great biological advantage of this continuous cropping method is one which should be especially important under British conditions. It maintains the woodland humus, and prevents the soil erosion and leaching which follow the exposure of the ground on clear-felling.

The other feature of the close canopy plantation is the entire absence of ground-flora, partly owing to the dense shade and perhaps to some extent also to the presence of a carpet of conifer needle-leaves. These give an acid surface layer and apparently tend to form *mor* humus.

CHAPTER 8

MOORLANDS AND BOGS

THERE is no good definition of moors and moorlands. Almost any open country, especially if it is wild and uninhabited, may be called a moor in popular parlance. Thus it might be desirable not to use the term at all in trying to describe vegetation or habitats. It is, however, possible to use it both in a general sense and also in a more precise way. Here, in the general sense, we can use it to indicate habitats with acid or strongly base-deficient and boggy soils, and in doing this we are, in essence, using a definition coined by a north-country farmer, who said that moor was land that was too poor to be cultivated. We can also use the term moor more precisely to describe the sort of vegetation found growing on this land. The vegetation of acid upland soils is very often largely composed of small heathery shrubs, especially heather or bilberry, and these types we might describe as heather or bilberry moors. Sometimes references are made to " grass-moors," and these are really either run-down grasslands with much Nardus or boggy grasslands with much Molinia. The implied distinction in calling them moors rather than grasslands would be mainly that their soils were of high acidity and low base-status, and so consequently infertile. Many moors have a large proportion of members of the sedge family (*Cyperaceae*) in their vegetation, particularly of the two types called deer-grass (*Scirpus caespitosus*) and cotton-grass (*Eriophorum* spp.). These should perhaps more correctly be called deer-sedge and cotton-sedge respectively, and the moors described as " sedge-moors " ; and this terminology has been used in the present book. Finally, there is no objection to including within the general term the range of boggy moors, which are more usefully called bogs or, often in local parlance, " mosses." These are generally distinguished by the presence of bog-moss (*Sphagnum*) but they fall into the same range of habitats. The essential feature of all these moors in our limited scientific meaning is thus that they have extremely lime-poor soils.

In dealing with moorland vegetation, we may first describe the moors of drier type dominated by bilberry or heather. It will be convenient next to consider the wettest area of moorland—bogs—before going on to consider those of intermediate character, which

PLATE XXIII

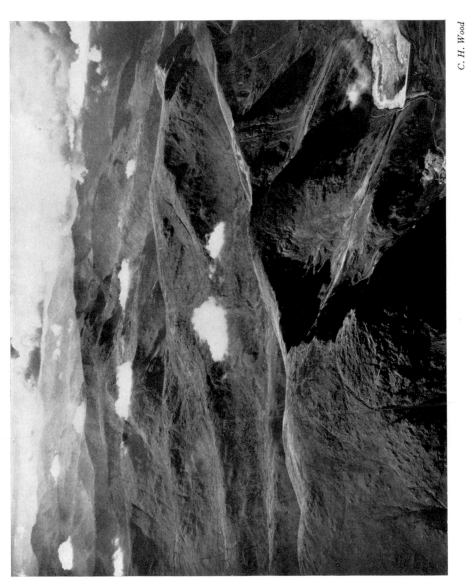

C. H. Wood

Aerial view of High Street, Westmorland. The foreground ridge marks the line of the Roman road from Lancaster and Kendal to Penrith and the Great Wall; the former tree limit is faintly shown in the left centre

PLATE XXIV

C. H. Wood

Aerial view of Gordale Scar, a limestone rift in the Pennines actually yield the commonest vegetational types. This is not a very logical arrangement, but it will save a vast amount of description and give, perhaps, a clearer general picture. The difficulty is that a great part of moorland vegetation is composed of mixtures—either of a variety of intermixed plant species or of a *mosaic* of patches of different sorts of plants. We want to see how this came about without getting too much involved in describing the mixtures.

BILBERRY-MOOR OR VACCINIUM-EDGE

The type of moorland which is rather aptly described under this name occupies a comparatively small area, but a very distinct series of habitats. It is particularly characteristic of the gritstone edges and screes among the Pennine cotton-sedge moors (see Fig. 28), or some of the high and narrow ridges in Scotland and the Lake District, and of the sandstone escarpments in north-east Yorkshire. The habitats are dry with extremely acid *mor* peat. The dominant plant, bilberry (*Vaccinium myrtillus*) is often accompanied by the cowberry (*V. vitis-idaea*), and there are usually also mosses present, such as *Pleurozium schreberi*, *Rhytidiadelphus loreus*, *Dicranum majus* and *Hylocomium splendens*. On the whole, these tend to be more abundant in Western Britain, while cowberry is perhaps most common in the east.

Even to-day, the sites occupied by Vaccinium-edge are often associated with the upper margins of woodland. They frequently also coincide with a group of interesting northern and arctic plants, which includes species such as the dwarf cornel (*Chamaepericlymenum suecicum*), chickweed wintergreen (*Trientalis europaea*) and cow-wheat (*Melampyrum pratense*).

The community as a whole, even including bilberry, is very sensitive to moor-burning, which favours the extension of heather over the sites and eliminates the interesting species. There can be little doubt that in its original state the Vaccinium community came from a corresponding woodland community characteristic both of high-level British woodlands and also of the North European coniferous forests. When the woodland is partly or wholly destroyed there is a marked tendency for the Vaccinia to be replaced by heather (*Calluna*) as the light intensity increases. Heather-moor is thus formed, though some of the associated plants may still remain. In this sequence of

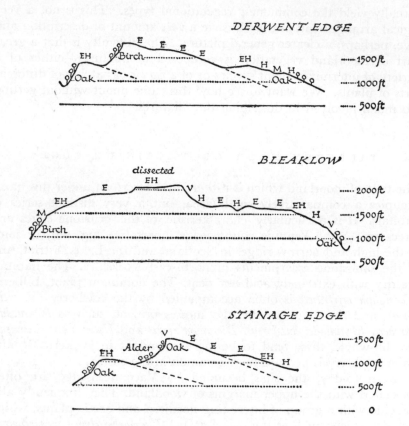

FIG. 28.—Pennine plateaux, edges and shelves : V, Bilberry edge ; H, Heather moor ; E, Cotton-sedge " moss " ; M, Molinia. Vertical scale x 2. The chain lines mark the dip of the rocks.

events, bilberry survives as a dominant only where the soil is particularly dry and porous, at high levels outside the altitudinal range of heather, or among large block-screes where a certain amount of shade and shelter comes from the boulders. Though bilberry is characteristic of drier and more acid soils than heather, it has a much wider tolerance of shade, and it is therefore more characteristic of woodlands and their margins than is the heather.

HEATHER-MOOR

By far the commonest and most accessible type of moorland in the lower upland zones is heather-moor, a unit of vegetation of which most people would first think if asked to describe a moorland. Heather-moors are especially widespread all along the lower eastern flanks of the Scottish Highlands and the Pennines. They are the predominant form of moorland in north-east Yorkshire and in Galloway, and are, in fact, well represented in all our mountain areas. The areas covered by heather-moor are generally those of pronounced slope, and as a general rule the annual rainfall is moderate, commonly between 35 in. and 45 in., probably always permitting a definite period of soil-drying in summer, so that soil humidity is then very similar to that of an oak-wood. To some extent, of course, the rainfall and slope are related —heather-moor being confined to the more pronounced slopes in zones of higher rainfall.

The vegetation is often almost entirely composed of the heather or ling (*Calluna vulgaris*), to the exclusion of almost all other flowering plants, but sometimes other " heathers " (heaths or bell-heathers in common parlance) also occur, such as fine-leaved heath (*Erica cinerea*) in drier areas, and cross-leaved heath (*Erica tetralix*) in damper places. With the latter is likely to be the heath-rush (*Juncus squarrosus*).

Some idea of the average composition of heather-moor may be gained from the following list which gives the plants commonly recorded in over 100 separate square-metre " quadrats." These ranged in geographical distribution from Central Wales to Sutherland. The numbers given imply, taking for example the case of bilberry, that on an average three quadrats out of ten would be likely to contain this plant. The crosses signify that the plant so marked was present in more than 5 per cent of the areas examined. Plants present less often are not recorded, in order to keep the list within reasonable limits. Heather was the only abundant plant in every sample.

Calluna vulgaris, heather or ling	10
Agrostis tenuis, bent	+
Carex binervis, heath-sedge	+
Deschampsia flexuosa, hair-grass	2
Empetrum nigrum, crowberry	1

Erica cinerea, finc-leaved heath	+
E. tetralix, cross-leaved heath	I
Festuca ovina, sheep's fescue	+
Galium saxatile, heath bedstraw	I
Juncus squarrosus, moor-rush	+
Nardus stricta, mat-grass	+
Potentilla erecta, tormentil	+
Vaccinium myrtillus, bilberry	3
V. vitis-idaea, cowberry	+

The four mosses most often present were:

Campylopus flexuosus	2
Hylocomium schreberi	I
Hypnum cupressiforme	4
Webera nutans	+

and the four most frequent lichens:

Cladonia coccifera	I
C. floerkeana	+
C. sylvatica agg.	+
Lecidia granulosa	I

It will be seen that the commonest flowering plant present (apart from heather) is the bilberry, generally in a stunted form under the shade of the heather. Mosses are the other common associated plants, and of these the commonest is *Hypnum cupressiforme*, generally a form of the variety *ericetorum*. Of lichens the most noticeable is usually the much-branched *Cladonia sylvatica* agg. but a search often reveals *C. coccifera* with red spore-bearing structures. Sooner or later almost every type of common moorland plant can be found in heather-moor. There is a great variation in composition, partly because heather-moor in Britain covers an extremely wide range of climate, of latitude and of altitude, and partly because it is almost always used as grouse-moor, and, in order to maintain the heather in a state suitable for grouse food, the moors are burnt at intervals. The frequency of the burnings, as well as the manner and season in which they are carried out, greatly affects the moor-flora. Furthermore, in order to increase the area of grouse-moor, many of the damper moors which would not normally be covered by heather have been drained and burnt to convert them into heather-moor. The result is that although some form of heather-moor is now perhaps the most widely-spread moorland type, we do not really know what a natural heather-moor looks like. But we know that on such a moor, left untreated, the

PLATE 21

B. A. Crouch

a. Cross-leaved heath and ling. Haystacks, Buttermere; September

B. A. Crouch

b. Bog-moss (*Sphagnum rubellum*) and non-tufted cotton-grass, Buttermere Moss
September

DAMP MOORLAND, CUMBERLAND

PLATE 22

John Markham

a. Deer-grass and heather moor in the Highlands. June

Eric Hosking

b. A cotton-grass " moss " in the Southern Pennines, Yorkshire. June heather would grow long and " leggy," leaving numerous openings in which other species could develop. Thus an unburnt or infrequently burnt heather-moor tends to have a more varied flora than one which is burnt regularly, and burning is largely responsible for such uniformity as is found. In an example from St. Ives, in West Yorkshire, an area under examination by the Yorkshire Naturalists' Union, and apparently regularly burnt, only one sample area (of 1 sq. m.) in 20 contained any flowering plants other than heather, a good example of the way in which regular burning limits the number of species present.

Heather-moor utilised as grouse-moor is generally burnt at regular intervals of from 7 to 15 years. After burning, the heather usually recolonises the area by a new development of shoots from the woody roots, which, buried in the peat, normally survive the burning of the upper parts. When burning is slow or unduly prolonged, the surface peat may become hot enough to kill even the heather roots ; then the recolonisation must come from seeds. Heather produces vast numbers of very minute seeds, weighing about 10,000 to the gram. These are liberated and easily blown about during dry periods. The success of heather on burnt moorland is primarily due to these two properties, of the roots and the seeds respectively. Of other plants which can persist after burning, cotton-sedge (*Eriophorum vaginatum*), deer-sedge (*Scirpus caespitosus*) and purple moor-grass (*Molinia*) do so in virtue of their dense tufts of leaf bases. The mat-grass (*Nardus stricta*) and moor-rush (*Juncus squarrosus*) both have underground parts (respectively rhizome and rootstock) which survive burning. When these are present, and especially on rather damper moors and where sheep-grazing is heavy, heather-burning may lead to an extension in quantity of these grass-like species, because, while the burnt vegetation is re-establishing itself, the sheep prefer to graze on the young heather, which is thus handicapped in the competition to re-cover the peat surface. Nevertheless, on the whole, regular moor-burning on the drier moors tends to favour the maintainance of heather-moor and to eliminate other species of flowering plants. The earliest associates of the ling to reappear after burning are usually lichens, particularly *Cladonia coccifera* and *Lecidia granulosa*, which come in very early. Mosses come later, usually appearing when a little shade has been re-established, though *Webera nutans* is often characteristic of the earliest stages. All of these owe their dispersal to minute spores.

In describing heather-moor, a distinction is often made between

M.M.   L the vegetation types found on deep and on shallow peat. That a difference does exist is largely due to the production of heather-moor from other types of vegetation on deep peat by drainage and other treatment. The distinction between " fat " moors and " thin " moors might, however, be justified on other grounds, because most of the heather-moors on thin peat are known to have arisen from woodland, sometimes within quite recent times. On the other hand, the process of heather-moor formation can actually be watched in some places, where upland oak- or birch-woods are slowly degenerating to be replaced by heather. Elsewhere, grasslands which we know or can infer to have been derived from woodland are slowly drifting towards heather as the high rainfall leaches the soil. In Scotland, the replacement of pine-wood by heather-moor is known to have taken place, and although pine and birch can regenerate on moorland soils of this type, they are unable to do so when the moor is regularly burnt. Arguing from examples of this sort and also from the comparison of the former distribution of woodland and the present distribution of heather-moor, it seems certain that most of our existing heather-moor on thin peat has replaced woodland. It thus bears a general resemblance to the *heaths* of Southern England, which have arisen wherever forest has been cleared from poor and porous soils. It is beyond question that in flora and fauna the lowland heaths and upland heather-moors tend to grade into one another. It is, however, convenient to separate them, partly because certain characteristic heath species are not found in the uplands, and vice versa. Thus some species like the small furze (*Ulex minor*) seem to be confined to lowland heaths, while *Empetrum nigrum* is perhaps normally a moor species. Certain animals are still more restricted. Thus a butterfly, the silver-studded blue (*Plebejus argus*), is always associated with heather, but as Dr. E. B. Ford has shown, it is always southern and lowland in its distribution. The much greater abundance of both insects and of birds on heathland is also a sufficient proof of noteworthy differences in habitat.

Heather-moor and bilberry-edge are distinctive among moorland vegetation types in being dominated by woody shrubs as well as in being characteristically found on *mor* peats, over soils showing podsolic tendencies. When they occur on deep peats, it is because these have been drained, either as a result of natural desiccation or artificially. Heather-moor on these sites grades into damp moorlands and bogs, just as elsewhere it shows signs of being derived from woodlands and grasslands. On its upper margins, above about 2,000 ft., it merges into the montane heaths—in which usually bilberry and other small shrubs become equally abundant (see Fig. 17). Thus heather-moor occupies almost a central position among upland vegetation. As a general rule it is found on a very clearly defined type of habitat, and thus is very useful for comparative purposes in the field. It is perhaps worth pointing out that isolated plants of heather have no such indicator value. They can be found over a great range of altitudes and humidities.

BOG VEGETATION

At the other extreme from the mainly porous and well-drained montane habitats lie those in which drainage is deficient so that water constantly accumulates. Because of the high rainfall, these waterlogged places predominate in most upland areas in Britain, except where the slopes are steep. They are marked by the presence of deep peat, and are now or were formerly covered by bog vegetation. The place-name which corresponds to these bog-peats in Britain, wherever Scandinavian peoples once settled, is " moss," a term which has the merit of describing an essential feature of the original vegetation—the presence of bog-moss—and so of distinguishing it from the drier " moor," on which other plants are more noticeable.

The general form of such a bog vegetation in its original and natural state is very characteristic. The surface is almost completely covered by bog-mosses, particularly *S. papillosum*, and through this *Sphagnum* carpet project the scattered shoots of the many grassy or sedgy plants, which may include the moor-grass (*Molinia*), deer-sedge (*Scirpus caespitosus*) or cotton-sedge (*Eriophorum*), and almost always the bog asphodel (*Narthecium*) (see Pl. XX, p. 125). Along with these are short and slender shoots of heather (*Calluna*), cross-leaved heath (*Erica tetralix*) or bog-myrtle (*Myrica gale*), rarely much exceeding 6 in. in height. On the carpet of bog-moss are to be found liverworts which are almost confined to this habitat, such as the unobtrusive *Odontoschisma sphagni* and the striking brown or red *Pleurozia purpurea*. Here also are insect-catching plants, particularly the sundews (*Drosera rotundifolia* and *D. anglica*). The natural state of the vegetation on a well-developed bog is thus marked by three features—a more or less continuous cover of bog-moss, a special community of small plants which live on this carpet and a somewhat stunted vegetation of flowering plants growing through it. In order to avoid frequent repetition, it will be convenient to describe this condition of a bog surface as that marked by a " continuous Sphagnum-cover."

Wherever such a Sphagnum-cover is well developed, active peat formation is taking place, or, putting it in another way, the bog is growing and, as we have already seen, constant development or re-adjustments among the species must be taking place—such, for example, as the slow transition from more eutrophic to oligotrophic types. The larger plants growing in the Sphagnum-cover are those able to keep pace with the rising level of the bog-moss, and the larger grasses (*Molinia*) and sedges, deer-sedge and cotton-sedge, are particularly successful in doing this, although they generally lose their tufted character in doing so (see Pl. XX, p. 125). They produce roots each year just below the bog-moss surface, while the shrubby plants such as heather, sweet gale and cross-leaved heath, have roots or slender shoots running horizontally in the same region.

The bog-mosses themselves also show change. The surface of such a developing bog is rarely uniform, and in the damper hollows the chief bog-moss is usually *S. cuspidatum*, a somewhat narrow-leaved form. The most abundant and widespread species is, however, almost always *S. papillosum*, a blunt-leaved and generally yellowish species, though often *S. rubellum*, frequently more or less red as its name implies, and with narrow leaves, is also well represented in the slightly higher places. Two other species seem to be representative of old-established and little-damaged bogs, *S. magellanicum*, tinged with a metallic red, and the small and slender *S. tenellum*.

The vegetation of existing bogs shows extreme diversity and it includes a very large number of plant species. Some of the most frequent and widespread are given in the following list, which also attempts a rather rough comparison of different localities. The numbers given represent the number of times one would expect to find the named species if 10 samples of bog surface each of 1 square metre in area were examined. These figures are averages reduced from a large number of records taken at various altitudes. They thus simply represent the average vegetation of areas of bog and deep peat, and are taken on approximately similar and slight slopes. The numbers do not indicate which plants are actually most abundant, simply those most often present. The letters *a*, *la* and *f*, meaning *abundant*, *locally abundant* and *frequent* respectively, have therefore been added to the species which merit these descriptions in the different areas. A cross means that the species is present.

THE COMMONER PLANTS IN REPRESENTATIVE SAMPLES OF BOG VEGETATION

	Connemara	*Rannoch Moor*	*Stainmoor*
Andromeda polifolia, bog rosemary	—	—	+
Calluna vulgaris, heather	10	10	10 f
Carex panicea, carnation sedge	+	+	—
Drosera anglica, long-leaved sundew	3	+	—
D. rotundifolia, round-leaved sundew	8	6	6
Empetrum nigrum, crowberry	—	—	+
Erica tetralix, cross-leaved heath	9	9	10 f
Eriophorum angustifolium, cotton-sedge	4	9	8
E. vaginatum, tufted cotton-sedge	+	4	9 f
Molinia caerulea, purple moor-grass	10 a	6	—
Myrica gale, bog-myrtle	5 la	3	—
Narthecium ossifragum, bog asphodel	7	8	8
Vaccinium oxycoccus, cranberry	—	+	5
Pinguicula spp., butterwort	+	+	—
Potentilla erecta, tormentil	+	+	—
Rhynchospora alba, white beak-sedge	2 l	+	—
Rubus chamaemorus, cloudberry	—	—	+
Schoenus nigricans, black bog-rush	8 la	—	—
Scirpus caespitosum, deer-sedge	8	10	2
Utricularia spp., bladderwort	+	+	—
Mosses			
Breutelia chrysocoma	4	—	—
Campylopus atrovirens	3	+	—
Rhacomitrium lanuginosum	4	+	—
Sphagnum spp., bog-moss	10	10 a	10 la
Liverworts			
Odontoschisma sphagni	+	3	+
Pleurozia purpurea	6	3	—
Gymnocolea inflata	—	—	+
Lichens			
Cladonia sylvatica agg.	5	+	5
C. uncialis	—	+	+

MOLINIA-SPHAGNUM   BOGS

The record for Connemara in the above list describes an example of actively growing and extending bogs in regions of very high rainfall. Developing bogs of this general type are found elsewhere along the western margins of Ireland and Britain as well as in Connemara, but elsewhere they do not always make up such a large proportion of the vegetation as in the Connemara mountains, where indeed they may overrun the whole of the lower slopes.   The commonest type of "western" bog has a vegetation in which the purple moor-grass (*Molinia*) and the bog-myrtle (*Myrica*) are associated with an almost continuous carpet of bog-moss.   Where the rainfall is unusually high, as in the example cited, and the soil-water has probably never receded from the peat surface, the *Molinia-Myrica* bogs may contain also an abundance of the black bog-rush (*Schoenus nigricans*) and often also the white beak-sedge (*Rhynchospora alba*).   The permanently wet nature of the peat in these localities is frequently shown also by the presence of plants, elsewhere and more normally found in the margins of lakes and pools, such as the common reed (*Phragmites communis*), the reed horsetail (*Equisetum fluviatile*), slender sedge (*Carex lasiocarpa*) and bog-bean (*Menyanthes trifoliata*).

The third type of bog illustrated in the list is one of which extensive areas are still to be found in the Northern Pennines, particularly in the Stainmore region and also in the higher parts of Bowland Forest. These bogs differ from those of the far west mainly in the absence of the moor-grass and its associates, the beak-sedges and bog-myrtle. The cotton-sedges become more prominent, and so do the cross-leaved heath and heather.   Particularly characteristic are the cranberry and the rarer bog-rosemary.   Insectivorous plants are now represented mainly by a single species of sundew, the round-leaved, and equally noticeable is the absence of the liverwort, *Pleurozia purpurea*.

Intermediate between the Stainmore and Connemara types is the general form of bog common in the Western Highlands of Scotland, illustrated by a sample from Rannoch Moor. Both deer-sedge (*Scirpus*) and moor-grass are usually prominent, though great diversity in the composition of bog vegetation occurs in this area and the figures given are simply an average of a large number of samples.   For this reason, indeed, it is often hard to describe any bog types in a simple manner because they usually have no plant entirely dominant as does, for example, a heather-moor, but instead usually include a great mixture of plants in each standard area. Thus on average a square metre of typical bog vegetation will usually contain at least 12 species.

The examples given of these three main types are associated climatically with decreasing intensities of rainfall. The Connemara example is from an annual rainfall of 90-100 in., the Rannoch Moor site from one of probably about 70-75 in., while the Stainmore region has a rainfall of about 55 in. per annum. A comparison of the figures suggests that the balance in composition of the vegetation depends partly at least on the humidity of the climate, operating no doubt through its effect on soil humidity and soil aeration.

However, the pattern of the bog vegetation in any one of the mountain areas can usually be related also and in a broad way to changing altitude. Thus among the western mountains, from Kendal to Fort William and beyond, the lowermost bogs have commonly Sphagnum, mainly associated with bog-myrtle and purple moor-grass. Bog-myrtle does not, however, reach an altitude much exceeding 1,000 ft. (e.g. on Rannoch Moor), and its range falls to 700 or 800 ft. in Sutherland and Caithness, and to still less in the western islands. At higher levels, deer-sedge and heather generally become more common, though they, in turn, get scarce above about 2,000 ft. The sheathed cotton-sedge often becomes abundant at about 1,500 ft. and persists to much greater heights than heather. The highest bogs also often include the crowberry (*Empetrum nigrum*) and cloudberry (*Rubus chamaemorus*), as well as Vacciniums (particularly mountain blaeberry, *Vaccinium uliginosum*). The Sphagnum carpet is also different and is often composed mainly of *Sphagnum acutifolium* (agg.), the usually abundant *S. papillosum* being much less common or absent while the brown *S. fuscum* is at times very noticeable.

It is, however, rare to find growing bogs at high altitudes with a complete Sphagnum-cover. Almost always in the high bogs, the peat is dissected in all directions by drainage-channels, a feature that is well shown in the fine photograph of Sghoran Dubh in Plate 23, p. 160. In dissected bogs of this type, the sheathed cotton-sedge is almost always the most prominent of the grass-like species. It is usually accompanied by much heather, and although most of the bog-species can be found here and there, the Sphagnum carpet is absent and the balance of the different species entirely changed. The proportions of these subordinate species found in any particular area depend mainly upon the degree of dissection and the resultant drainage (see p. 157).

MIXED MOORS

There are large areas covered by deep peat in the British uplands and most of them we should expect to be bog on climatic grounds. Over a large proportion of this area the Sphagnum-cover is incomplete or absent. Often this may be ascribed to erosion and dissection, or if not, it may be associated with greater slope and increased drainage. But we often hesitate to ascribe the absence or scarcity of the bog-moss to these reasons, for Sphagnum bogs at times are found on steeper slopes than those which elsewhere lack them. Generally speaking, also, we note that the same species of plants are found as occur with the Sphagnum-cover, though their appearance is different and their size and vigour is usually much increased when the Sphagnum-cover disappears. Hence, running parallel to the main bog types, is a very diverse series of " mixed moors," marked by varying proportions of the larger plants, by the absence of a *continuous* Sphagnum-cover, and by decreasing proportions of the characteristic but smaller bog species.

These plant communities normally occur on fairly deep peat, generally 3 ft. or more in depth, which shows by its composition that Sphagnum must have been an important element in its formation. Thus the probability is that these various forms of " mixed " moorland are derived from some form of bog, which has no doubt been most easily changed, often with loss of Sphagnum, on the steeper slopes where the peat is more easily drained. To avoid undue complication of description we may think of these " mixed " moors as lying on peat formed by what we can call " blanket bog " (see p. 65), recognising that this is a conveniently vague term for peat-forming vegetation, which no doubt resembled in a general way the existing bog types described above, varying in composition with slope, altitude and rainfall.

In the area they cover, the innumerable variants of the " mixed " moor condition must be almost the most widely spread form of British moorland. Two main types are recognisable. In the Scottish Highlands particularly the golden brown of the hills in late summer is due to the abundance of deer-sedge, so that much of the

Western Highlands is said to be covered by " Scirpus-moor "—actually by a range of plant communities in which at times Molinia, heather and cotton-sedge respectively may be almost as frequent as the deer-sedge.

Elsewhere a mixture of heather and cotton-sedge, often with numerous mosses, is frequently met with, showing marked seasonal changes of aspect, being flecked with white when the cotton-sedge heads are ripe in spring and purple when the heather blooms in late summer. No distinctive name has been given to this type of moor, probably the most extensive British type, as it certainly is along the eastern margins of the Highland zone and in Northern England. It has often perhaps been regarded as an intermediate between heather-moor and the " cotton-grass moss," described below, but the emphasis in all these types of moorland vegetation should properly be laid on the original blanket-bog vegetation from which they were derived. If this in a way resembled existing upland bog vegetation, as we should suspect, then it must have consisted of numerous species and the " mixed " types of plant community must more nearly resemble it.

Although these mixed types of moorland vegetation are often developed among the mountains where drainage is better or where erosion of the peat has taken place, they also occur on gentle slopes in some places which at present seem to have a climate too dry for wide-spread upland bog-growth. Particularly is this the case in Caithness, and in areas like Lune Forest, between Stainmoor and Teesdale, where the average annual rainfall now is only of the order of 30 to 40 in., considerably below the figure of about 55 in. which seems to represent climatic conditions certainly characteristic of bog develop-ment. Similar conditions probably occur elsewhere, notably in the Eastern Highlands of Scotland and in many parts of Ireland, away from the high mountains. In all these places the appearance of the vegetation, in which most of the typical bog species are still represented, and still more, the structure of the underlying peat, which contains the abundant remains of Sphagnum, both suggest very strongly that such localities represent areas in which more humid conditions of climate must formerly have prevailed.

In the Southern Pennines, in contrast, there are large areas of former bog almost entirely covered by tussocks of cotton-sedge, often to the exclusion of almost all other plants. The sheathed cotton-sedge is the dominant, but the narrow-leaved species (*E. angustifolium*) is also generally present. Occasionally associates may be found, particularly at times crowberry and bilberry, the mosses, *Campylopus flexuosus* and *Pohlia nutans*, and the liverwort, *Calypogeia*. The cloudberry (*Rubus chamaemorus*) is local and is more often present at the higher levels. Bog mosses and the small species of the Sphagnum-cover are normally quite absent. The great Pennine " cotton-grass mosses " are generally wild and desolate in the extreme for most of the year. They have their moments of unforgettable colour, especially when the cotton-sedge heads are ripe and white in May or June (see Pl. 22b, p. 145), for at the same time the adjacent " edges " are often splashed with the bright yellow-green of young bilberry leaves.

The " cotton-grass mosses " cover some 500 sq. ml. in the Southern Pennines. Over much of this area, the annual rainfall is in the range of 50 to 60 in., as we saw in an earlier chapter (p. 39), and there are no very obvious grounds for supposing that all these areas are necessarily outside the range of climate favourable for bog growth. Their topography, for example, is often very similar to that of the Stainmoor district, which possesses a similar rainfall and may still support Sphagnum-bog. The cotton-sedge bogs of the Southern Pennines have no counterpart in other European mountain areas, and as their vegetation is extremely different from that of other parts of upland Britain, its origin and development is worthy of a further discussion, to which we shall presently return. This is the more necessary because they were early recognised as a distinctive type of British vegetation, and a great deal of our knowledge of moorland ecology has centred round them. It may perhaps be useful to emphasise two points at this stage. Poverty in associated species seems to be especially characteristic of the Southern Pennines. " Mosses " with cotton-sedge abundant are not uncommon elsewhere in the uplands, as indeed the frequency of such names as White Moss denotes, and particularly is this the case on dissected peat. Most of these areas actually approach or belong to the mixed heather-cotton-sedge type to which reference was made earlier, a form of vegetation distinguished by its more numerous associated species.

A survey of the existing types of upland vegetation on deep peat thus reveals a varied series of plant communities of which some possess a more or less continuous Sphagnum-cover, while in others, in fact in the majority, the Sphagnum-cover is incomplete or lacking. On the whole, though the proportions vary greatly, the same larger plants are frequent in both types, so that we may suspect that the two sorts are related, even though there are great differences in their appearance. The four main bog types tend to be distinguished by abundance of black beak-rush, of Molinia (and sweet gale), of deer-sedge and cotton-sedge. There are also four fairly extensive types of " mixed " moorland without continuous Sphagnum-cover. Two of these are " dissected bogs " and " high-level bogs," both obviously derived types, and in two others, deer-sedge or cotton-sedge, both usually associated with heather and with cross-leaved heath, are the most abundant plants. Finally, there are the extensive areas of cotton-sedge moss or of heather-moor, which usually show no obvious connection in composition with the original bog sequence.

Speaking generally, then, the types of mixed moorland seem to have been derived from bogs by the elimination of the Sphagnum-cover, with a corresponding increase in the larger species remaining. The ecologist wants to know why these changes have taken place, and if they can be related to any of the trends of soil or other conditions that it is possible to detect.

CHANGES IN BOG VEGETATION

In almost any of the main bog areas there can be found numerous signs of the effects of human interference upon the bog vegetation. The chief agencies causing changes in the vegetation are burning, draining and grazing. The oldest and easiest method of modifying moorland is undoubtedly by burning it. It may appear odd that this method can be used to modify the vegetation of water-logged bogs. Nevertheless, most of the taller bog plants have a high fat content, and there are periods in autumn and spring when their dried remains will burn with great ease. Particularly is this true of the grasses and the woody stems of heathers and bog-myrtle. The effects of burning are at first to damage the woody plants more than the grass-like ones and also to destroy, partly at least, the bog-moss surface with its sensitive species. The first effects are thus often a temporary disappearance of heather, heaths and bog-myrtle, as well as a reduction in the number of species present. Some of the curious mixtures of deer-sedge and Molinia found here and there in the West Highlands seem to have arisen in this way.

Where the effects of burning are augmented by draining, they are often extremely marked. Draining alone mainly alters the balance of abundance between the bog-mosses and the larger flowering plants, leading to the development of tussocky moorland in which heather, along with deer-sedge or cotton-sedge, predominates. If there are pines or birches near at hand, they are likely to spread on to the drained area. All of these changes are primarily due to the penetration of air into the soil, and this, by permitting the more rapid breakdown of the soil organic matter, causes chemical changes which also favours the plants mentioned above. These flourish at the expense of other true bog plants, such as the black beak-rush and the bog-myrtle, as well as those growing as part of the Sphagnum-cover. It is usually hard to separate the effects of draining and of burning, because when draining is used burning is almost always added. The effects of draining alone are most easily seen on dissected areas—where the eroded gullies prevent the passage of moor fires. It will usually be found that a greater proportion of bog species survives in dissected areas, particularly the smaller species, the mosses and lichens, which are so characteristic of the Sphagnum-covered bog. The tenacity with which these species persist in such places suggests that burning and grazing are often the most potent agencies of elimination.

The effects of grazing are also, in practice, almost invariably mixed up with those produced by burning and draining, and so are often not easily distinguished. They are, however, of two sorts : the effects of treading and manuring on the bog surface, and the selective effects due to grazing some plants more than others. Bog-moss is particularly sensitive to treading and the Sphagnum-cover soon disappears, especially when this effect is added to those produced by burning or draining. While this is taking place other rather specialised mosses appear which grow mainly on dung or on animal remains. The commonest of these is perhaps *Tetraplodon mnioides*, but species of *Splachnum* are also frequent.

About the selective effects of grazing we know very little. The plants eaten certainly depend both on the particular grazing animal and the season of the year. Most moorland plants are grazed to some extent when the shoots are young, and the young flowering shoots of cotton-sedge (often called " moss-crops ") are greedily pulled and eaten in spring by both deer and sheep and are supposed to increase lactation. Deer and Highland cattle appear to graze the young leaves also. Sheep, however, seem to prefer deer-sedge and moor-grass. All of these animals graze freely on the young shoots of ling and heathers, and many of the moorland insects are particularly selective in this respect, defoliating the heathers and bilberry but leaving the grass-like species almost untouched. While it is difficult to assess the comparative effects of the different types of stock, there is one well-marked difference. Sheep graze so very much more closely than the larger animals that they destroy many more of the smaller species. They have also a greater effect on the surface—" puddling " it along their runways instead of breaking through it as cattle do. Their effects are usually accentuated by the much greater numbers employed.

In general, the moorland plants belong to the same two main types as woodland ones (p. 122). Some species like the heathers have their growing points at the ends of the shoots, while the grass-like types have their growing points at the base of the leaves and hence usually buried in the depths of a tussock or near the ground. It is obvious that both grazing and fire will alike tend to damage the former type in such a way as to prevent the shoots from growing again, and thus we may expect that the general effects of these treatments may be somewhat alike, though, because it is more continuous, the grazing effect is usually more permanent. Both tend towards the replacement of the very mixed bog vegetation by types in which a few of the grass-like forms may predominate and in which the numbers of species is greatly diminished.

Speaking generally, however, the effects of these disturbances on bog vegetation are threefold. The first sign of change is often that the Sphagnum-cover ceases to be continuous and, very often, even if it has recovered continuity after damage, the number of species in it will be small. Particularly sensitive to modifying agencies are some of the widely distributed species of *Sphagnum* (e.g. *S. magellanicum* and *S. tenellum*), as well as small plants like the sundews and the liverwort, *Pleurozia purpurea*. Many of the rarer bog plants (e.g. *Scheuchzeria palustris, Andromeda polifolia*) and sedges like *Carex paupercula, C. limosa* and *C. lasiocarpa*, also belong to this category, even though because of their limited distribution they are not quite so useful as indicators.

The second sign of change is that the smooth, mossy surface with scattered shoots coming through it is replaced by an irregular tussocky surface, with mosses and smaller species becoming increasingly rare. The commonest state is for the tussocks to be mainly composed of sheathed cotton-sedge, with bushes of heather, although, along the western margins, both blue moor-grass and deer-sedge may be abundant at times.

A third sign of modification is the appearance of certain mosses and liverworts which are presumably associated with a somewhat higher salt-content of the surface peat (as a result of oxidation) or with the decreased competition. Notable among these are plants of the "mixed moor," such as the mosses *Aulacomnium palustre*, *Plagiothecium undulatum*, *Polytrichum commune*, *Dicranum scoparium* and *Campylopus flexuosus*. Among liverworts, *Diplophyllum albicans*, *Lophozia ventricosa* and *Ptilidium ciliare* are significant in this respect.

A final feature of these changes is a great reduction in the number of species, most easily seen if comparisons are made on the basis of standard small areas such as a square metre or square yard. The typical 12 or more species in a square metre of Connemara bog is reduced to 3 or 4 in the cotton-sedge moors of the Southern Pennines.

If we use these signs as tests in the examination of British upland vegetation on deep peat, we are led to the conclusion that almost all of it represents some form of bog vegetation greatly modified from its original condition; and while in some cases there are, as we have already seen, grounds for believing that natural drainage or changes in climate have contributed much to the modifications observed, over very large areas human activities have been the main modifying agency. In the Stainmore Forest, areas of Sphagnum bog are known to have changed in response to burning or grazing, either to cotton-sedge moor or to heather-moor, in the last forty years, and similar effects have been noted in the Lake District and in the Bowland Forest area. One very useful guide to such changes is the frequency with which marked differences in vegetation exist on opposite sides of a boundary fence, especially when the barrier separates owners with different interests. Several cases exist where the one side of such a fence is preserved for game and carries mainly heather, while another side, being common land or owned by a hill farmer, is predominantly cotton-sedge. The differences are due to the differences in treatment adopted along the lines indicated earlier.

The recognition of the fact that many of our moorland types of vegetation are derived from Sphagnum bogs, and in particular that forms of cotton-sedge moor may be so derived, led naturally to a consideration of the possibility that the moorlands of the Southern Pennines may once have belonged to the general British bog type and that they may have reached their present condition as the result of the long continued action of modifying factors. If we were to apply to their vegetation the tests used to detect modification, then we should immediately conclude that they were the most modified bog areas in Britain. At the same time it should be recognised that there are certain difficulties in the way of this assumption. The peat in the Southern Pennines is usually about 3-6 ft. in thickness, very dark in colour and almost structureless, except for the fibrous remains of cotton-sedge tussocks usually found at all levels in the peat. Taking into account the dominance of cotton-sedge on the surface, those who had worked on this subject had concluded that the peat had been almost wholly formed by cotton-sedge, or, in effect, that there had been no marked change in the bog vegetation. It is impossible to reconcile this view with what has happened and is happening in the other bog areas, and we must either conclude that the Southern Pennines are startlingly different from the other mountain areas in some respect or else seek in some way to revise the original conclusion as to the origin of their peat.

In the Southern Pennines, both W. B. Crump and Mrs. M. Bulman had pointed out earlier the existence here and there in peat cuttings of long and continuous layers of Sphagnum peat which had preserved the bog-moss structure little altered. These were considered to represent long depressions in a peat surface in which the bog-moss had once grown luxuriantly and to a considerable depth. More recent investigation has shown that bog-moss was once universally common in the Southern Pennines, though the remains are now usually so much compressed and humified as to be unrecognisable without detailed microscopic examination. A long series of such observations was made by my technical assistant, H. O. Dransfield, who later was unfortunately killed on the Atlantic patrol as a flight-lieutenant in Coastal Command. Peat samples were taken just below the surface at a depth of 4 in. and from sites widely distributed over the Southern Pennines on cotton-sedge moors. The microscopic examination of these samples showed that bog-moss remains (leaves and spores) were always present and normally in profusion, though occasionally, in the shallow peats, they might be so much decomposed and humified as to be almost unrecognisable. Comparative estimates suggested that the bog-moss was formerly at least as common as it is now on the great

Stainmore bogs. The fact is the more remarkable when it is remembered that over the areas examined, which covered some 30 miles of moorland, Sphagnum was not even seen. Indeed, at present, the characteristic peat-forming species of bog-moss are not to be seen on the Southern Pennines cotton-sedge mosses, though other forms may occur in peaty flushes outside the main peat masses. Evidently, then, the vegetation of the peat surface as a whole has changed remarkably, and the assumption seems to be justified that the changes from Sphagnum bog to cotton-sedge, which are known to have taken place recently in the Stainmore and Bowland Forest areas, must have ensued at an earlier date over wide areas in the Southern Pennines.

It would perhaps be unwise to assume from the present evidence that the bog vegetation of the area was exactly the same as that of the Stainmore and Bowland Forest areas, even although the topographic and climatic conditions are so strikingly similar as to render a close resemblance in the vegetation probable. One difficulty is that of finding traces of all the bog species in the peat. Experience has shown that the remains of bog plants decay in aerated peat at very different rates. The twigs of heather and cross-leaved heath, in particular, and also of the deer-sedge, are destroyed comparatively quickly, while the fibrous remains of cotton-sedge are particularly resistant and are usually recognisable long after other visible structures have disappeared. In peat like that most common in the Southern Pennines, which is much decayed and usually lacking in easily recognisable structures, it may well be that the obvious remains of heather, heaths and deer-sedge in the peat have disintegrated, even though microscopic examination shows an abundance of pollen of heath-like and sedge-like plants, indicating their former presence. It is, moreover, well to remember that the heaths are not represented in bog peat by the large and shrubby individuals found, for example, in old heather-moor, but by the slender and stunted twigs characteristic of growing bogs. These are not very prominent even in fresh peat, and they must disappear still more quickly during peat decay.

The conclusion that large areas of the present cotton-sedge moors once resembled Sphagnum bogs is not one which rests entirely on the evidence already outlined. The early stages of bog modification often pass through a stage with heather as abundant as cotton-sedge, and according to the recollection of experienced keepers and shepherds there has been a very great decrease in the proportion of heather in

PLATE 23

John Markham

Sghoran Dubh, Inverness-shire: a high-level peat-bog showing marked dissection. The adjacent slopes are glacially steepened

PLATE 24

John Markham

Peat-buried timber (pine) and gentle sloping ground, characteristic of extensive peat development the Southern Pennines in the last 50 or 60 years, and a corresponding increase of unmixed cotton-sedge. At a still earlier stage, in 1813, John Farey, a knowledgeable and well-informed writer who was commissioned by the Board of Agriculture to draw up a *General View of the Agriculture of Derbyshire*, wrote of the upland peat-mosses that they were " formed of great accumulations of the grey Bog-moss (*Sphagnum palustre*), Cotton Grass (*Eriophorum polystachion*), Heaths (*Ericas*), Marsh Horsetail (*Equisetum palustre*), rushy bents and other small aquatic plants which can still be seen growing on the edges and wetter parts." I think that the order in which Farey arranged the plants is not the least instructive part of this list, because if he had visited to-day the bogs he mentions in his book, nothing would lead him to mention bog-moss at all, for it is absent. It seems certain that it was abundant 140 years ago.

Still a third line of inquiry may be of interest also in connection with these vegetation changes. The beautiful bog rosemary (*Andromeda polifolia*) is now an extremely rare plant in the Southern Pennines. In 1942 there appear to have been only two stations where occasional plants still survived, a newly-found one containing only a few plants on the Ringinglow Bog, near Sheffield, and one near Halifax at Lighthazels, where Dr. W. A. Sledge had seen the plant. There were formerly many records of this plant (probably about 10-12 in the period 1870-1890), so that it was evidently far more widely spread 60 to 70 years ago. Still earlier, in 1835, H. C. Watson had written of it in the *New Botanist's Guide* : " Abundant in all that group of mountains that separates Yorkshire from Lancashire."

It is perhaps generally known among naturalists that the spread of civilisation in England has greatly affected our flora, and Sir Edward Salisbury has shown us that of the species which have disappeared, a large proportion, probably the majority, have been plants of wet places. Andromeda comes within this category, and it is of particular interest because it is a species which spreads and establishes itself on the Sphagnum cover of bogs. It maintains itself subsequently, on drainage for example, only where the original vegetation is not too profoundly modified. Thus it still survives in some abundance in parts of the Stainmore Sphagnum-bogs and also on similar areas with Sphagnum-cover in the Bowland Forest and the English Lake District. It seems, therefore, that in 1836 there must have been many areas in the Southern Pennines which still retained a strong resemblance to the conditions of the original bog vegetation, presumably with Sphagnum abundant as in the existing upland sites of Andromeda to-day. There is thus evidence that at least the last stages in the change from Sphagnum-bog to cotton-sedge moor have been completed within the last 100 years or so. They may, of course, have been going on for a much longer time, because the Andromeda sites, for example, prove generally to be on the deep Sphagnum peat of " mosses " which would probably be the last to change. Indeed, the peat on one site, examined since in detail by Dr. V. M. Conway, has shown that the main changes are comparatively recent, within the last 100-150 years.

A survey of the observed or detectable changes brought about in bog vegetation leaves little doubt that potent and widespread causes of change have been the various forms of human interference. These have meant a transition of the general form :

bog ———→ mixed moor ———→ cotton-sedge moor or
heather-moor

The actual path of the changes and the final results depend partly on terrain and largely on the duration and intensity of the agents employed. The effects undoubtedly show a general resemblance to those produced by natural agencies which have led to drying of the peat, and similar changes could doubtless be produced also by climatic desiccation. The agencies associated with man are, however, far more effective in changing the vegetation, producing also a notable reduction in its variety and very often leading to the elimination of shrubby species.

It is evident that these changes are mainly those associated with bog degeneration. There must also have been upgrade or developmental changes during which the original forest vegetation or the mineral soil changed over to fully-developed bogs on deep peat. Logically, we should now search for these developmental stages, even though the search will involve the widening of the scope of our inquiry.

CHAPTER 9

VEGETATION AND HABITAT

RELIEF FACTORS

W H I L E the moors and "mosses" of the Southern Pennines owe something of their special character to the changes in vegetation that have just been described, many of their striking features are associated with the land-forms which result from their geological structure. The dissected plateaux of which they are composed show a strong tendency to separate into a series of gently sloping shelves separated by "edges" which are usually capped by coarse sandstones of the Millstone Grit type. On these shelves, according to their height and rainfall, may be heather-moor (700 to 1,000 ft.), cotton-sedge moss (1,000 to 1,500 ft.) or, at the highest levels, the much-dissected peat-bogs of summits like Kinder Scout or Bleaklow. The exposed escarpment slopes are often "bilberry edges"; the more sheltered may still support birch-woods or even oak-woods at lower levels (see Fig. 28, p. 142). Characteristically, the natural state of the valley sides would be oak-woods, merging into birches along the bilberry edges, but the slopes are now most of them grasslands in which wavy hair-grass often predominates, its dark-green foliage contrasting with the lighter greens of the bents and Yorkshire fog (*Holcus lanatus*), which pick out the mineral flushes. Here and there (Fig. 28) are degenerating woodlands of birch with Molinia associated with areas flushed by peaty water from above. The preponderance of soils covered with acid *mor*, or with oxidised bog peat which is often still more acid, limits the flora severely to those species which can tolerate this peculiarity. A noticeable scarcity of mosses, liverworts and lichens has often been attributed with some plausibility to atmospheric pollution from the neighbouring industrial areas.

The general form of the Pennine hills remains similar farther north, although the presence of huge shelves of Carboniferous limestone gives a special character, as we have already seen (p. 9), to the Craven Uplands, just as it does to the hills of Derbyshire, Westmorland and Clare. The apparent bareness of the limestone pavements is belied by the extremely rich flora otherwise associated with this rock, which contrasts remarkably in species with that of the adjacent sandstones and shales of the Lower Carboniferous. The frequent presence of glacial drifts, sometimes calcareous, sometimes derived from slaty rocks and otherwise from siliceous sources, gives an added variability to the vegetation, which thus affords a unique field for working out the varied influence of geological structure and of climatic variations, though in practice there is also a severe handicap due to the long-continued and overriding influence of man.

There is another interesting feature of the moorlands of the district. The deer-sedge (*Scirpus caespitosus*) is a very local plant in the Southern Pennines. It is rather more frequent in the Central Pennines, occasionally on basin-peats, which though often much dissected, preserve many elements indicative of the original bog-flora. On peats which belong more obviously to the blanket-bog type, the deer-sedge is mainly, if not wholly, confined to the lower margins of the peat masses, where it may be at times, also associated with the presence of typical peat-forming Sphagna. The example shown in Fig. 29 gives

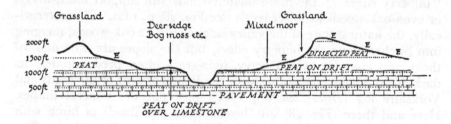

FIG. 29.—Arrangement of moorland vegetation in the Craven uplands—Cable Rake to Simon Fell. (Somewhat diagrammatic.) Rainfall 50 inches. Vertical scale x 2.

a good illustration of the altitudinal and topographic zonations on the west of Ingleborough, where the higher cotton-sedge mosses are of the species-poor type found in the Southern Pennines. We could, perhaps, take the view that the sequence shown in this figure :

(1) deer-sedge with bog-moss (lowest)
(2) mixed moor (heather, deer-sedge and cotton-sedge)
(3) cotton-sedge moss
(4) dissected cotton-sedge moss (highest),

represents, on the whole, an age series, the oldest and most naturally modified bogs lying at the highest level.

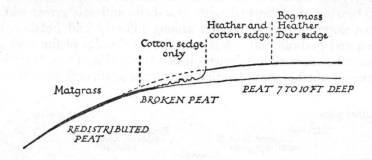

FIG. 30.—Distribution of peat-plants on High Borrow Moss (Westmorland).

Farther north, deer-sedge becomes increasingly frequent, though still strongly western in distribution (e.g. in the Southern Uplands), and very often at the lower levels when present. In all this central country, however, the peat-bogs show a bewildering variety of aspect, undoubtedly due largely to the varying intensity of recent modification by man and of erosion by rain and weathering. Good fragments of primitive aspect remain in the Bowland Forest, the Lake District and in Western Galloway. Not infrequently they show a marginal arrangement like that shown in Fig. 30, illustrating another aspect of the interrelations of deer-sedge and cotton-sedge, the former remaining on the less oxidised and less acid peats in the damper part of the bog.

One of the interesting variations on the long shelf and steep escarpment type of structure comes when the rock strata diverge appreciably from the horizontal. With porous strata in particular, such a dip has appreciable effects on the vegetation wherever over-steepened slopes occur. There are excellent examples of this in north-east Yorkshire (see Fig. 31), where the prevailing sandstone plateaux are usually covered by heather moor, and intersected at intervals by deep valleys. The rock strata dip gently towards the east and south, so that in some of the valleys running north and south (in which such factors as exposure to light and heat are more or less similar on each side) the western of the two valley slopes tends to be flushed by salt-rich water

emerging from the rocks, while the eastern slope is leached and any
water which penetrates is drained away. Thus in the example figured
(Fig. 31) the flushed slope has a *mull* humus on soil of brown-earth
type, bearing an oak-wood with blue-bells and soft grass, while the
eastern slope has a few birches among bilberry and heather, a *mor*
humus and podsolic soil. A good effect of the dip of the rock strata
on montane vegetation is shown on Ben Wyvis (Fig. 17, p. 81), where it
determines whether the vegetation is montane heath or flushed grassland.

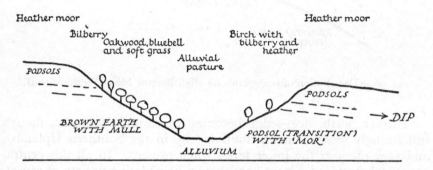

FIG. 31.—Effect of the dip of the rock strata on vegetation. (North-east Yorkshire.)

The dip of the strata may, however, produce other results, and these
may be illustrated further while at the same time reference is made to
another region, which strikingly illustrates the influence of topography
upon vegetation. Much of Eastern Skye belongs essentially to the
shelf and escarpment type of structure, its character being largely due
to the gently-sloping and resistant beds of basalt, either sills or lava
flows, lying among soft sandstones and shales. Each of the exposed
layers of basalt presents a nearly impermeable surface from which the
softer deposits have been removed by ice-action. The climate is
humid and the larger shelves are now peat-covered and clothed by
bogs of deer-sedge and moor-grass. The little crags are capped by
basalt (a " basic " rock) so that the tendency is for soils of the brown-
earth type to persist for a considerable time on the steep slopes. On
these can still be found vestigial woodlands of oak and hazel, but most
of the slopes have been cleared and converted into good grasslands,
round which the existence of the crofter population centres. In Elgol
and Strathaird particularly, from which the example in Fig. 32 is

taken, there are some admirable examples of this type showing the influence of topography and geological structure upon human distribution. Near-by also are the homesteads of Torran, a small but populous centre which represents an oasis of limestone among a desert of moorland on granite and sandstones.

The section illustrated in Fig. 32 is also interesting because of the great difference in the details of soil development on the two slopes.

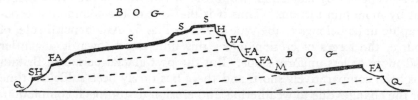

FIG. 32.—Effects of the dip of the rock strata on grassland and peat distribution in the Elgol district of Skye. The shelves and ledges are basaltic lava flows. Vertical scale x 2. Q, Oak; H, Heather; FA, Fescue-Bent grassland; M, Molinia grassland; S, Deer-sedge.

On the upper part of the western slope, above 500 ft., soil formation has been almost negligible except occasionally where there has been an accumulation of gravelly detritus as a result of rain-wash. On most of the slope the peat rests directly on the washed and leached rock surface, and it seems as though the downward seepage of peaty water has served both to sterilise and to protect the lower rock surfaces. In this upper part, the influence of the dipping strata of base-rich rock (basalt) on the vegetation is otherwise hardly discernible except where the main flushes emerge. These are marked by the presence of the black bog-rush (*Schoenus nigricans*), appearing in autumn as light-grey streaks among the golden-olive of the deer-sedge bog. Below 500 ft. soil formation has been nearly as vigorous as on the eastern slopes, where it continues to the uppermost crest, and it shows a similar pattern, although the influence of the water drainage makes boggy areas more frequent on the west. On the east, peat seepage has little influence, although the crests are more leached and bear much heather. The brown-earth type of soil persists longest near the steepest and least stable areas, particularly on the upper parts of the screes and on the fans below gullies. This soil carries a Festuca-Agrostis grassland, including much vernal grass (*Anthoxanthum*).

In most of these examples we see in an extreme manner the repeti-

tion of a topographic form—namely, platform, crag and scree, which is
characteristic of many British upland areas. When it is not associated
with structural features, as in the cases considered, it is often due, as
we have earlier seen (p. 18), to the strong tendency among British
mountains for many of the higher zones to exhibit comparatively
gentle slopes which may represent ancient and pre-glacial land forms.
Below these are generally the glaciated main valleys with their sides
over-steepened by ice-action, while the lateral valleys are often gorges
cut by mountain torrents. Thus it is that one of the commonest topographic units belongs to the type given in Fig. 8. As a general rule, of
course, the forces of erosion make this unit trend towards a gentler
and more or less uniform slope. But the post-glacial period in Britain
has been comparatively short, and there has rarely been sufficient time
for the changes due to weathering and erosion to approach completion.
Thus the general form commonly persists, though its biological character is affected by the trends due to the effects of climate on soil
development and vegetation cover, such as have already been indicated
in connection with Fig. 31. One of the commonest of the early stages
of development which can still be found in a more or less natural
state is that given in Fig. 33. The natural vegetation on the lower
slopes, when little altered by human interference, is oak-wood with
birch abundant at the upper limits or on knolls, and mixed woods or

FIG. 33.—Original vegetation types on the seaward aspects of the Western Scottish
Highlands. Deer-sedge bog above, woodland on the slopes oversteepened by ice,
25-foot beach below. (See text.)

" ash-streaks " running down the gullies. The lower part of the oak-wood generally includes other trees and shrubs with a moderately high base-requirement like gean (*Prunus avium*) and hazel (*Corylus avellana*), and it usually merges below into an alder type of alluvial woodland, often alder and ash on gravel, in the valley bottom. The vegetation of the zone above the wood depends largely upon the degree of slope, and the rainfall. Where the slope is not very acute, say 1 in 10 (6°) or less, a common type of vegetation is likely to be a bog of deer-sedge and its associates.

A second characteristic type of mountain country to-day is a form that shows mainly oak-woods and grasslands, both montane and sub-montane, the latter having been induced by biotic agencies. There is comparatively little visible heather-moor or bog-land. The oak-wood and grassland type is especially common in the Scottish Highlands around Ben Lawers and Loch Tay, and it may be noted that it is associated with three conditions which are not always present else-where. These are the presence of a rock (mica-schist) which is friable and which readily yields an open soil, a comparatively low rainfall, and extremely steep slopes at higher levels which insure good drainage. Originally similar units of vegetation existed in the Lake District and among the higher Welsh hills, where there is generally a similar steep-ness of slope, and the bed-rock is commonly also of a base-rich volcanic type (see p. 12). There is, however, a much higher rainfall, and, moreover, there is reason to believe that the slopes were mostly denuded of their woodlands at an early period, and this no doubt accounts for the great prevalence of bracken on the lower slopes (see Pl. 20b, p. 113). The high rainfall has also led to the leaching of the grasslands so induced and to marked effects of downward seepage from the little bogs on the cols and shelves. As a result there has been a widespread exten-sion of mat-grass and moor-rush on the upper slopes (Pl. XV, p. 108).

Any one who travels north to Fort William by the West Highland railway line or, for that matter, to Inverness by the old Highland railway, will easily be able to see still another common variant of this general type in which the middle slopes, below the deer-grass bogs, are now occupied by extensive Molinia-Myrica swamps which mingle with the remains of the upper woodlands and are often clearly replacing them. The slopes in this case are usually about 1 in 6 or 1 in 7 (8-9°), and this variant is most abundant in regions of high rainfall, particularly where the natural degeneration of woodland by leaching and bog seepage is still proceeding (see Fig. 34). It is usually associated with smaller zones of oak-wood and a greater proportion of birch-wood, and it is apparently an intermediate state leading on to a condition which is commonest in the north-west of the Highland zone.

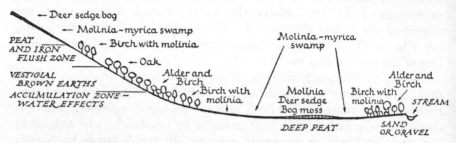

FIG. 34.—Reconstruction of ideal hillside during phase of bog development.

In the region of high rainfall represented by Glen Shiel, Glen Clunie and Glen Garry, for example, the remnants of woodland show a marked preference for certain types of site. The general aspect of the country is mainly that of birch-wood and bog, and the examples given in Figs. 35 and 36 serve to illustrate the topographic relations. The detailed example illustrated in Fig. 35 shows that the birch-wood remains only on the lowest part of the steep slope (40-47°) and on the stabilised scree below, where the angle falls to about 35° and the soil is essentially of the brown-earth type. (In the particular example figured the ground-flora is of the grassy type, bent (*Agrostis*) and vernal grass (*Anthoxanthum*), with much wood-sorrel (*Oxalis acetosella*) and the fine moss, *Hypnum cristra-castrensis*.)

Above the wood the general slope is less (20-30°) and the vegetation mainly variants of deer-sedge bog, with heather and moor-grass and bog-moss frequent. On the more pronounced shelves the peat is commonly 3 ft. deep (slope 22°) and there it must have been developing for a considerable time, so that all the upper part of the slope has been affected by bog seepage. The steeper craggy part has clearly protected the remaining woodland area against seepage from above, although there are numerous signs of the influence of the latter on the upper part of the wood, for a wet peaty soil with bog-moss and moor-grass is found along the upper fringes. Moreover, in the wood each little gully has below it a striking iron-flush, which can be traced downwards for several yards as a streak of ochreous precipitate in the woodland soil.

The influence of the wet climate is not, however, confined to the upper slopes. On the lowest part, where the angle is only 13-14°, the percolating waters emerge at the surface and produce a zone of Molinia-Myrica bog. The soil is waterlogged peat, which is usually more than 2 ft. deep and in places contains the remains of alder and birch timber. The area was presumably damp woodland in its original condition. The transition area from this swamp to the birch woodland has a vegetation mainly of moor-grass and heather, on peaty and leached soil, overlying old scree and sloping at an angle of 24°. This resembles in slope the zone above the wood, but there is a far greater depth of soil, while the drainage comes from the brown-earth soils just above, and these two factors together have retarded the onset of bog conditions.

The detailed examination of sites of this type shows very clearly how the maintenance of woodland depends on the flush effects and better drainage found on unstable or recently stabilised areas. Both are apparently necessary, for better drainage alone can be found on exposed knolls where, however, leaching has normally led to the establishment of *mor* humus and then to incipient waterlogging. No doubt also, in the examples considered, the existence of a crag serves as an upper protection, both against downward seepage and also against the attacks of grazing animals. Thus in the area which is

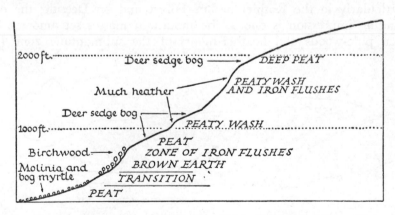

FIG. 35.—Transect of Rattachan hillside, Glen Shiel. Rainfall 80 inches. True scale. Quartzite rock.

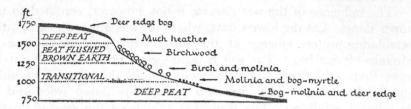

FIG. 36.—Bog and birchwood—Doire na Achlaise, Glen Loine. Rainfall 100 inches.
True scale.

characteristically bog and birch-wood, the woodland remnants are
almost all topographically influenced, hanging to the upper screes and
to the lines of erosion represented by the streams as shown in Figs.
36 and 37. The stream lines (*allts* in Gaelic) are characteristically
occupied by a more varied woodland, as they represent lines of still
active erosion (see p. 119). The zone of Molinia-Myrica swamp
extends over most of the valley alluvia, alder trees being confined to
the stream banks, while farther away from the streams there are
usually considerable areas in which deer-sedge and heather are
becoming abundant.

The western unit of bog and birch-wood contrasts very markedly
with the characteristic eastern one in the same latitude and at somewhat similar altitudes of about 700-1,000 ft. Around the Cairngorms,
particularly in the Rothiemurchus Forest and on Deeside, the outstanding impression is one of the mountain masses set amongst the
open pine-woods and heather-moors of the submontane zone (see

FIG. 37.—Doire na Achlaise, detail of tree distribution in relation to rock outcrops
and stream lines.

Pl. 5, p. 22). These are associated with relatively low rainfall, often annually below 40 in., and are best developed on porous gravels and sands of glacial origin, often with negligible slope, and showing a marked tendency to be podsolised. The topographic unit is thus a sandy or gravelly plain or a shallow valley, from which rise the steeper slopes of the high hills (Fig. 3). These have a higher rainfall and the submontane slopes are for the most part peat-covered with deer-sedge bog containing much heather. Thus the zonation is often climatic rather than topographic. Common among these eastern hills are dry slopes with high-level Vaccinium heaths (p. 90), while the high-level basins and gentler slopes are occupied by deep, much dissected peat and degenerate bogs, with a vegetation in which cotton-sedge and heather are especially abundant (Pl. 23, p. 160).

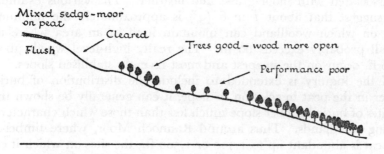

FIG. 38.—Field diagram showing performance of pines in upper part of the Black Wood of Rannoch.

The Rothiemurchus pine forests seem to be independent of slope and in many places they are regenerating freely. Farther west, however, as, for example, in the Black Wood of Rannoch, there is little or no regeneration at present. The rainfall in this locality is probably a good deal higher, and although the substrata are similar, originally glacial sands and gravels now showing podsolic features, the pine-wood is only well developed where the slopes are about 1 in 7 (8°) or more, rather than less, on account of the ridgy nature of the ground. In between the ridges are small depressions occupied by little Molinia-Sphagnum bogs, where, in spite of lower acidity, the performance of the pines is very poor. Above the wood is deer-sedge moor—some of it on deep peat and all on more gentle slopes, such as are shown in the field diagrams given in Figs. 20 and 38. The general impression gleaned from this area is that the pine forest is gradually failing as bog seepage from above, slowly works downward, though any such conclusions are complicated by the felling operations that have taken place recently and in the past. However, generally speaking, this conclusion would fit the numerous relics of woodland that can be found round the head of Loch Rannoch, for these remnants show a striking dependence on slope. In this area well-developed woods of pine and of birch occur on slopes of 1 in 4 or 1 in 5 (14-11°) at altitudes between 1,000 and 1,500 ft. An extensive birch-wood containing much oak occurs on slopes between 1 in 2 and 1 in 3 (27° to 18°) up to nearly 2,000 ft., the oak, however, being at lower altitudes and on the best-drained but least stable areas. Vestigial birch scrub can be found at various places on slopes of as little as 1 in 7 and 1 in 8 (9° or 8°) associated with moor-grass, and heather. The various examples thus suggest that about 1 in 6 (9°) is approximately the minimum slope on which woodland can maintain itself in an area where the rainfall probably exceeds 60 in. The really high-level woods above 1,500 ft. occur on the steepest and most recently stabilised slopes.

If the inquiry is extended to include the distribution of buried timber in the peat in relation to slope, it can generally be shown that the sites of buried timber slope much less than those which characterise existing woodlands. Thus around Rannoch Moor, where timber in the peat is abundant up to 1,400 or 1,500 ft., the sites on which it can be seen rarely have a slope of 1 in 10 (6°), and the steepest one observed, on the south side of Meall Leath na Doire, was of 7° (about 1 in 9). The same feature is illustrated in Fig. 39, which represents average data for the eastern part of the Lake District. Putting the matter in a more generalised way, the illustration indicates that ancient woodlands in the Lake District were buried in peat on gentle slopes averaging 1 in 10 or less down to a level of 900 ft. On steeper slopes, averaging 1 in 2 or 3, natural woodland still persists up to about 1,800 ft. These effects are associated with an annual rainfall exceeding 70 in. Clearly the differences could be ascribed to the beneficial effects of increased " soil creep," or flushing, and the decreased chance of waterlogging on the steeper slopes. In contrast, on the areas of gentle slope, we might anticipate that leached conditions and waterlogging could become established at a comparatively early date in the high-level soils, no doubt extending downward through seepage as time went on.

We have to add on to this series of descriptions one other feature

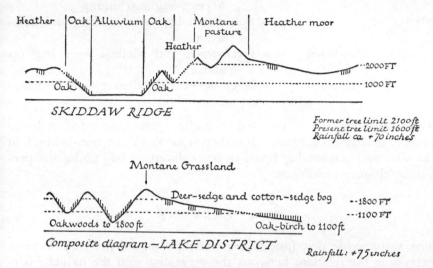

FIG. 39.—Composite diagrams comparing slopes and altitudes of present high-level woodland and timber buried in peat. Lake District : rainfall 75 inches. Vertical scale x 2. Buried timber shown as vertical lines below the profiles.

of importance. Running parallel to these various topographic types on the hillsides is a range of developments seen on the valley floors. These are generally alluvial deposits more or less overlaid by peat and almost always converted to human use. But the deposition stages of such alluvia are still to be found here and there, and under natural conditions these bear alder or alder-ash woodlands merging, on the side away from the stream, through a zone of birch into Myrica-Molinia swamp (see Fig. 34). The central and more peaty parts of these swamps ultimately develop much bog-moss and deer-sedge. On old alluvia, especially in the west, one may find that almost the whole surface is covered with deep peat and possesses deer-sedge-Sphagnum bog on its surface, the trees being at this stage limited to a few birches along the stream margins.

The series of topographic stages described above are of value not only in bringing out the relations between vegetation and habitat, but also in helping to elucidate the stages through which bog vegetation is apparently developing. The discernible facts suggest that the development proceeds through stages such as these :

1. Alder-wood ⟶ Birch-wood and Molinia ⟶ Molinia-Myrica-bogmoss swamp
⟶ Sphagnum bog with Molinia and deer-sedge

or 2. Oak-wood ⟶ Birch-wood and Molinia ⟶ bog (as above)

or 3. Oak-wood ⟶ Birch-wood with bilberry ⟶ Heather-moor

These transitions are accelerated by higher rainfall, retarded by lower rainfall or base-rich rocks. Heather-moor is almost non-existent in the west and presumably tends to be replaced by bog under the prevailing climatic conditions.

SOIL FACTORS

The topographic descriptions are evidently one of the easy ways of expressing the relations between the vegetation and the habitat, particularly if attention is paid to the possible connecting factors. Undoubtedly, if we are to explain more fully the relations between vegetation and soil, we must constantly pay attention to the fact that we are dealing with two or more dynamic systems which may or may not be in equilibrium with each other. On the one hand we have trends of topography and of soil development, while on the other we have biological successions, both in soil or vegetation and in animal communities, which may on the whole keep pace with the habitat changes, but which certainly do tend to lag behind them and which, moreover, have certainly been greatly affected by human interference. The relation between the vegetation of different areas and the soil is thus not always a simple one.

The broad understanding of these relationships is probably best obtained, as suggested above, by considering the different vegetation types as responses to the trends of soil and surface which have already been noted (Chapter 3). Thus in the wetter parts of the uplands the trends of soil development are assumed to be :

(a) brown-earths ⟶ podsolic soils ⟶ peats or bog soils
and

(b) eutrophic peats ⟶ oligotrophic peats.

We may suppose that there are corresponding trends of vegetation which we may call plant successions—keeping pace with soil changes. Thus the trends in series (a) are broadly paralleled by the vegetation series :

oakwood ——→ pine-heath forest ——→ moor or bog.

But the vegetation series is more complex than that of soils because there are biotically induced plant communities which are equivalent to those mentioned and which are found in the same soil types. Thus we have as more or less equivalent :

oak-wood, Festuca-Agrostis grassland, juniper scrub and birch-wood, on soils of *brown-earth* type.

pine-forest, heather-moor, and birch-wood, with heathy shrubs, on soils of *podsolic* tendency.

But oak-wood, for example, may occur on soils which bear the ground-flora of heathy shrubs normally associated with leached soils. The oaks are then rooted in a better and less leached soil below. Thus there may be a discrepancy between some feature of the vegetation and the overall character of the soil. The discrepancy is often due to the greater rapidity of change in the surface layers, particularly in the humus, which is much exposed to change or even to removal when the original woodland cover has, at some time, been disturbed. It will be noted that in the example mentioned above there is likely to be a lag equal to the average life span of an oak in the change from oak-wood to another sort of vegetation.

The trend in the character of the mineral soil in wet climates is towards the production of a base-poor and acid soil. The establishment of this condition is followed by biological changes in the soil humus, notably by the replacement of *mull* humus by *mor* humus or by *bog* peat, depending on humidity. The biological character of the soil is thus completely changed and, in either case, it becomes deficient in available nitrogen. There are corresponding changes in the vegetation, marked often by a change in the characteristic trees, pine and birch instead of oak. More frequently, woodland degeneration in response to these or other conditions is associated with the presence of characteristic indicator plants, particularly the shrubs, heather and bilberry with *mor*, juniper with *mull* and bog-myrtle on swamp soils. The root systems of these shrubs reflect the changes in soil conditions. On nitrogen-deficient *mor*, the typical plants have strongly developed *mycorrhiza*, coral-like root structures associated with special fungi, which are believed to assist in obtaining nitrogen from the undecomposed humus. Bog-myrtle, in contrast, has root-nodules which are capable of fixing nitrogen from the air, and presumably this enables the plant to grow on swamp soils. Moor-grass, which grows with it, is believed to be also a mycorrhizal species. In juniper, however, mycorrhiza, if present, appear to be quantitatively unimportant and the more striking feature is the extent of the root system, which penetrates to a considerable depth, and to soils of higher base-status. It is presumably on account of this that the plant is able to persist and to produce *mull* humus long after its surroundings and the surface soil have become leached.

The trend towards diminishing base-status, increased acidity and low available nitrogen in mineral soils is also evident in bog-peats, where it is paralleled by the development of more oligotrophic vegetation—that is, of plants with low salt requirements. Generally speaking, the most characteristic oligotrophic bog vegetation is the type associated with the Sphagnum-cover of growing bogs, generally with deer-sedge present. Moor-grass and bog-myrtle swamps, although also containing bog-moss, normally occur on peats of higher ash content. So, too, does the black bog-rush (*Schoenus*) in many of its habitats, if not in all.

Cotton-sedge, however, may at times be found on peat with an ash content slightly higher than that typical for deer-sedge bog, and this is probably the result of the peat having been partly oxidised or of the vegetation on it having been burnt. Dr. G. K. Frazer observed that planted trees may grow better on cotton-sedge-covered peat of this type, presumably owing to the increased availability of salts. In contrast, some of the much-dissected cotton-sedge-covered peats in the Pennines are often so severely leached that the total ash contents may be below 1 per cent of the dry weight. As a result such peats are usually extremely acid. Thus cotton-sedge can tolerate, or perhaps better, can persist on, peats of very low ash content, and much of its success as a peat plant is due to its inertia—that is to say, to its ability to persist under changing soil conditions.

Such characteristics as the salt requirements of plants are known to depend, however, upon other soil properties such as acidity and oxygen content. For example, the moor-grass may be found growing on oxygen-poor peats with a moderately high salt content and low acidity. It will, however, also grow on highly acid and salt-poor peat, but apparently it will do this only when the peat contains a certain adequate amount of oxygen. Presumably the presence of oxygen permits the absorption of salts from solutions of very low concentration and high acidity. The effective soil relations are possibly also shown in the manner in which the characteristic bog-plants are related to soil acidity. Generally speaking, we should expect a higher acidity to be associated with a low base content and hence with low ash in the peat. As long as we deal with deep bog-peats, this is, on the whole, true, though complications may occur if the roots of the plants can reach the mineral soil below. On bog peats, the sheathed cotton-sedge is most abundant on the more acid peats, those whose pH value is 3·8 or less. Deer-sedge is characteristic of peats of lower acidity (pH 3·8 to 4·6) and moor-grass and bog-myrtle together normally indicate a still less acid type of peat (pH above 4·3). The black bog-rush is limited to peats of the lowest degrees of acidity. Thus in one respect at least these plants can be arranged in a regular series.

Another series can be arranged to represent the humidity relations of typical moorland vegetation types.

The Vaccinium edge represents the driest as well as the most acid of all moorland habitats, though one which is limited in area. The most extensive of the dry areas are usually covered by heather-moor, while cotton-sedge indicates damper conditions. In the Southern Pennines, Mr. W. B. Crump found that the peat of typical heather-moors had an average " relative humidity " (water content/humus content) of about 2-3 in summer, which is similar to that of sandy oak-woods in the same district. At the same time of year, the relative humidity of peat from the cotton-sedge moors averaged about 6·0. This latter figure is much lower than those derived from peat with a considerable Sphagnum cover, for these rarely give a relative humidity in summer of less than 10. Usually the value is much higher, often so high that it is difficult to get a good sample on account of the ease with which the water squeezes out of the peat during collection. The relative humidity of deep moor-peats without Sphagnum often lies in the range 7-10 in summer, and these peats commonly have deer-sedge present on them, in amounts which often increase with increasing humidity. It must be realised, however, that these broad statements refer to the drier conditions observed—and that, because of the frequent rain, great variability of the water content is common in the wetter moorland soils. The figures given in the following table must thus only be taken to express the type of result observed under comparable conditions of collection and estimation.

Table 10

COMPARABLE RANGES OF ACIDITY (AS pH) AND RELATIVE HUMIDITY IN MOORLAND SOILS IN RELATION TO VEGETATION TYPES

	Relative Humidity	*pH*
Vaccinium-edge	1-1·5	2·8-3·3
Heather-moor	2-3	3·4-3·7
Cotton-sedge moor	6-7	3·2-3·8
Mixed deer-sedge moor	7-10	3·8-4·3
Sphagnum bog with frequent :		
Molinia and *Myrica*		4·7-5·4
Deer-sedge	10 or more	3·8-4·6
Cotton-sedge		3·6-4·0

The influence of humidity is exerted principally through its effect on soil aeration so that the drier soils are also the best aerated, while those with a high relative humidity (above 10) may be taken to be oxygen-deficient or even " reducing " (p. 70) for most of the year. Generally speaking, then, the better aerated soils are, as we have already seen, the most acid.

For reasons indicated at the beginning of this chapter, we do not expect a narrow and invariable relationship between vegetation and habitat as defined by physical and chemical factors. The vegetation is often unbalanced, as it were, alteration having lagged behind any changes induced by disturbance. The larger plants, in particular, almost always show considerable inertia in response to environmental changes, and this is, indeed, one reason why they generally become dominant when, for example, a bog surface is disturbed by treatments such as burning and grazing. Starting from two different sorts of habitat and vegetation, treatment may yield peats of apparently similar humidity, aeration and acidity, which differ considerably in their vegetation. This may mean, of course, that we cannot as yet diagnose the real habitat factors, but it certainly suggests that previous history is at least as important as existing habitat conditions in determining the vegetation.

CHAPTER 10

ECOLOGICAL HISTORY

T H E previous discussion of our upland areas and the changes they have undergone makes it evident that human influence has had much to do with shaping the existing upland vegetation. As a result it is becoming increasingly clear that we ought strictly to try and view our ecological problems against an appropriate background of human history. At the same time, in dealing both with the vegetation and with the montane habitats, we have found it necessary to stress the fact that the montane habitats as a class are unstable and that they are still subject to considerable secular changes, due to weathering, erosion and leaching, which have profound effects on the distribution and properties of the plant and animal communities. It seems clear, therefore, that it would be at least a useful exercise to try to reconstruct the ecological history of some upland areas with the hope of expanding our knowledge of the way in which habitat and living organisms have interacted. Scientifically, of course, the matter is of some importance, because we seek to verify or to disprove our ideas on the factors which have led to vegetational change.

We are fortunate in having sufficient evidence to enable us to look at two sample areas from one point of view, though the material is at present not sufficient to enable us to do more. The sample areas are, as it happens, of sharply contrasted type, for they are respectively, a mainly montane area, the English Lake District, and a large bog in the midst of Southern Pennine moorlands. We shall perhaps be able, after considering pertinent details drawn from these examples, to discuss the problems involved in a more general manner.

THE LAKE DISTRICT

The record of the ecological history of the Lake District is preserved in the sediments of its numerous lakes and tarns. The sediment column provides continuous information on the soils and vegetation of the district since the basins were last occupied by ice. Because of the position within the Lake District of the Ferry House laboratory of the Freshwater Biological Association, it has been possible to obtain and examine cores of sediment from nearly all the lakes and larger tarns of the district. The record of past vegetation is found in the sediments as pollen grains, which do not decay under aquatic conditions, but are preserved in the accumulating mud. Most British trees are wind-pollinated and produce very large quantities of pollen, and the proportion of the pollen of different kinds of tree in the samples from successive levels gives a measure of relative importance of each species at each level. From counts of the proportional representation of each tree and other plants in the total pollen at each successive level, a "pollen diagram" such as that shown in Fig. 40 can be prepared, giving a picture of the changing proportions of the different trees, shrubs and herbs throughout the time represented by the diagram. Parallel chemical analyses of many series of samples have provided information about the soils of the drainage basin of each lake through the same period.

The sediment column of these lakes and tarns represents the time since the end of glaciation at each site. In the large valley lakes such as Windermere and Ennerdale Water, the lowest sediments are laminated clays containing no organic remains; these were formed by seasonal deposition from active glaciers. One can picture the inner valleys, such as Great Langdale, Troutbeck and Upper Ennerdale, still occupied by valley glaciers, from the snouts of which would emerge turbid glacier streams. There is no direct evidence for the date of this early stage in Lake District history, but a date has been obtained from a small basin near the north-west shore of Windermere. During the time when laminated clays were forming in the large lakes, into which glaciers were draining, a hollow was formed there by the melting of a block of dead ice which had been enclosed in gravels deposited at an earlier stage in the retreat of the ice; such a hollow is called a kettle-hole, and water accumulates in it to form a kettle-hole lake. This one has now been filled in by the growth of aquatic vegetation, and is known as Blelham Bog. At some time within the long period represented by laminated clays in Windermere, mud containing remains of algae, lichens, and minute invertebrate animals including Cladocera, was accumulating at the bottom of this kettle-hole, and this mud has been dated in Cambridge by the technique of radiocarbon dating to approximately 12,350 B.C. We know then that by this date there was no longer any ice in the lowlands round Windermere.

The pollen preserved in the algal mud at the bottom of the Blelham Bog profile shows what the vegetation of the surrounding country was like at this time. This pollen is derived almost entirely from herbaceous plants, the only woody plants represented being willows, juniper, the dwarf birch *Betula nana*, and the sea buckthorn, *Hippophae*. Among the herbaceous plants, grasses and sedges predominate, but species of *Rumex* (dock) contributed an appreciable part of the pollen rain. Many other herbs were present, including the rock-rose (*Helianthemum*), meadow-rue (*Thalictrum*), wormwood (*Artemisia*) and meadow-sweet (*Filipendula ulmaria*). This assemblage of plants suggests a rich herbaceous vegetation, or grass-sedge tundra, with bushes of willow, dwarf birch and juniper, and occasional plants of the sea buckthorn (which can flourish only in open habitats where the vegetation cover is not continuous, and is now confined in this country to the sea coasts). This type of vegetation is now known to have been very widespread in Britain during the Late-glacial period between about 12,350 B.C. and 8,300 B.C. In the colder parts of this period, laminated clays appear to have accumulated in all the big valley lakes, but from about 10,000 B.C. to 8,800 B.C. there was a compara-tively warm interval, an interstadial, during which all active ice and probably all permanent snowbeds disappeared from the Lake District mountains. During this interval, woods of silver birch grew in the valleys, and a more stable plant cover developed on the hills; organic muds containing remains of algae, notably diatoms, and small animals, began to accumulate in the lakes. This warmer interval was followed by a cold period, lasting from about 8,800 to 8,300 B.C., during which permanent snowfields and small corrie glaciers once more developed in the central Lake District, and melt-water from these small glaciers laid down an upper layer of laminated clay in the large lakes. The highest tarns now occupy the sites of these latest small glaciers, and the sediments in these began to accumulate only after the melting of these glaciers at about 8,300 B.C. This date marks the final end of glaciation in Britain.

The Post-glacial organic muds which have accumulated in all the lakes since the rapid improvement in climate at about this date, contain in their pollen records of the changing vegetation of the surrounding land. The muds also contain very many silica shells of diatoms, a few remains of other algae, and fragments of certain small animals of the zooplankton. The inorganic fraction of the mud, comprising about 75-90 per cent of the dry weight, has been washed in from the land surface and was originally part of the mineral soil of the drainage basin. The fraction, from 10 to 25 per cent of the dry weight, which is organic in composition, seems to consist (apart from the micro-fossils already mentioned) of very finely divided plant debris, and of structureless decayed organic matter derived from the organic material in soils of the drainage basins. From estimates of the proportions of different pollens at different levels, and from parallel chemical analyses which tell us many things about the soils which were washed in at each level, it has been possible to reconstruct the ecological history of the Lake District throughout the Post-glacial period since about 8,300 B.C.

One striking fact which has emerged is that all through the first half of the period, that is, until about 3,000 B.C., practically all the pollen in the deposits of all the lakes came from trees. Once the improving climate at the

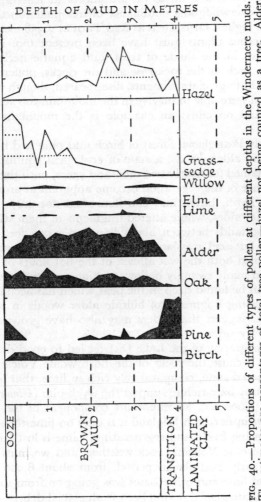

FIG. 40.—Proportions of different types of pollen at different depths in the Windermere muds. The estimates are percentages of total tree pollen—hazel not being counted as a tree. Alder averages about 50 per cent of the tree pollen.

final end of the Ice Age permitted the growth of trees, first birch woods and later pine, hazel, oak and elm, with, later still, alder woods spread across the whole of the landscape up to an altitude of at least 2,500 feet. This is proved by the overwhelming dominance of tree pollen in the lower sediment of even the highest tarns, such as Red Tarn at 2,356 feet on Helvellyn. Certainly herbaceous plants must have been present too, but only those which can survive in the shade of trees, and aquatic herbs. The shade-intolerant herbs, such as the rock-rose and the docks, pollen of which had been common in Late-glacial sediments, disappeared, though we can suppose that some of them were able to survive in the mountain-top vegetation above the tree limit, and on cliffs: an example is the mountain sorrel, *Oxyria digyna*.

After the early Post-glacial forest of birch and pine had been succeeded by mixed-oak and alder woods, a state of ecological equilibrium seems to have been maintained for nearly two thousand years, until the first traces of human disturbance of the vegetation become apparent at around 3,000 B.C. Oakwoods with hazel, birch, and elm flourished not only on the steeper slopes of the valley sides, where altered fragments of them still remain, but on the high moorlands between about 800 and 2,000 feet, where today nothing is found but acid grasslands, heather moors, and bogs. Alder woods must have occupied both the wet alluvia of the flat floors of the U-shaped main valleys, and many swampy hollows at higher altitudes, where remains of alder wood can be found deep in the peat which has accumulated subsequently. The existing fragments of hillside alder woods in Martindale, at about 1,000 feet, suggest that alders may also have grown in the mixed woods of the valley sides.

The steep topography of the Lake District led to good drainage, and it must have been because the rocks of the Borrowdale Volcanic Series are, in their unweathered state, comparatively rich in lime, that soils in general were still sufficiently base-rich to support the wych-elm (*Ulmus glabra*) which was until about 3,000 B.C. an important component of the Lake District woods. Nowadays in northern England it is only on limestone soils that this tree is found growing freely and regenerating. Lime is lost fairly rapidly as surfaces of Borrowdale Volcanic rock weather, and we must suppose that throughout this early Post-glacial period, from about 8,000 to 3,000 B.C. continuous loss of lime and other bases was going on from soils which had at the end of the Late-glacial period been fresh glacial debris—that is, finely ground samples of unweathered or little-weathered native rock.

The leaching of soils by rainwater is a very rapid process in an oceanic climate and on well-drained slopes. As a result, by about 3,000 B.C., the Lake District soils must have progressed some way towards increasing acidity. From work on chemical analysis of lake sediments, F. J. H. Mackereth reached the conclusion that it is possible to differentiate between periods with a high rate of erosion, and periods with a high rate of leaching of the land surface. Calcium, sodium and potassium are fairly readily removed from comminuted igneous rock by leaching, and calcium, in the form of calcite in these rocks, is the most readily soluble in rainwater. The highest content of calcium in the lake sediments occurs in the lower laminated clays, where erosive processes were so active that rock flour still containing most of its original calcium content was deposited in the lake basins before it had been exposed to leaching processes for any appreciable time. In all Post-glacial sediments, calcium is in rather low quantity compared with the source rocks, indicating rapid removal of this base from skeletal soils by leaching during the Late-glacial period. Sodium and potassium, being combined in minerals less readily soluble than calcite, can be used as broad indicators of erosion rates during the Post-glacial period. After the establishment of a stable forest cover during the opening centuries of the Post-glacial period, there is to be seen in all the sediment profiles a period of deposition of mineral material comparatively low in sodium and potassium. Mackereth interprets this as a period of soil stability when the rate of erosion was low, so that mineral particles remained in position in the soil for a sufficiently long time for leaching to become effective, and so to lower the sodium and potassium content drastically, before those mineral particles were eventually removed by slow denudation and carried into the lake basins. This early Post-glacial period, after the establishment of a continuous forest cover, between perhaps 7,500 and 3,000 B.C., was therefore a period of slow erosion and comparatively rapid leaching: that is, a period during which the base-status of the soils must have been considerably reduced. At the same time, as Mackereth points out, this rapid leaching must have enriched the lake waters in bases, and so one would expect this to have been a period of comparatively high productivity in the lakes. That this is so is apparent from the richness in both numbers and species of the diatom flora of such lakes as Windermere and Esthwaite during this period. This diatom flora includes species now found only in waters much richer in lime than any Lake District lake at the present day.

The evidence from chemical analysis of the sediments of many lakes points to the centuries around 3,000 B.C. as the time when this ecological equilibrium of the early Post-glacial period was first upset. This horizon can be identified by pollen analysis, as it is distinguished by a sharp fall in the percentage of elm pollen. Because of widespread interest in the nature and causes of the vegetation changes at this horizon, many radiocarbon datings have been carried out in north-west Europe, and all fall within a few centuries on either side of 3,000 B.C. In the Lake District, this horizon has been dated in the sediments of three tarns by the Copenhagen Carbon-14

Dating Laboratory, and the three dates lie between 3150 B.C. and 3390 B.C., each date ± 120 years. This is accepted as evidence for the synchroneity of this horizon, since the difference between the dates is due to the uncertainty of the method.

At this horizon in the profiles, there is at many sites a decrease in the percentage of organic matter in the sediments and an increase in sodium and potassium—that is, the indications are of an increase in erosion rate, with increased input to the lakes of comparatively unweathered mineral soils. In some lakes, this can be seen as a visible band of clay or silty mud in the profile. At the sites where these vigorous signs of soil erosion are present, there is also an episode in the pollen diagrams which indicates temporary clearance of the forest, either accompanying or just after the steep fall in elm pollen. In these clearance episodes, pollen of grasses and of the ribwort plantain, *Plantago lanceolata*, indicates openings in the forest, and the appearance for the first time in the Post-glacial period of the ribwort plantain, a plant always associated with man's activities, is firm evidence for the presence of man. The dates, just before 3,000 B.C. coincide with what is now known to be the opening of the Neolithic period, when new techniques of pastoral farming and agriculture were introduced into north-west Europe by immigrating peoples. It has been established by Continental archaeologists that the domestic animals—mainly cattle—of at least some of these peoples were fed on leaves of deciduous trees, because at this time there were no natural grasslands in Europe except the high montane grasslands. Elm leaves are among the most nutritious of all those available, and to this day there are primitive pastoralists in Asia who feed their cattle on elm leaves. The steep fall in elm pollen at about 3,000 B.C. is therefore confidently attributed by many authorities to Neolithic farmers, who are thought to have lopped the leafy branches for fodder for stalled cattle and so prevented the trees from flowering. In the Lake District, if this is the correct explanation of the elm fall, it is probable that the human exploitation of the elm, which thereafter failed to regenerate, only brought about the final failure of a species which was already in precarious balance as the result of several millennia of continuous and rapid soil leaching. The pollen diagram in Fig. 40 shows that after this episode, the elm was never again a significant component of Lake District woodlands.

The evidence in lake sediments for forest clearance, vegetation changes, and soil erosion at *c*. 3,000 B.C. is strongest in certain parts of the Lake District—the head of Great Langdale, the coastal plain of S.W. Cumberland, and the eastern part of the central mountains. Remains of early Neolithic occupation of the area are found on the Cumberland coastal plain, in settlements such as the one at Ehenside Tarn, and in the axe-factory sites at the head of Great Langdale and on Scafell, where a band of fine-grained tuff in the local Borrowdale Volcanic rocks was exploited to produce large axes of polished stone with which it was possible to fell trees. The presence of roughed-out axes in the coastal settlements and the absence of finished axes at the factory sites suggests that the finishing and polishing processes were carried out at the coastal settlements. It is now thought probable by archaeologists that the earliest phase of activity of the axe factories began in the Early Neolithic period, at about 3,000 B.C., though at this early stage, production was for local use only. This corresponds very closely with the dating of the first (and apparently human) interference with the primeval vegetation—an interference which is most clearly marked in the areas of early Neolithic occupation. The activity of the axe factories continued for many centuries, and the main phase of production for export to other parts of Britain seems to date from the middle Neolithic period. In the sediments of Blea Tarn and Angle Tarn, both within two miles of the main axe factory on Pike of Stickle in Great Langdale, the horizon of forest clearance, soil erosion, and increased run-off has been dated by radiocarbon to c. 3,150 B.C. and 3,260 B.C. respectively.

As a result of recent work in both archaeology and historical ecology, therefore, it is now necessary to date the earliest onset of human influence on the Lake District landscape to a much earlier period than had hitherto been supposed. These Neolithic people who worked the axe factories have left few traces of themselves, apart from the factory wastes, in the central Lake District. The settlement sites of this early Neolithic period are known from the West Cumberland coastal plain, at Ehenside Tarn and other places, where Great Langdale axes and rough-outs have been found, associated with hearths, pottery, worked flints and other artifacts. At these sites, the pollen record suggests that corn-growing as well as pastoral farming formed part of the way of life of these early Neolithic people. Few or no fuerary monuments of this date are known in the district.

The effect on the upland vegetation of the central Lake District of these Neolithic people was comparatively slight and transient, except on the elm. The exception is the way in which the forest disturbance and consequent soil erosion, at higher altitudes, reinforced natural processes which were already tending to destroy the ecological equilibrium. At Angle Tarn, 1,800 feet, for instance, the increased erosion rate which set in at about 3,000 B.C. seems to have continued thereafter, and so did the process of reduction in the amount of tree pollen which began with the Elm Decline. In what appears to have been approximately the next thousand years, the forest around this tarn became largely replaced by acid grassland, peaty soils with bog myrtle, and heather moorland. This can be interpreted as a natural degenerative process at this altitude, consequent on particularly rapid soil leaching and podsolisation.

That this natural replacement of forest by moorland did not take place at lower altitudes is shown by the analyses from Blea Tarn, Langdale, at nearly 700 feet. There, pollen analysis of the sediments reinforces the results of observation of the present state of the drainage basin, to show that woodland persisted there until the last century or so and that no deforestation took place. On the steep well-drained slopes around Blea Tarn, one supposes that flushed habitats remained, and the soils consequently continued as free-draining forest brown-earths. Because there was apparently little human activity in the Blea Tarn area after the end of the active period of the axe factories, this forest remained in existence, as post-Elm Decline secondary forest, modified by the Neolithic episode to the extent that elm had virtually disappeared and ash had appeared as a forest component.

On the western, northern and north-eastern fells of the Lake District, at altitudes between 700 and 900 feet, a later phase of human occupation and land use belongs to what can be broadly described as the Bronze Age, though as yet no dates are available and metal objects are very scarce. The remains of this phase are stone cairns, which occur in profusion in these uplands, and appear to include both burial cairns and cairns of unknown significance in which no burials are found. Urns of Middle Bronze Age type have been found in some of the cairns which were excavated unscientifically in the nineteenth century. Associated with them are often stone hut-circles, which may belong to the period of the burial cairns or to a much later one.

All these remains agree in suggesting the presence of a considerable upland population in these intermediate slopes, avoiding both the highest altitudes and the densely wooded and swampy valley bottoms. The generally accepted view that the Bronze Age, or later part of the Sub-Boreal period, was a period of drier climate than the present, means that these hillsides were probably less inhospitable then as dwelling-places than would be thought now. The evidence from pollen analysis of the sediments of upland tarns such as Devoke Water, surrounded by these cairns, and Haweswater in the east, together with evidence of considerable local settlement at this time, shows that at some distance above the 3,000 B.C. horizon there occurs an episode suggesting considerable clearance of the upland woods. Oak pollen is much reduced, and there is a corresponding increase in the pollen of grasses and of herbs of grassland such as ribwort plantain, sheeps sorrel, and tormentil; there is also an increase in the pollen of heather (*Calluna vulgaris*). This episode seems to have continued for an appreciable time, but it is followed in the pollen diagrams by a period of regeneration of the oak woods, so that clearly the forms of land use which were practised by these peoples did not lead to severe deterioration of the upland soils. The appearance of *Calluna* at this horizon on the uplands between 700 and 900 feet does suggest however that some podsolisation of soils was going on, possibly as a result of human exploitation. This is borne out by the appearance in lake sediments at this level of a more acid type of humus. In contrast with the later clearance episode, there is little or no evidence of cereal cultivation on the uplands during this "Bronze Age" occupation. On the whole, in these areas where the vegetation episode is well-marked, the soil history at this time is of accelerated erosion of mineral soils and consequent increase in the rate of accumulation of sediment in the lakes.

The next event in Lake District ecological history seems to have been a widespread shift to wetter conditions on the uplands. This is more clearly recorded in layers of acid *mor* humus, the old organic soils now preserved beneath blanket peat, than in the lake sediments. A striking visible relic of this shift is the layer of birch trunks and branches which can be seen at the base of about a metre of peat, usually at altitudes of about 1,500 to 1,900 feet, in many parts of the district, wherever subsequent erosion of the peat has exposed the wood layer in the sides of drainage channels. The birch trees were growing in an acid humus over a leached stony soil, and in the accumulating humus, or *mor*, pollen preservation was good because of the acidity, and the layers accumulated in temporal succession because the soil was too acid for earthworms and other members of the soil fauna which cause mixing. On the Lake District fells, wherever gentle slopes and impeded drainage allowed the accumulation of this acid humus, the extremely oceanic conditions tended to continue the process of paludification until peat-forming communities of *Sphagnum*, cotton sedge and *Calluna*, replaced the birch forest. Pollen analysis of profiles through the buried forest in various parts of the Lake District suggests that this change from forest to bog took place at approximately the same time in many places, though of course the processes discussed in Chapter 9 must have tended to bring about this vegetation change at various times and independently of climatic change. It is however now possible to recognise two distinct episodes of land use in the peat profiles, and the major horizon of buried timber falls between them. The earlier episode is that described in the preceding paragraph and tentatively ascribed to the Bronze Age, while the later episode, to be described in the following paragraph, corresponds in distribution with the "British settlements" and upland farmsteads of apparent Celtic or Romano-British date. This places the major change from forest to bog on the flatter fells of the Lake District between about 1,200 and 2,000 feet, in the first millennium B.C. It also suggests that widespread acceleration of this natural succession from forest to bog took place at the same time as the renewed growth of peat on the lowland raised bogs of the Lonsdale area, to the south of the Lake District, which has been dated by radiocarbon to the centuries between 800 and 500 B.C.

Above this evidence for climatic deterioration comes a very conspicuous episode of land use, recorded both in the upland blanket peats and in the sediments of nearly all the tarns above 700 feet. It is a striking horizon, where erosion processes clearly became very severe, producing a visible stratigraphic change in the sediment profile. This coincides with pollen evidence for almost complete replacement of the remaining upland woodlands by grasslands and heather moor, and at the same time, pollen of cultivated cereals and of weeds of arable land appears for the first time in these upland profiles, but the continuous curve for cereal pollen covers only a short time. This must indicate a period when native agriculture was locally stimulated, and corn-growing went on at higher altitudes than before or since. In many parts of the Lake District are traces, usually in the form of field banks, of high-lying farmsteads of a type dating from the first few centuries A.D. During this phase of intense farming activity in the hills, run-off must have increased very considerably, carrying with it increased amounts of both organic and inorganic soil which was deposited in the tarns. A very sudden increase in the amount of *Calluna* pollen is found whenever a layer of particularly organic material occurs at this horizon, and is interrupted as inwash of organic soil, probably *mor* humus from the topmost horizons of podsols, rich in secondary *Calluna* pollen. This shows how destruction of the forest cover can be seen to have led to soil deterioration and removal of the surface layers by rain-wash, as discussed on page 61.

In the valley lakes, the sediments record a different history. The episodes in vegetation history which have been described for the uplands appear in the valley lakes as more transient and temporary phenomena, and the main forest clearance comes later. The Windermere pollen diagram on page 185 shows, in the grass pollen curve, the earlier clearance episodes, between 2m and 1m below the mud surface, and the final permanent clearance in the topmost metre of mud. Though no dating of it has yet been possible, it seems on general historical grounds most probable that the main valley clearance corresponds with the Norse land-takes of the ninth and tenth centuries A.D., from which so many of the place-names of the central Lake District derive. Historians of the older school, notably W. G. Collingwood, believed that there was little if any Anglian settlement in the central Lake District, and that some at least of the upland collections of stone huts were probably still occupied by people of Celtic descent when the Norse settlers arrived and began for the first time to clear the valley woods. By the time of the Norman Conquest there was probably very little natural forest remaining in the Lake District, for the extension of sheep-farming which seems to have been initiated by the Norse would continue the process of deforestation of the uplands which had been begun by the Bronze Age and Celtic peoples. This process of continued expansion of grazing land into possibly secondary scrub woodland (with a few pockets of remaining forest as at Blea Tarn) would go on through the medieval centuries, under the encouragement given by the great Cistercian abbeys to the wool trade, and complete the destruction of Lake District forests. Destruction of the high forest is known to have proceeded further in areas such as High Furness which at present appear

Table 11

LAYERS IN THE RINGINGLOW BOG PEATS,
arranged in reference to the beginning of rapid bog-growth
and the beginning of the modern period

	Lower Bog—slope *1 in 20*	*Bog-Centre—slope* *1 in 30*	*Hillside—slope* *1 in 8*
Modern period	25 cm. peat. Heather abundant, some bog-moss, growth very slow.	100 cm. Sphagnum peat. Cotton-sedge on surface.	20 cm. dark peat, with heather dominant.
A.D. 1100			
	200 cm. Sphagnum peat. Rapid bog-growth.	250 cm. Sphagnum peat. Rapid bog-growth.	83 cm. bog-peat slow-growing with Sphagnum, cotton-sedge, heather.
500 B.C.			
Mid Transition Bog-bean zone			
1200 B.C.	80 cm. bog-peat, slow-growing with Sphagnum, cotton-sedge, heather.	190 cm. bog-peat slow-growing with Sphagnum, cotton-sedge, heather.	Peat with heather, 20 cm. in, say, 5,500 years.
2000 B.C.	100 cm. dark peat with alder and birch wood.		
		70 cm. dark humus with rushes, sedges,	
6200 B.C.	Rushes.	grass.	
Post-glacial	Pine probably dominant in many places, soil inorganic.		

M.M. O

well-wooded, under the demands of the local iron-smelters for charcoal. Though the Furness woods were probably never clear-felled, it is on record that there were times when scarcely a single full-grown tree remained; the oak-hazel woods were managed as coppice, to supply coppice poles for charcoal burning and for many small woodland industries.

Only with the eighteenth century was there a revival of interest in woodland when local landowners began to plant amenity woodlands based on the native forest, with the addition of aliens such as the sycamore and later the larch, of the beech which had never reached north-west England by natural spread, and of the native Scots pine which had almost or quite died out in the Lake District, though of course it had survived as a dominant forest tree over wide areas in Scotland. The vegetation change in the last two centuries can be identified at the top of the pollen diagrams by the re-appearance of pine pollen in quantity and the appearance of beech pollen.

Though the results of recent research have been to change to some extent the interpretation of the ecological history of the Lake District as originally set out by Professor Pearsall, his general conclusions have been modified, rather than basically altered. Further research has only confirmed the accuracy of his ecological insight, notably on the course of soil history, and reinforced his conclusion that "the effects of human occupation in such a district are to accelerate the pre-existing changes, but not necessarily to initiate them."

THE SOUTHERN PENNINE MOORLANDS

The great expanse of peaty moorland covering the rather flat summits of the Southern Pennines has been the subject of work by many ecologists, including the early investigations of the late Dr. T. W. Woodhead in the Huddersfield district, and the extensive work by Dr. V. M. Conway, and more recently by Dr. J. H. Tallis, on the moors above Sheffield, the Kinder summit, and the Snake Pass area. A consistent broad picture of the ecological history of the Southern Pennines emerges from these studies, though as yet it lacks the precision of radiocarbon dating. Horizons of vegetational change, as shown by pollen analysis, and of change in type of peat growth, can be correlated over a wide area, and have been tentatively dated on the basis of regional vegetation changes, the known facts of historical geography, and certain widely recognised periods of increased oceanity of climate. These horizons where rapid growth of unhumified *Sphagnum* peat succeeded a period of slow peat growth with considerable humification are called recur-rence surfaces, and a series of these was tentatively dated by the Swedish

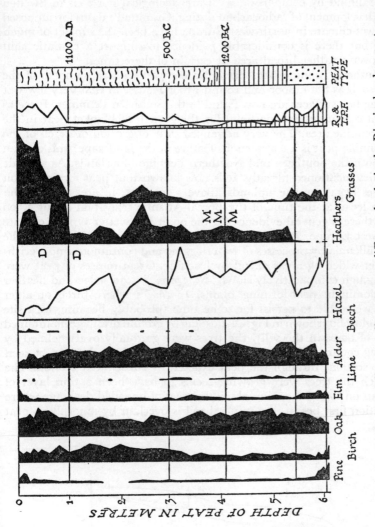

FIG. 42.—Proportions of different pollen types at different depths in the Ringinglow bog-peat, as percentages of total tree pollen. M, pollen of *Menyanthes*, the bog-bean; D, that of *Drosera*, the sundew. On the right are shown the three main types of peat, clayey at the bottom (shading dots), close and rather fibrous (shading lines) and mainly bog-moss above. T.P.F. (shaded) is tree pollen frequency and R, is its reciprocal.

botanist Granlund by comparison with archaeological horizons in Sweden before the development of radiocarbon dating. Granlund's dates for supposed periods of wet climate in north-west Europe have been the subject of much discussion, but there is considerable evidence to support a climatic shift operating over a rather broad area at certain of these times.

The Southern Pennine bogs present a contrast with those north of the Aire Gap, such as Stainmoor and round Moor House, in that very few wet and growing bog surfaces are now found in the Southern Pennines. It seems that present conditions are marginal for the growth of blanket peat in the Southern Pennine area. The very advanced state of erosion of much of the existing Pennine peat is a conspicuous feature of the landscape; this erosion occurs in both the Southern and Northern Pennine moorlands. As a result of the studies mentioned already, it is now known that peat formation on the Pennines began on the uplands above 1,200 feet, in areas where the slopes were least, at the time of the Boreal-Atlantic transition about 5,500 B.C., when there is general evidence for the onset of a wetter type of climate in north-west Europe. Peat formation extended progressively through the next four millennia by processes of waterlogging and continuous impoverishment of ever-widening areas of soil by leaching. Great masses of peat were built up, though comparatively slowly. *Sphagnum*, cotton sedge and heather were the dominant peat-forming plants. In places where birch or alder woodlands were able to persist for some time (probably because, as a site A in Ringinglow Bog shown in Fig. 42, flushing by ground drainage maintained the supply of bases in the soil), the trees were gradually overwhelmed by peat-forming communities and today their trunks and branches can be seen at the base sections through the peat exposed by subsequent erosion. The soil in which the trees were growing seems to have been a thin layer of peaty humus on top of the mineral soil. In areas of impeded drainage where peat formation first began, the mineral soil is overlain by amorphous peat

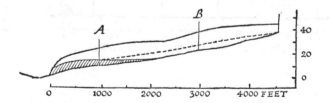

FIG. 42.—Slopes and peat depths in the Ringinglow bog—the shaded area being peat containing wood and the numbers feet.

containing the remains of a plant cover of rushes, sedges and certain grasses. This turned over to a bog vegetation of *Sphagnum*, cotton sedge and heather, of the same type as the vegetation which replaced the woodlands. The long period of this type of comparatively slow peat growth formed most of what Conway calls the Lower Peat; this ends in a Transition zone which marks the change-over to a greatly accelerated rate of peat growth, which formed the very fresh, unhumified Upper Peat, consisting mainly of *Sphagnum* remains but containing layers rich in cotton sedge or in heather. This soft, sometimes almost liquid, Upper Peat, is that which becomes very readily eroded once the surface skin of vegetation is broken by any means.

Over wide areas, some change clearly occurred in the bog vegetation, after which there seems to have been a rapid extension of drainage channels in peat which had ceased to grow actively; once this process was initiated, downcutting became very rapid in the soft Upper Peat, so that a multitude of deeply incised drainage channels came to dissect the remaining peat into isolated tabular blocks in many places. Elsewhere growth of peat on the interfluves continued until comparatively recent centuries. There has however been a complete change within recent centuries in the peat-forming vegetation, *Sphagnum* having been replaced by the sheathed cotton sedge, *Eriophorum vaginatum*, as the dominant plant over the whole of the South Pennine moors. As a result of detailed work on remains of *Sphagnum* in the Upper Peat, Tallis concludes that "*Eriophorum vaginatum* assumed dominance some time after the fourteenth century, as a result of human interference with the vegetation . . . the human activities having been attempts to drain the moorland surface by the construction of artificial channels, and burning periodically the surface of the drier moors in an attempt to improve the grazing for either sheep or grouse . . . The modifications produced resulted in a decline in the frequency of *Sphagnum* in the vegetation, but the almost total absence of *Sphagnum* at the present day can probably be ascribed to the atmospheric pollution of the last 150 years."

Conway's original work at Ringinglow Bog, see Fig. 42, has shown how at this altitude, 1,300 feet, near Sheffield a considerable expanse of peat, now nearly 20 feet deep at most, has built up on top of the original mineral soil on a slightly sloping area of hillside. Surrounding slopes have protected this area of bog from most of the effects of peat erosion, so an undisturbed profile is available for study, with evidence of continued peat formation up to the present day, though the growth-rate has been very slow in the topmost few centimetres. The inorganic soil at the base of the organic profiles has in it pollen of pine and heather, which, with some birch, is thought to have been the vegetation of the high Pennine moors during the Boreal period, before about 5,550 B.C. The special interest of the profile at Ringinglow is that it shows how the vegetation succession from forest to bog proceeded at different places on a sloping transect (Fig. 42) where drainage factors differentiated one site from another. Originally, as shown by closely-spaced peat borings, the area A on the west of the transect carried a woodland of alder and birch, which maintained itself for a long time after the area to the east of it had become bog. Local flushing of the area A, by comparatively base-laden drainage water from the upland area to the north of the transect, for a long time prevented the deterioration of the soil to the state where a bog vegetation took over. The area B had too little slope for the soil to dry out in summer, after the wet Atlantic climate set in at about 5,500 B.C., so peaty humus began to accumulate there, with a vegetation of rushes (*Juncus* spp.), sedges and grass. Probably scattered trees of alder and birch formed a transition from the woodland at A to the wet rushy swamp at B. As the organic soil continued to accumulate in area B, its surface would become completely cut off from the underlying mineral soil, and so extremely deficient in bases. When about 18 inches of peaty humus had collected, the vegetation had changed to a bog community of *Sphagnum*, cotton sedge and heather. This change must have gone on over wide areas of the Pennine plateau at about this time. The wood in area A, originally of alder, came to include more birch as time went on, and though the flushing by drainage water seems to have allowed tree growth to continue for something approaching 1000 years after the Boreal-Atlantic transition, the bog at B was continually encroaching downwards on to the eastern margin of the woodland. Eventually the wood peat accumulating at A was replaced by a bog peat similar to that at B, and one can suppose that by that time a bog vegetation of *Sphagnum*, cotton sedge and heather extended over the whole hillside now occupied by the bog. On the higher slopes to the north of the transect, heather moor was the vegetation, on thin *mor* peat.

After a long period of rather slow growth of this type of peat, conditions changed and the rate of peat growth accelerated. This forms the opening of Conway's Transition zone. At Ringinglow Bog the first recurrence surface is marked by remains of bog bean, *Menyanthes*, a plant of pools on bog surfaces, which provides additional evidence for the identification of this at a time when the bog surface became much wetter. The second recurrence surface, which forms the upper boundary of the Transition zone, is however in general the more striking vegetation change, and this is considered by both Conway and Tallis to be the most probable equivalent of the strong recurrence surface in lowland raised bogs which has been dated to about 500 B.C., the opening of the Sub-Atlantic period.

In all these peat profiles, the strongest representation in the pollen counts is of the local pollen of the vegetation of the bog surface—mainly sedge and *Calluna* pollen, and spores of *Sphagnum*. Tree pollen incorporated in these peats must come from the comparatively small areas of steeply sloping and flushed habitats on the higher hills, and, probably in much greater quantity, from woods marginal to the moorlands. Conway used the absolute quantity of tree pollen at each level—numbers of grains of tree pollen per unit weight or volume of peat—as an index of the rate of growth of the peat, assuming the yearly rain of tree pollen to have remained approximately constant. This method accentuates the characterisation of the periods of rapid peat growth, which can be primarily identified by stratigraphical change, reinforced by consideration of variations in quantity of *Sphagnum* spores. In Conway's profiles, there is a first horizon of lowered absolute frequency of tree pollen coinciding with the horizon of the Elm Decline, at about 3,000 B.C. Conway's interpretation of this was that the evironmental change at about 3,000 B.C., which is still not completely understood, included a climatic shift of such a kind as to accelerate the rate of peat growth on the Pennine plateau. An alternative explanation of course could be that there was a real decrease in the supply of tree pollen from the source areas, because of the onset of Neolithic farming, but as yet there has not been any demonstration that these early Neolithic people were widely active in the South Pennine area.

The two main recurrence surfaces at the beginning and end of the Transition zone are marked by changes in the amount of tree pollen which would agree with a period of slow-growing and highly humified peat, rapidly succeeded in each case by the onset of much more rapid growth of fresh, unhumified, peat mainly composed of *Sphagnum* remains. If the second of these recurrence surfaces is correctly identified with the main recurrence surface, the Grenz horizon, of lowland raised bogs at *c.* 500 B.C., then it seems very reasonable to adopt the suggestion of Conway that the earlier recurrence surface could well date from the same climatic episode as Granlund's RY IV, for which a date of 1200 B.C. was suggested. Somewhere before the end of the second millennium B.C., therefore, it seems that the blanket bogs of the Pennine plateau became much wetter, with a consequent greatly accelerated growth of peat, and that a second climatic shift in the direction of increased wetness can be traced in these peats at a horizon which seems to correspond with the lowland Grenz horizon at about 500 B.C.

Some ecologists consider that the increased run-off from the peat mantle which would be the consequence of an increase in total rainfall would of itself be enough to initiate erosion of the peat. There is however some evidence that in many places a considerable thickness of the Upper Peat had accumulated, after the climatic shift before erosion set in. Tallis has found in the Snake Pass area several profiles where two minor recurrence surfaces, with a characteristic succession of *Sphagnum* species forming a very fresh *Sphagnum* layer, occur well above the main surface equated with the Grenz; for these he suggests dates to compare with Granlund's most recent recurrent surfaces, at about 400 A.D. and 1300 A.D. In these places, rapid growth of peat was still going on at this time. The position of these horizons is in agreement with Conway's view that human influence on vegetation in the South Pennine area only became perceptible in the pollen diagrams at about 1100 A.D., though traces of man's presence had appeared at earlier horizons. Professor Pearsall pointed out that the prevalence in the Pennine place-names of Anglian and Scandinavian words for woods and clearings— for example, the Anglian *clough, dene, hey, haigh* and *hirst*, and the Scandinavian *birks, carr, royd* and *thwaite*—suggests that there were extensive woodlands still in existence when the English settlements began. The growth of the medieval wool trade, beginning with the establishment of the great Cistercian abbeys, must have led to the conversion of extensive areas of hill woodlands into grassland below the altitude of blanket-bog, and probably from this period date also attempts to drain the surfaces of the lower bogs, from which the drying out of their surfaces began. The question of peat erosion is further discussed in a later section, beginning on page 203.

THE NORTHERN PENNINE MOORLANDS

Study of the ecology and ecological history of the high plateau of the Northern Pennines has been stimulated by the acquisition by the Nature Conservancy (see Chapter 15) of the large Nature Reserve at Moor House, where a field laboratory has been founded. During the Boreal period, the light forest on the high northern plateau, up to about 2,500 feet, seems to have been mainly of birch, with some willow and juniper. This is from the evidence of wood fragments at the base of the peat, but in long pollen diagrams from valley bogs there is evidence for the importance of pine during the Late Boreal period (zone VIc). The formation of blanket peat on the Moor House Reserve dates from the Boreal-Atlantic transition, and in general seems to have followed the same pattern of development as that worked out by Conway for the Southern Pennines. The peat-forming vegeta-tion was similarly one of cotton sedge, *Sphagnum* and heather. At the higher altitudes an earlier type of peat deposit can be found beneath the blanket peat; this represents incorporation of peaty material with intercalated clay layers, and dates from the earliest part of the Post-glacial period when solifluction was still active at high altitudes. During Boreal and Atlantic times, Mesolithic peoples wandered over these high plateaux near the upper limit of tree growth, and Mesolithic stone flake tools of flint and chert have been found both in the mineral soils at the base of the blanket peat and in the lower peat deposits, of Atlantic age. At the same (Atlantic) levels in the peat have been found horns of wild cattle, *Bos* sp., which may well have been the quarry of these Mesolithic hunters. At 1,800 feet and upwards, the change in climate at about 500 B.C. seems to have resulted in a change to a regime in which erosion of peat, rather than deposition, predominated. Above 2,500 feet the peat cover has been almost entirely removed.

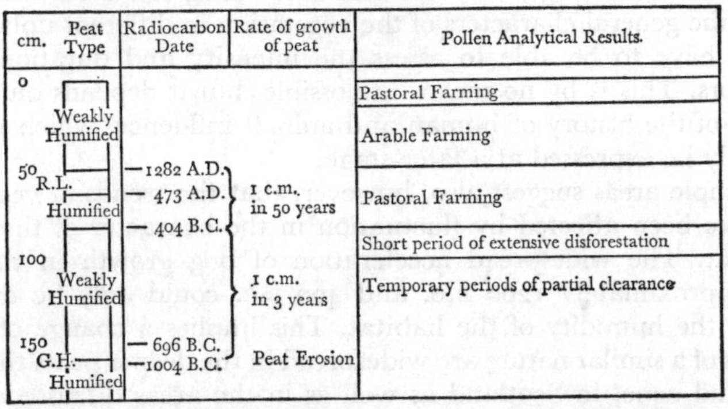

cm.	Peat Type	Radiocarbon Date	Rate of growth of peat	Pollen Analytical Results.
0				Pastoral Farming
	Weakly Humified			Arable Farming
50	R.L.	—1282 A.D.		
	Humified	— 473 A.D.	1 c.m. in 50 years	Pastoral Farming
		— 404 B.C.		Short period of extensive disforestation
100	Weakly Humified		1 c.m. in 3 years	Temporary periods of partial clearance
150	G.H.	— 696 B.C.		
	Humified	—1004 B.C.	Peat Erosion	

FIG. 43.—Peat profile at Tregaron Bog, and vegetation history, based on J. Turner (1965). GH—Grenzhorizont RL—Retardation Layer.

At lower altitudes, between c. 1,000 to 1,800 feet, in the Stainmoor area and near Moor House, peat accumulation proceeded with increased rapidity after the climatic deterioration and erosion processes were not so dominant. Bog surfaces at these altitudes in the Northern Pennines are in general now much wetter than the Southern Pennine moors, and in many areas on Stainmoor and near Moor House the growth of peat is still going on, where it is topographically least vulnerable to erosion.

CLIMATIC CHANGE

The sample areas so far discussed show that the trends of soil and vegetational change which have been recognised during the earlier chapters are now seen to have been subject in the past to changes in velocity, which can often be closely correlated with the intensity of human activity. The general effects of leaching and bog development thus seem to have been accelerated first during the period of influence of the Neolithic peoples, particularly in areas of concentration of these people. Their effect may well have been exerted along the upper margins of the woodlands, where we may suspect that the effects of environmental trend were already well marked. A larger influence on upland vegetation is found in areas where traces of Bronze Age settlement are abundant. Still more disturbance followed the coming of the Scandinavian peoples using iron, who first on a large scale cleared the valley woods and drained the valley swamps. They paved the way for the wholesale economic exploitations in more recent times, mainly those associated with sheep-farming and iron-smelting. We might take the view that the vegetation in different upland regions today depends largely on the rate at which the changes thus induced have progressed. And in order to "explain" the general characters of the vegetation in different upland areas, we should have to be able to assess the intensity and duration of these biotic factors. This is by no means impossible, but it depends on a greater knowledge of the history of human and animal influence, which can more conveniently be expressed at a later stage.

The sample areas suggest also, however, that the trends of vegetational change have been affected by fluctuation in the character of the physical environment. The widespread acceleration of bog growth in the period between approximately 1200 B.C. and 400 B.C. could only be due to an increase in the humidity of the habitat. This implies a change of climate. Indications of a similar nature are widespread in the deeper peats throughout the Highland zone, in Scotland as well as in the areas discussed in detail in this chapter. Work on the ecological history of the Scottish blanket peat is in progress, but still in a comparatively early stage. In lowland peats of Britain and north-west Europe there is now a wide range of observation which agrees with the dating provisionally adopted here.

Thus the Post-glacial period, as we have seen, is generally assumed to have included an era of optimum and probably drier climate followed by an era of climatic deterioration, presumably to a wetter and perhaps also a colder condition, which led to rapid peat accumulation and also to forest degeneration. At the time of the optimum climate, there was often in the Eastern Highlands some extension of birch and pine trees on to the deeper peats, particularly where drainage was possible around stream lines, and perhaps even more widely. The deterioration of climate led to a great extension of bog conditions on the slopes, particularly where downward seepage was possible, and this resulted in large areas of woodland on *mor* soils being replaced by bog. Many of the signs of buried timber in the peat belong to this era, though they will possibly prove to be of almost all ages. Thus, though peat accumulation in the uplands has probably been a continuous process, it thus appears to have suffered a period of retardation and a later period of acceleration. Generally, it is probable that much of the shallower upland peat of less than 3 ft. in depth belongs mainly to the later period of accelerated bog-growth. The deeper peats, particularly those at higher altitudes and those in basins, are normally of much greater age, and it is these which, especially in the eastern uplands, show most clearly the signs of varying rates of peat accumulation. There is one other interesting feature which arises in this connection. The vegetation now found on these eastern peats is, as a rule, not that characteristic of growing bogs and, as we have also seen, there is good reason to believe that the rainfall of eastern hills is now often below that characteristic of blanket-bog areas. Technically, of course, bog-growth can continue on the surface of basin-bogs, even when the rainfall is well below the blanket-bog limits, but on sloping areas bog-growth is especially dependent on rainfall conditions, and it is on or near sloping areas in the eastern hills that we see the signs that bog-growth was formerly active but is now in abeyance. The problem we cannot as yet answer is how much of this cessation of bog-growth can be attributed to climatic change and how much to human interference, particularly perhaps to draining and burning.

The conclusions we can make with a fair degree of certainty about the eastern peats are less easy to apply to the region of high rainfall in the Western Highlands. Within this region it is less easy to correlate the limited data available with other areas, and this is perhaps because more attention needs to be paid to the influence of topographic factors upon the peat succession. If the present high rainfall has been continuous throughout the Post-glacial period, it might be that marked changes of bog-growth have not always occurred at the same times as elsewhere, although there are good records and abundant signs of this for adjacent marginal areas of lower rainfall and particularly for the big "raised bogs" along the western seaboard: Tregaron and Borth Bogs, Chat Moss on the borders of Cheshire and Lancashire, the North Lancashire and Solway Mosses.

In particular, the elegant and precise work of Dr. Judith Turner on the vegetation history at Tregaron Bog (Fig. 43), has set a pattern which it is hoped will be followed at other sites. A close series of radiocarbon dates has enabled Dr. Turner to trace the vegetation history of the dry land surrounding this great raised bog, and to date precisely the changes in rate of bog growth, giving an accurate estimate of the rate of growth before and after the climatic deterioration in the last millennium B.C. Detailed pollen analysis of later peat has shown a particularly striking change in land use on the surrounding uplands, which was dated to within a century of the foundation of the nearby Cistercian monastery of Strata Florida in 1164 A.D., thereby substantiating Professor Pearsall's ideas on Cistercian influence as set out in Chapter 13.

PEAT EROSION

Of course, if erosion of soil and of rock has taken place on such a considerable scale, we should perhaps also anticipate that the softer material, peat, must also have suffered greatly from erosion. Almost everybody who has written about mountain peats in Britain has commented on the frequency with which they show dissection. Often they are entirely cut up by peat-haggs into tabular masses a few yards in diameter or else the surface is intersected in all directions by deep drainage channels, cut by running water down to the basement rock or clay (Plate X, p. 53).

On the higher " mosses," both dissections and drainage channels have often originated from the cutting back of the stream gullies and drainage channels into the high plateaux, and they might thus be a direct result of the normal development of erosion on the mountain surface. But a peat-moss on an undulating or gently sloping upland surface naturally develops a drainage system of its own, and the way in which it does so can be studied in part along the edge of any peat-cutting after wet weather or, on a larger and natural scale, it is very well shown in many places on Rannoch Moor. At first the drainage water runs along the ground surface in hollows under the peat. Finally, the surface peat collapses into the channel so excavated and a visible system of drainage gullies arises which spreads, at first slowly, but gradually more rapidly as the adjacent peat dries and cracks, for the cracks serve as drains and are themselves rapidly excavated into gullies.

Erosion systems in peat may and do arise in still another way, and that is as a result of "bog-flows." Large and deep masses of peat hold enormous volumes of water, so that often the surface vegetation and peat represents a thin crust on a liquid mass. After periods of heavy rain, such peat surfaces may become too weak to retain the great weight of liquid beneath, so that the bog bursts or flows with destructive effects on the surrounding soils and vegetation. After it has " flowed " the peat surface is usually left in a chaotic condition, torn and thrown about in every direction, and it then develops an astonishingly mixed flora. Local histories and traditions in peat-covered country record many instances of " bog-flows." Indeed, just around the Solway Firth, as well as in parts of Scotland, many of the larger peat-bogs are normally called " flows," which may suggest that bog-bursts were formerly much more numerous. There are two reasons why it is probable that bog-bursts are now less frequent than formerly. The widespread draining of peat-moors by man is one, and the second, partly caused by this, is that the peat is usually now covered by mats of coarse vegetation that offer a great deal of resistance to splitting, much more than would be the case if the surface were still a spongy mass of bog-moss.

Thus it is very hard to decide by direct observation to-day between two divergent views which are frequently held. Some observers think that a peat-bog starts, grows to maturity and ultimately degenerates. Thus the peat must finally reach a dissected condition, no matter which of the three methods of degeneration described above develops first. The alternative view is that peat dissection has resulted mainly from some form of drying, either as a result of climatic change or as a result of burning and drainage, influenced as well, of course, by the natural tendency of every stream to cut back into its gathering grounds. Both views doubtless contain a considerable measure of truth, but the former one perhaps helps best to explain the enormous amount of peat erosion which can be seen in the wetter, blanket-bog parts of Britain, while the after-effects of drying the peat surface might be expected to be more pronounced in the drier eastern uplands.

While this discussion of peat erosion is partly a digression, it is also essential to the proper appreciation of the present condition of British moorlands, for if erosion of upland peat is a natural result of its mode of development it must be taken into account in describing the vegetation sequence. There are certainly some conditions under which peat dissection is a natural outcome of the physical conditions. These may occur, for instance, on some of the tabular hills of limited extent. There bog development has overflowed the margin, and retrogression has followed. On the steeper upland slopes, too, peat becomes unstable when a certain depth is exceeded. A deep peat-bog on a slope is comparable to a drop of viscous fluid. It will either flow or develop its own internal drainage system. Finally, where peat development has taken place over limestone, in places where the cracks are blocked by glacial drifts or glacial-lake sediments, there is almost always a development of sink-holes from which widespread peat retrogression follows. Further, where rainfall has always been high, it is probable that there was rapid peat growth in the early Post-glacial period with a resultant overstepping of physical boundaries which has later led to rapid cutting back and erosion. One may say generally that on sloping terrain high rainfall will accelerate peat accumulation in the first instance, but it will also accelerate peat erosion when instability sets in.

PLANT SUCCESSION

Familiarity with upland vegetation leaves one impression very firmly fixed in the mind of the observer, and that is the idea that the vegetation is in a constant state of flux. It matters little whether we have to deal with the changing surface of the mountain-top or of crag and scree, or whether we examine the present status of the upland woodlands, grasslands and moorlands. In almost every case we find it necessary to suppose that change has taken place and is taking place. There is, of course, no better example of this than is provided by the study of the plant remains preserved in peat-bogs, for they give a record, if we can read it, of the vegetation changes on one particular area. To the plant ecologist this idea of the mutability of natural vegetation is, of course, a commonplace, and one of the reasons for ecological interest in peat vegetation is that it is often possible to verify theory by studies of the sequence of plant remains preserved in the peat. In this way we can often describe the series of vegetation types, and recognise that different types of vegetation follow one another in what is usually called a plant succession.

By way of recapitulation, it may be useful to describe and briefly discuss the broad outlines of the plant succession in upland Britain.

On all upland soils of more or less normal slope, say 1 in 20, the general post-glacial succession of plants has tended to follow the sequence,

arctic vegetation ⟶ woodland ⟶ bog

We can make various refinements in this sequence by describing in detail the stages of woodland succession as, for example,

open pine-birch woodland ⟶ alder and sometimes oak-woods ⟶ damp birch-woods and Molinia
or pine-birch ⟶ oak ⟶ heather with pine or birch.

We can also recognise that bog development probably passed through two main stages like :

grassy swamp   ⟶   Sphagnum-cover with sedges and
(Molinia-Myrica-Sphagnum)   heathers

but these are mainly refinements in detail.

The second idea that has emerged is that the upland bogs almost always show signs of degeneration. These changes are apparently of the type :

bog with   ⟶   mixed   ⟶   sedge *with*   ⟶   sedge *or*
Sphagnum-cover   moor   heather-moor   heather-moor

We may recognise that both human activities or natural causes (e.g. peat retrogression) can bring these about, and the method of doing this will also affect their detailed composition.

If we can assume that these two types of plant succession have been common ones, then it must also be conceded that the rate at which they have progressed has been very variable. Acceleration or retardation has been brought about by three groups of factors ; topographic, climatic, and human (biotic). On at least one occasion in the past, an increase in climatic humidity has accelerated the developmental process, while the combined effects of low temperature and of the unstable topography resulting from it have even maintained traces of the first sub-arctic phase at high altitudes.

Generally speaking, however, in the uplands topography, slope and rock structure have exerted a preponderant influence on the plant successions. On steeper slopes, surface instability and mineral flush effects have generally retarded the development of leached soils and of humus accumulation, though peaty flushes have often accelerated such changes. The better drainage has altered the course of the vegetation changes, often through oak-wood and heather-moor, for example, so that sometimes perhaps only a deterioration of climate can have turned such sites into bog.

Lastly, topography has had enormous influence not only in transferring the influence of one habitat to another—e.g. the down-wash of peaty water from upland bogs—but also, through physical instability and erosion, of introducing bog retrogression or other physical changes into the habitats.

Two other things need to be noted about this succession. In the eastern part of the Highland zone, the deterioration of climate produced an acceleration which is not now being maintained. Except in basins, active bog-growth has ceased, and what we see are mainly somewhat stabilised phases and particularly a greater variety of retrogressive ones. In the west, in contrast, there are as a rule marked signs of over-development at the high altitudes and clear signs of continued bog development below.

There are, then, three things to take into account in describing upland vegetation : development, mature condition and subsequent changes. The development has passed through the equivalents of the extraordinarily wide range of upland vegetations considered in Chapters 5, 6 and 7. These may be viewed as responses mainly to the variety of topography and rock structure.

They have tended gradually to become merged beneath a mature bog cover of a generally uniform type though apparently still showing the influence (p. 193) of the climatic conditions and probably of other conditions that have controlled the developmental history.

The uniformity in aspect of the bog cover gives way, under the influence of the general topographical instability, of climatic change and of biotic activity, to a second almost infinitely variable range of plant groupings. A common series has been that associated with desiccation (following the sequence outlined in Table 10, p. 180) but getting into different " steady states " which obviously depend on drainage (whether natural or artificial) and on climate.

In addition, man has influenced the plant groupings in many other ways. These obviously may alter any stage in the above series —either upgrade or downgrade. Thus there are obviously large differences between different parts of the uplands which are due to the varying intensity of human occupation and exploitation. Indeed it is not too much to say that the differences between one part of the Highland zone and another from this cause are probably greater than those induced by any other factors. It would be very interesting if we could develop this idea and arrange our forms of upland vegetation in such a way as to represent the degree of human interference they indicate. Perhaps this is impossible—but when we come later to consider the history of animal life on the uplands, more can certainly be done towards indicating which are the primitive parts of the upland zone and which the most modified.

PLATE 25

John Markham

Nesting ground of ptarmigan and dotterel. Cairngorms, June

PLATE 26

John Markham

a. Dotterel at home in *Rhacomitrium* grassland, Inverness-shire. June

Eric Hosking

b. Nest and eggs of golden plover, Yorkshire. June

MOUNTAIN BIRDS

CHAPTER II

UPLAND ANIMALS—THE INVERTEBRATES

O N E of the most noticeable features of upland life is the apparent smallness of the animal population, and this is perhaps particularly the case on moorlands. It may, of course, be partly a camouflage effect, for moorlands usually show a mosaic of colour into which the greys and browns of moorland animals very easily fade. On the high grasslands, animals are not only more easily seen but may also be more numerous—at any rate until the high crags and the mountain-tops are reached : there, a real sterility seems to rule. If we may for the moment confine our attention to moorlands in the strict sense, then we may attribute the smallness of the animal population largely to the special characters of the peaty soil. The slow rate of decay found in moorland soils permits only a small annual turnover of vegetation, and it therefore follows that it will maintain only a com-paratively small animal population. The effects of the moorland soils are, however, qualitative as well as quantitative. The unusual soil conditions not only give rise to somewhat specialised types of vegetation, they also directly control the soil fauna and may affect indirectly even the largest animals.

For example, we have already drawn attention to the marked deficiency of mineral bases, and of lime in particular, that characterises moorland soil. Thus the only moorland member of the mollusca is *Arion ater*, the black slug, a species practically without a shell. Snails as a class require lime in order to make their shells, and as upland forms they are therefore absent from moorlands in the strict sense and are confined in the uplands to limited areas of grassland and sub-alpine rocks, relatively rich in lime.

Growing mammals also require considerable quantities of lime salts, particularly of phosphate, in order to produce their skeletons. It appears to be generally known that cattle will not *grow* satisfactorily on moorland habitats owing to the lime deficiency, although the hardier breeds (e.g. Highland Kyloes) can maintain themselves there when mature. The inadequacy of the lime supply for large mammals may be illustrated by other facts. A very striking one is the observation (see, for example, F. Darling) that on many Scottish moorlands, red deer are so avid for lime that they will eat the cast antlers or even the bones of dead animals. The practical results of this are that basic slag, which includes calcium phosphate, is the best pasture manure for moorland soils.

An ecological result is that because vegetation types vary in their lime content, or, more accurately, in their base contents, they can exert, at least to some extent, a controlling influence on the animal population. Thus, in a general way, the " pattern " of vegetation, since it is based on nutritional factors, also affects the success or failure of larger animals—well illustrated not only by the above facts but by others discussed in later pages (p. 248, deer forests). The same factors must have equally profound effects on the distribution of the smaller creatures.

We have noticed already (p. 72) that other characteristics of moorland soils are that they contain a very limited soil fauna, and that among their more easily ascertained features is the absence of earthworms. This fact finds its counterpart in the parallel absence of moles, though both earthworms and moles may occur on the less typical and more calcarous grassland soils which possess a more commonplace fauna.

Because soil properties very largely determine the types of vegetation, and as special types of plant tend to have associated with them particular animals, each plant community tends to have its own characteristic animal community. This feature is, as we shall see later (p. 215), very clearly shown by the insect populations, for many insects, especially in their larval stages, are *phytophagous*, feeding on plants, and often causing galls or " mining " (i.e. boring holes) in the tissue of certain species only. These are accompanied by characteristic predatory and carnivorous forms and also by carrion-eaters, both types tending to have a wider and more universal distribution.

Hence, one method of distinguishing animal communities is that of utilising as a basis the larger and more distinct plant communities and attempting to describe the animals characteristic of each. The value of this method is that it results in a correlation, even if an indirect one, with distinctive features of the habitat. Unfortunately, the information on which a complete treatment of this kind could be based is almost non-existent, although, as subsequent pages will show, enough is available to demonstrate the value of this method of approach. It is, however, extremely difficult to apply it successfully to all animals, particularly to those with a considerable mobility.

Birds, in particular, and mammalian predators in most cases, may need a more general method of survey and so will be considered separately.

A third method of approach to the subject would be to try and identify natural or existing communities of animals and plants, and to examine their more noteworthy characteristics. We can distinguish, for example, certain well-established groupings such as grouse-moor, deer-forest and sheep-walk, and it will be profitable to consider how far these can be regarded as natural. In this class also come the new State Forests, which, though not strictly either moorland or mountain, have certainly had a very great influence alike on upland vegetation and animal life.

Following on these lines of approach we shall attempt to deal first with the smaller invertebrate animals in relation to types of vegetation ; secondly, with the general characters of the vertebrate fauna ; and thirdly, with types of vertebrate communities.

INVERTEBRATE ANIMALS OF GRASSLANDS AND MOORLANDS

In dealing with the invertebrate animals of the uplands many difficulties stand in the way of a complete or even a logical description. Not only is the number of species involved extremely large, but even their identification is often a matter only to be attempted by specialists. Hence, few observers have been able to deal with all the types represented, and it is far from easy to give a comparative description. Thus the following account can be little more than an attempt to indicate the place occupied and the part played by these smaller animals in the general field of moorland ecology.

The main factors that determine the nature of the upland invertebrate fauna are clearly three in number : the soil characters, the vegetation cover and the physical conditions of temperature and humidity. In a general way, the pattern of the invertebrate animal groupings follows the soil and vegetation. Excluding, for the present, the montane habitats above 2,000 ft., the main groupings are either those of the grasslands (and occasional vestigial woodlands) or of the moorlands in the stricter sense. The grassland and woodland faunas merge into those of the lowlands, but differ particularly in the smaller number of species and a more limited ecological character. Thus faunistically the grasslands are of three main sorts—ranging from the rich and varied types on base-rich soils to the poor ones on acid and base-deficient *mors*. Wherever such rocks as limestone, basalt and dolerite outcrop, there are grasslands of sheep's fescue, with many other herbs and grasses, distinguished among upland habitats by the presence of snails, ants and earthworms, and characterised by a great variety of insect larvae. Though this type is of widespread distribution in British mountains, it covers a limited area. It is perhaps more noticeable on the igneous rocks of Eastern Scotland, but of course finds its fullest expression in Southern England on the chalk downs. In the north and west, it is nearly always recognisable also because it harbours moles and practically always rabbits.

The second and commonest faunistic type is that of the poorer Festuca-Agrostis grasslands on base-deficient soils on which snails are replaced by slugs and where ants are absent and earthworms scarce. Dipterous larvae are not infrequent, particularly leather-jackets, *Tipula* spp., and here come in some of the characteristic smaller moths of the uplands, their larvae feeding chiefly on the roots of grasses and sedges. In this category Prof. Heslop Harrison records *Procus strigilis*, *Petilampa minima* and *Arenostola pygmina*. Dr. M. J. D. White tells me that another characteristic insect is the small speckled short-horned grasshopper (*Myrmeleotettix maculatus*).

The third faunistic type is that of the damp and extreme base-deficient or acid soils of a peaty type bearing the moor mat-grass (*Nardus*), or blue moor-grass (*Molinia*). Here a visible soil fauna is usually absent, though slugs may persist on the surface. Certain moths are often noticeable, particularly forms feeding on the mat-grass or moor-grass (see p. 218). The fox-moth (*Macrothylacia rubi*), one of the commonest moorland species, comes here feeding on mat-grass, and so does the antler-moth (*Cerapterix gramineus*), which at times occurs in enormous numbers. Another fairly characteristic species is the small rush-moth (*Coleophora caespititiella*), which lives as a larva in the fruits of the moor-rush (*Juncus squarrosus*). These damp grasslands grade into the moorlands and bogs from which they are sometimes derived, and their insect populations reflect mainly the differences in the character of the vegetation.

Moorlands in the strict sense are, like these very acid grasslands, also characterised by a fauna from which soil animals are virtually absent, though a few occur, mainly minute mites (*Acarina*) and spring-tails (*Collembola*), which are found in the litter above the drier types of heather-moor (e.g. *Mydonius nivalis*, *Lepidocyrtus cyaneus* and *L. lanuginosus*). The scarcity of soil animals is due largely to the oxygen deficiency of the wetter moorland soils, and this is also no doubt associated with the fact that when moorland insects are phytophagous they live almost entirely on the leaves of moorland plants—less often on the stems and very rarely on the roots. Because of the absence of soil organisms, the distinctive faunal types on moorlands are mainly groupings of insects associated particularly with the special moorland plants. But there is also a very distinctive element that belongs to the Sphagnum-cover, and this may occur in association with a variety of plants of different types. A somewhat specialised fauna on the wetter moors is that occupying the little peaty tarns and lochans. This includes many truly aquatic species as well as those mainly associated with Sphagnum.

While the animals of the Sphagnum-cover have not received so much attention as the plants, there are known to be present many species of animalcula, including many Rhizopods, of which, according to J. M. Brown, species of *Heliopera*, *Placocysta*, *Hyalosphenia* and *Nebela* (e.g. *N. scotica*) are restricted to this habitat; also recorded are the tardigrade, *Macrobiotus hufelandi*, and numerous rotifers. The peat commonly contains also the remains of aquatic mites (*Diplodontius despiciens* is recorded) and almost every sample shows curious flask-shaped objects which are the spermatophores of small aquatic crustacea (copepods); *Moraria sphagnicola* and *Canthocamptus weberi* in particular are regularly associated with Sphagnum and with the liverwort, *Gymnocolea inflata*. In the pools on the peat surface, crustacea of the water-flea type (Cladocera), *Strebloceris serricaudatus* and *Ancantholeberis cur-virostris* are widely distributed. Particularly characteristic of the drier bog-moss surfaces are also the scale-insects, *Orthezia cataphracta* and *Newsteadia floccosa*, both of which may also come from moss under heather. On the bog-moss cover in addition there are likely to be certain special beetles as well as the spiders *Pirata piraticus* and *Lycosa palustris*, while many smaller species of spider, *Hilaira* and *Erigone* spp., may live just beneath the mossy surface. The combination of Sphagnum with the moor-grass *Molinia* generally results in the appearance of a grasshopper (*Mecostethus grossus*), which elsewhere tends to be a species associated with boggy places in the subarctic tundra, according to Dr. M. J. D. White, who also associates the long-horned grass-hopper, *Metrioptera brachyptera*, with such moist places when they contain cross-leaved heath (*Erica tetralix*).

Of insects in and near moorland pools and runnels, the water-beetles and dragon-flies are perhaps most noticeable. Of the latter, some of the species of *Sympetrum* and particularly the striking *S. scoticum* and *S. striolatum* (subs *nigrifemur*) are noteworthy, the former having black males and yellow females, while the latter is particularly a species of the western margins of Britain. More widespread is the four-spotted Libellula (*L. quadrimaculata*), while in Scotland *Somatochlora arctica* may also occur, a rare and local form with very marked arctic-alpine affinities. All of these probably feed mainly on the midge larvae which abound in peaty waters.

The water-beetles are represented in such places particularly by *Hydroporus morio*, often occurring also with *H. obscurus* and *H. tristis*, the latter of which is generally associated with Sphagnum. *Agabus congener* and *A. arcticus* are often regarded as the stock examples of northern and alpine forms occurring in the high peaty pools and tarns. The only whirligig-beetle, *Gyrinus*, found in this type of habitat is *G. minutus*, which is generally found above 1,000 ft.

The smaller water-boatmen (*Corixids*) are at times numerous. Particularly associated with peaty moorland habitats are *Sigara nigro-lineata* and *S. wollastoni*, both common above 1,500 ft. The two species of pond-skater, *Gerris costai* and *G. gibbifer*, may be found still higher, up to at least 2,500 ft. *Velia currens* is perhaps commoner at lower levels, and so, too, is the larger water-boatman, *Notonecta glauca*.

Equally noticeable at times (in more senses than one) are the hordes of midges (*Chironomids*) and other dipterous flies like the black-flies (*Simulium* spp.), which may also occur, though they are not necessarily confined to moorlands. The midge larvae, living in the peaty mud, are peculiar in their ability to absorb oxygen from sur-roundings containing this gas only in very low concentrations. The *Simulium* larvae, on the other hand, are found attached to stones in *moving* water as they require abundant oxygen.

The scarcity of oxygen in the soil must be one of the most important factors limiting the soil fauna on wet moors. In fact, when moors of this general type are dominated by cotton-sedges (*Eriophorum vaginatum* and *E. angustifolium*), their barrenness is intensified by the almost complete lack of insect species living or feeding on the cotton-sedges.

Though, for example, dozens of moths are recorded for moorlands, only one of them, *Celaena haworthii*, the cotton-sedge or " cotton-grass " moth, feeds on cotton-sedge, its larvae burrowing into (" mining ") the stems (Pl. 30, p. 245). Among the few smaller insects associated with cotton-sedge is the cecidomyiid gall-gnat, *Stenospatha eriophori*, found by Professor Heslop Harrison, who believes it to be probably not uncommon but overlooked. Another fly often associated with cotton-sedge is a daddy-longlegs, *Tipula subnodicornis*, about whose mode of life it would be interesting to have further details. Even predators like spiders are scarce, though, according to Bristowe, *Sitticus floricola* is a characteristic inhabitant of the fluffy heads. Here occurs, however, one of the most specialised of the moorland insects, *Plateumaris discolor*, a beetle, which is adapted to overcome the absence of oxygen in its habitat (see below). For the rest, cotton-sedge moors are dependent for their insect population largely on the species living on the somewhat occasional associated plants. Among these, one of the most widespread is a peculiar syrphid fly, a melanic (or dark) form of *Melanostoma mellinum*, which, both in the Pennines and the Western Highlands, is characteristically associated with the cloud-berry (*Rubus chamaemorus*), an almost constant member of the higher cotton-sedge moors. Two Empids (*E. lucida* and *E. snowdoniana*) also occur with cloudberry in this habitat.

The scarcity of insects on cotton-sedge moors is one of the remark-able features of this habitat. It is balanced also by the very small population of insect-feeding birds. The only figures available suggest that this may be as low as 5 to 10 per 100 acres of moorland of this type. The birds are mainly meadow-pipits.

The beetle mentioned above, *Plateumaris discolor*, is undoubtedly one of the most interesting of moorland species. It belongs to a group of reed-beetles, of which there are over 20 species in the lowlands on Britain, mostly of the genus *Donacia*. They spend most of their lives as larvae or pupae on the buried roots and rhizomes of the water plants found in lowland ponds and waterways, and their elytra have been recorded from lowland peat. *Plateumaris discolor*, on the other hand, is distinct among these Donacine beetles in occurring as an upland species on the roots of the cotton-grasses or cotton-sedges (*Eriophorum* spp.). Where it has been sought for, it ascends to nearly 2,000 ft., and in the lowlands it appears to be replaced by a similar species, *P. sericea*, found in reeds. Both are fairly large (1 cm. long) and extremely handsome insects, showing a great range of metallic colour from the typically brassy, through golden, coppery and purple to nearly black. The remarkable feature of these beetles is that their larvae always occur below the mud-level and, consequently, in an environment devoid of oxygen. They are found only on plants with large intercellular air-spaces, and they obtain their oxygen by tapping these cavities. For this purpose they possess at the anal end two hollow spines which communicate with their tracheal system and also penetrate the plants' intercellular air-spaces. Thus there is a continuous channel through which air can be obtained. When it is full-grown, the larva constructs a thin, oval, transparent cocoon attached to the roots of the plant. This cocoon is full of air and communicates with the air-spaces of the plant by a hole eaten through the root-cortex. In this cocoon, the pupal stages, which are without the respiratory spines, are passed through very rapidly, but the adult beetles, though apparently mature by September, remain in the cocoon until the following June. They can doubtless maintain the connection between the cocoon and the air in the plant by using their mandibles.

If cotton-sedge is a poor medium for insect life, the deer-sedge (*Trichophorum casspitosum*) must be still worse. In spite of careful search, I have never seen any insect associated with this plant. But Professor Heslop Harrison, though having no proof of the existence of any insect associate, has observed that grass-moths of the genus *Crambus* come to rest on the deer-sedge tufts, and he accordingly suspects that some of them may feed on the plant in the larval condition. Mr. W. D. Hincks has also unearthed a record of the coccid, *Ripersia scirpi* Green, as having been found " concealed at the base of stems of *Trichophorum caespitosum* in boggy ground, Camberley, June 1920." It seems clear, however, that deer-sedge, even if edible to the larger ruminants, is not very attractive to insects. On the other hand, it is not a plant which covers large tracts of country by itself. The deer-sedge moors thus almost always have a fairly large fauna of the insect species which are associated with heather and moor-grass (*Molinia*). Here also occur such species as the coccid or scale-insect, *Eriococcus devoniensis*, which galls the cross-leaved heath (*Erica tetralix*) throughout Britain, causing a spiral twist on the stems. The insect population of deer-sedge moors in the Western Highlands would probably repay careful investigation, as it inhabits one of the more primitive of British plant communities.

Damp moors including heather in their vegetation are also characterised at times by "plagues" of the so-called heather-beetles,
well known to sportsmen, at least by name, on account of the damage
they produce at times on the wetter grouse-moors.   The damage is
generally caused by one particular heather-beetle, *Lochmaea suturalis,*
an insect about a quarter of an inch long and dark brown or black
in colour, though the wing-covers may be yellowish (Pl. 28a, p. 225).
It feeds on the bark and leaves of the ling or heather, stripping the
young stems and, by killing them, reducing the amount of food
available for grouse.   The plants attacked often acquire a characteristic
foxy red.   The eggs of Lochmaea have been found mainly on Sphagnum, but as plagues of Lochmaea have occurred on moors on which
Sphagnum is absent it is probable that the eggs are more widely distributed in nature.   Their successful incubation does, however, seem
to depend on the air being moist and upon it having a relative
humidity of more than 70 per cent of saturation.   The larvae feed on
the young heather, mainly in July and August, and, when they are
full-grown, burrow into the surface of the soil (about an inch below it)
and hibernate there, emerging as adults in the following spring when
the air becomes warm.

In order to reduce the severity of "plagues" of Lochmaea, it is
recommended that heather-burning should, as far as practicable, be
carried out in July and August when the larvae may be easily destroyed
whilst feeding on the leafy shoots.   Increased drainage, which eliminates
Sphagnum and increases the dryness of the surface soil, is also advocated
as tending to prevent the successful incubation of the eggs.

Heather-burning, and even drainage, may have certain disad-
vantages.   For example, if burning is carried out in July it may harm
young birds.   Hence the attempt has been made to find other organisms
that will prey on or parasitise the heather-beetle.   At present no
suitable organism of either of these types has been found, though the
search has revealed something of the natural enemies of Lochmaea.
The commonest of these appears to be a ladybird-beetle, *Coccinella
hieroglyphica* (Pl. 28b), which has a life-cycle corresponding in type
and in time with Lochmaea.   It is, however, rarely very abundant,
and nothing that is known at present suggests that it could serve to
reduce the heather-beetle "plagues."   Indeed, in the Western Isles,
where such plagues have been frequent, Coccinella seems to be unable
to maintain itself.

The moorland beetles include other forms which feed on heather—for example, *Haltica britteni*—and there are in addition heather-weevils, small insects about an eighth of an inch long. The widely distributed weevil, *Micrelus ericae*, is almost unique among moorland insects, in mining into ling stems. The much less common *Strophosomus sus* is another weevil which is found in the roots (Pl. 28c, p. 225). All of these may be present on drier heather-moors.

Predatory moorland forms include the spiders, *Lycosa nigriceps* and *L. amentata*, as well as the handsome carabid beetles. The most striking of the latter is *Carabus nitens*, at home in most types of moorland. It is mainly a metallic green in colour, but the elytra are bordered with crimson, the thorax is crimson and the head copper-coloured. Both more sober in appearance and more frequent are *C. arvensis*, often in grassy places, and *C. violaceus*, which, in captivity, has been observed to eat five or six heather-beetles a day. Both also occur under stones on mountains. Among other moorland beetles are certain species of *Bradycellus* and *Feronia*, of which *B. assimilis* and *F. adstrictus* seem to be associated with heather-moors, and there are also tiger-beetles of which, perhaps, *Cicindela campestris* is the most common on the moors.

The most noticeable insects on our moorlands are often the very many species of Lepidoptera (moths and butterflies), some of which occur at times in great abundance. The moorland species (in the strict sense) show certain peculiarities. In the first place they include hardly any butterflies, only two species being at all characteristic—namely, the large heath, *Coenonympha tullia* (see Pl. 30, p. 245), and the green hairstreak, *Callophrys rubi*. The latter of these is not even restricted to moorlands. As it feeds on leguminous plants like gorse and broom, it prefers the shelter of hollows and sheltered banks shunning the open moor. The former the large heath, almost always feeds on Molinia, the purple moor-grass, and so tends to follow its range, though it is said also to use the white beak-sedge (*Rhynchospora alba*) as food. Another butterfly, the Scotch argus or northern brown (*Erebia aethiops*) (Pl. 30), also haunts Molinia slacks in the Western Highlands and Islands. It is often particularly noticeable among the remains of the ancient pine- and birch-woods, and hence, perhaps, can hardly be considered as a strictly moorland species. The dark green fritillary (*Argynnis aglaia*) is similarly associated with the moorland margins of ancient woodlands.

The moorland moths are much more numerous and some of them

also frequent Molinia. Among these is the drinker-moth (*Philudoria potatoria*), whose larvae are at times very common on some of the moorland isles, such as Rhum, up to 1,500 ft. It extends in similar places south into England. Associated with this in the Molinia-Myrica bogs is the Scottish argent-and-sable (*Eulype subhastata*), found generally in the Highlands and Islands, wherever Myrica grows (Pl. 30, p. 245). Two tortricid moths, *Argyroploce dimidiana* and *A. mygindana*, of which the former is the commoner, also occur. Their larvae are found in tents spun in the leaves of the bog-myrtle.

On the whole, however, the moorland moth population is composed more particularly of species whose larvae feed on heathers (both *Calluna* and *Erica*) or *Vaccinium* spp. (bilberry and cowberry). Some 50 or more species of this general type are known in contrast to the one species, for example, of *Celaena*, already mentioned as feeding on cotton-sedge. Among those of the moths which show preferences for particular moorland plants, the species feeding on bilberry and other *Vaccinium* sp. tend to have much wider distribution than moorlands in the strict sense, because the food-plants are equally at home in a wide range of montane habitats and are also characteristic of open woodlands. Thus the Vaccinium feeders, *Anarta cordigera* and *A. melanopa*, both go very high. More widespread are such species as the northern spinach (*Lygris populata*), the smoky wave-moth (*Scopula ternata*) and the golden-rod brindle (*Lithomoia solidaginus*). Most of the moorland species have larvae feeding on the leaves of plants and only rarely on roots or stem. But as we have seen, there are also some species found mainly on the upland grasslands that feed chiefly on the roots of grasses and sedges. These, as one might expect, are not characteristic of deep peat or waterlogged soils.

Two other common moorland moths are the moor-carpet (*Entephria caesiata*) and the northern eggar (*Lasiocampa callunae*), both of which feed preferably on ling and so tend to follow the distribution of that plant, though both, and the latter in particular, have a much wider possible range of food-plant. Another common moorland moth, the fox-moth (*Macrothylacia rubi*) is equally at home on grasslands, where it lives on the moor mat-grass (*Nardus*). Also associated with heathery moors are the heath-pug, *Eupithecia nanata*, the little yellow underwing, *Anarta myrtilli* (Pl. 30), the common heath-moth, *Ematurga atomaria*, and the emperor-moth, *Saturnia pavonia*. Though the last of these is at times extremely numerous on moors, it feeds also on much more widely distributed plants, such as creeping willow (*Salix repens*) and meadowsweet (*Filipendula ulmaria*).

Though moths are always present and very noticeable on moors, the actual numbers revealed in the only available estimates are rather small. Occasionally, however, certain moths and other insects, like the heather beetle, may be present in enormous numbers and then they may completely defoliate the heather or, at times, bilberry. The northern eggar, fox-moth, emperor-moth and vapourer-moth (*Orgyia antiqua*) have all been observed in great abundance in this manner. At such times in particular they are subject to attack by parasitic insects or predators of various sorts.

Thus the vapourer-moth occurred in some areas in great abundance in 1945, when Professor Heslop Harrison noticed that its egg-masses were almost invariably parasitised by a small hymenopteron, *Trichogramma* sp. Over 300 egg-masses were examined, equivalent to tens of thousands of eggs, and all were so attacked. Dr. Fraser Darling, commenting on the scarcity of emperor-moths in some places, observed that three out of four cocoons were infected by Chalcid flies. Another characteristic moth parasite on moors is the ichneumon, *Ophion undulatus* Grav., which is often found in the cocoons of the northern eggar-moth.

A large proportion of the moorland moths consists (as Elgee pointed out) of species found also in woodland. These include particularly the species feeding on bilberry and cowberry. Further, the remainder, including most of the ericetal forms, seem to have been derived from woodland types, for the species most resembling them usually occur in open woods. The best-known example of this is probably the northern eggar-moth (*Lasiocampa callunae*) (Pl. 30, p. 245), which is now regarded as a moorland race of the oak-eggar, *L. quercus*. Elgee gives many other examples in illustration. In this feature the moths resemble certain larger animals such as red deer and grouse. The former was originally an animal of the open woodlands, while our British red grouse seems to have been derived from the same ancestral stock as the Scandinavian ryper or willow-grouse, a bird of the woodland margins and arctic scrub. All of this is logical enough when it is remembered that much of our moorland was originally forest. We can perhaps see the processes at work in the example of the Hebridean wood-mouse, *Apodemus hebridensis*, which in the islands is a species of open moorlands with well-marked local races.

Its habitat appears to be more limited than that of the corresponding mainland form, the common wood-mouse, *A. sylvaticus.*

The beetles and moths, because of their larger size and brighter colouring, are often the most noticeable moorland insects, and hence there is a good deal of information about them. They are, however, accompanied by numerous other forms which also merit passing attention even if their ecology is often less fully known. I have summarised the following outline mainly from Professor Heslop Harrison's notes.

Plant-bugs in particular are often common, well represented by the striking *Zicrona caerulea,* a member of the Hemiptera-Heteroptera which occurs on ling. *Orthotylus ericetorum* is also recorded below heathers. Of the Hemiptera-Homoptera, the psyllid *Rhinocola ericae,* despite its specific name, is also attached to the heather or ling as well as to the heaths (*Erica* spp.), and it may be very abundant at times. Other frequent Homoptera on moorlands include *Neophilaenus lineatus, Cixius nervosus, Dicraneura flavipennis, Deltocephalus pulicaris* and *Psammotettix striatus*; while J. M. Brown records below heather *Ulopa reticulata* and *Aphrodes bifasciatus.* On the barer and wetter moorlands, and perhaps particularly on those of the deer-grass type, another psyllid, *Livia juncorum,* makes very conspicuous galls on various species of rush, while we have already referred to the coccid or scale-insect, *Eriococcus devoniensis,* which makes galls on cross-leaved heath. The so-called snowy fly, *Tetralicia ericae,* also affects the same species.

Of the other arachnid groups, the harvestmen (*Phalangiideae*) are represented by *Mitopus morio, Oligolophus tridens* and *Nemastoma lugubre,* while the false scorpion, *Obisium muscorum,* is at times plentiful. Of the moorland spiders, *Lycosa nigriceps, L. amentata* and *Tarentula andrenivora* are perhaps most typical, the former more often in the open and the latter among the heather. But mention should also be made of *Aranea cornuta* and *A. patagiata,* which make neat webs and shelters among rushes, while *A. quadrata* and *A. diadema* in particular may block small moorland ravines.

Bees and their allies are common enough as moorland visitors, if possibly not very characteristic of the most peaty habitats. Professor Heslop Harrison tells me that the bumble-bee, *Bombus lapponicus,* is almost entirely a Vaccinium insect, and strictly moorland, and so, too, is *B. jonellus* var. *hebridensis.* In the Hebrides, *B. smithianus,* a bright orange species in general appearance, replaces the mainland *B.*

muscorum and favours the moorlands. In addition to these bumble-bees, most of the heathers, and bilberry also, have their *Andrena* visitors.

The only attempt that seems to have been made to present a complete picture of a moorland animal community (including insects) is one which is being carried out by the Yorkshire Naturalists' Union, who are making a detailed study of heather-moor. So far, however, only preliminary reports are available. The method they are employing is to try to estimate the relative proportions of the species present in standard areas dominated entirely by heather, *Calluna* (see p. 143). Thus the insects are recorded from " quadrats " 20 metres square, that is, with an area of 400 sq. m. Only approximate numbers can be given, and, of course, there is great variation both from day to day and from season to season. But in some detailed observations that we owe to Mr. C. A. Cheetham, an approximate and fairly typical figure for the number of insects in September was 1,100 insects in the stated area—i.e. about 3 to 1 square metre. On a fine and sunny day in March, the number in the air was rather higher, about 5 above 1 square metre of surface. The greater part of these numbers was made up of small, two-winged flies (*Diptera*), the species varying greatly with the season. Much remains to be done in finding out what these insects feed on and in what manner they spend the winter months.

In this area at present most fully described, which was an " intake " on which heather moor had redeveloped, the more noteworthy insects recorded by Mr. Cheetham were as follows, the numbers given in brackets being those in the standard area of 400 sq. m. Starting in March, when they first became numerous, the midge *Metriocnemus fuscipes* appeared in small local swarms of 20 to 50, while two beetles were noticeable, *Aphodius lapponum*, a dung-feeder, and *Catops chrysome-loides*, a carrion-feeder. In April another midge, *Syndiamesa pilosa* (800) was the most numerous insect with a frequency of about 2 per sq. m., and a frequent fly was *Chortophila aestiva* (200). Several other flies which persisted in numbers all the summer till September also first appeared at this time—e.g. *Sepsis cynipsea* (200), " a restless species with a black spot in the wing-tip," and a sawfly, *Dolerus* sp., which appeared first in March, and in April reached a maximum of 300 per 400 sq. m. A somewhat more specialised fly numerous in April was the fungus-midge, *Boletina sciarina* (800). With it, but much less frequent, were *Coprophila vagans, Aneurina urbana* and *Orthellia caesarion*, all feeding on decaying animal matter.

The most noticeable fly in May was *Bibio reticulatus* (about 800). The common heath-moth (20) was noticeable in both May and June, as later were its caterpillars. Odd caterpillars of the emperor-moth, *Saturnia pavonia*, were also seen at this time, as was the froth of the so-called cuckoo-spit, *Philaenus leucopthalamus*, the mature insect being plentiful (maximum 800) until September. The most noticeable form in July was an empid fly, *Rhamphomyia sulcata* (200), which is carnivorous both as a larva and as a fly.

The autumn species of daddy-longlegs was *Tipula pagana. T. rufina* was the first to appear in the new year. Of the bibionids, which were now less frequent, *Bibio lepidus* was found as late as November. A small moth, *Exapate congelatella*, was also present in November; this feeds on bilberry and heather. In winter there was little except the so-called winter midges, *Trichocera saltator*, at first, but later (in February) *T. hiemalis*.

This extremely brief summary of the commoner species does enable us to picture something of the numbers and variety of insect life which may occur on a heather-moor. Numerically, moths and beetles were relatively infrequent in this example. From the same source we know that this insect population was associated in this particular case with two nests of meadow-pipits in an area of some 300 × 100 yards—that is, an area roughly equal to 100 of the standard areas for insect study. No other birds nested in the area studied, though grouse visited it.

INVERTEBRATE ANIMALS OF THE MOUNTAIN-TOPS AND FLUSHES

The strictly montane animals merit a special consideration as they differ considerably from those enumerated above. Our vegetation survey of the mountain habitats in an earlier section suggested that four main types could easily be distinguished. By far the most extensive of these is some form of grassland often associated with heath plants such as Vaccinium. Equally characteristic, though less extensive, is some form of " mountain-top detritus," often with the Rhacomitrium moss-heath developing over it. Finally, occupying small areas, but often containing the most interesting plants and animals, are the crags and flushes. We may take this outline as a useful basis for the consideration of the invertebrate population, for though systematic inquiry as to the whole population of any one of the areas is lacking, it is still possible to make out the same sort of pattern in the organisms which have been recorded on mountains in Britain. For practical purposes, the upper limit of heather-moor (about 2,000 ft.) is a good dividing line between the typical moorlands and the more truly mountain areas, and from our present point of view it will be best to consider as mountain species those occurring mainly above this line.

The employment of this distinction also has the advantage of cutting out the very large number of moorland species that feed on the heathers, for these naturally tend to be infrequent above 2,000 ft. On the other hand, the species which feed on *Vaccinium* or crowberry (*Empetrum*) and particularly on the grasses, come to be relatively the most important, though the majority of them are actually more abundant at lower levels than they are on the mountain summits,

Here come in most of the moths found at higher altitudes and probably many of the flies. But some of the more conspicuous seem to be truly or mainly montane. Among the most noticeable of mountain insects are two species of daddy-longlegs, *Tipula macrocera* and *T. excisa*, which I, at least, always seem to find on mountain-top detritus in summer. The former of these presumably has grass-feeding larvae, but Mr. C. A. Cheetham thinks that *T. excisa* lives on decaying vegetable matter among the stones. It is, therefore, more truly restricted to such places, while *T. macrocera* is often found on the high grasslands, like *T. alpium*, also a common mountain form, in early summer. Generally these larger Diptera seem to be the most frequent of insects at higher altitudes, and their larvae are certainly characteristic inhabitants of high-level soils. From mountain summits bearing detritus and a Rhacomitrium grassland (p. 82), a fungus-midge, *Boletina groenlandica*, is also recorded as common, and certain empids are at times abundant, especially perhaps *Empis verralli*, but also at high levels, *E. lucida* and *Rhamphomyia fumipennis*, both of which have been observed to prey on *E. verralli*.

Equally noticeable, though perhaps much more local in its distribution, is the characteristic mountain butterfly, *Erebia epiphron*, the mountain-ringlet (Pl. 30, p. 245), which is also a grass-feeder in the larval state, and a species of the alpine grasslands.

PLATE 27

Eric Hosking

a. Hen merlin. June

Eric Hosking

b. Ring-ouzel in rough grassland, mainly *Molinia*. May

BIRDS OF THE YORKSHIRE MOORS

PLATE 28

MOORLAND INSECTS

S. Beaufoy

a. Heather beetle (*Lochmaea suturalis*)

S. Beaufoy

b. Ladybird (*Coccinella hieroglyphica*)

S. Beaufoy

c. Heather weevil (*Strophosomus lateralis*)

S. Beaufoy

d. Brown silver-lines moth (*Lithina chlorosata*)

There are, so Mr. E. A. Cockayne tells me, four British species of moth which are confined to the highest levels. These, as one might perhaps expect, are not grass-feeders. They live among the moss-heath types of vegetation and it seems probable, according to the same authority, that their larvae feed mainly on the crowberry (*Empetrum nigrum*) in the natural state. They are all confined to the highest Scottish summits as far as at present known. Their names are *Amathis alpicola* (subsp. *alpina*), the black mountain moth, *Psodos coracina*, the broad-bordered white underwing, *Anarta melanopa* (Pl. 30, p. 245) and *Zygaena exulans*, the mountain burnet moth. According to Dr. Fraser Darling, the larvae of the latter feed also on moss-campion, azalea and cyphel.

Mr. R. B. Benson has made detailed studies of the sawflies occurring at high altitudes in Britain—mainly on the higher Scotch mountains. The alpine sawflies he found tend to fall into certain characteristic groups. Some of them feed on plants with a wide altitudinal range and have themselves usually a wide range. Thus feeding on *Vaccinium* are three species of *Pristiphora*, *P. quercus*, *P. mollis* and *P. coactula*. Grass-feeders, though rather poorly represented, include *Pachynematus clibrichellus*, *P. obductus* and *Dolerus aeneus*, not restricted to the mountain zone. The first named, indeed, occasionally reaches sea-level—e.g. near Wick in Caithness. Perhaps the range of altitude is often related to that of the food-plant. Thus *Pristiphora hyperborea* has larvae which feed on willows such as *Salix herbacea* and *S. phylicifolia*, and although it is generally truly alpine, it comes down to 1,000 ft. in Teesdale and even to sea level in County Mayo, presumably with *Salix phylicifolia*, which is characteristic of both localities. In contrast, *Pontania herbacea*, which is a sawfly widely distributed on British mountains though restricted to high levels, feeds and forms striking red galls on the dwarf willow, *Salix herbacea*, and appears to have here in Britain no alternative " host." *Pontania femoralis*, much more widely distributed in the altitudinal sense, is another gall-maker on a wide range of species of willow, both alpine (e.g. *S. lapponum*, *S. arbuscula*) and lowland. According to Professor Heslop Harrison, it follows *S. andersoniana* and *S. phylicifolia* down to about 300 ft., in Northumberland and Durham. *Pontania pustulator* and *P. phylicifoliae* are both attached to *Salix phylicifolia*, and follow its range.

Magnifications of insects on opposite page : *a. Lochmaea* x 3. 5 ; *b. Coccinella* x 4. 5; *c. Strophosomus* x 3 ; *d. Lithina* x 1.

While, of course, almost any winged insect found in the vicinity may be carried by high wind up on to a mountain (or vice versa), there is perhaps generally a marked tendency for ground insects to predominate on mountain summits and indeed for flightless insects to be found there. Thus among the sawflies especially remarkable on British high mountains is *Amauronematus abnormis*, only known from Mt. Braeriach in the Cairngorms. This is unusual in that the female is short-winged and flightless. Otherwise a species of high arctic latitudes and apparently incapable of extensive migration, it is no doubt to be regarded as a relic of former glacial conditions. Similarly, perhaps the most characteristic insects of the mountain-top detritus are the flightless weevils and ground-beetles living among the stones (lapidicole). Of these varied types, the weevils are mainly phytophagous, feeding probably on grass roots. *Otiorrhynchus arcticus* var. *blandus* is a mainly Scotch form, while *O. nodosus* occurs also on other mountains in England and Wales. Both are flightless.

The alpine ground-beetles are predators and hence not directly related to the vegetation. In almost every mountain region in Britain is *Nebria gyllenhali*, as also is *Carabus glabratus*. Another form, *Leistus montanus*, is perhaps somewhat more localised, while two other mountain species, *Miscodera arctica* and *Feronia adstricta*, are high-moor species as well as montane. All of these are ground-beetles, and, though winged, probably never fly, and are also dark-coloured.

Dark and dingy colours are often characteristic of mountain insects —the tendency also being evident in the mountain spiders. It is, at any rate often, though not necessarily, the case that alpine insects are small. On the other hand, it should also be noted that they usually live below ground among the crevices of the rock detritus, and it has been shown that this habitat is not subject to the very great diurnal ranges of temperature observed in the air above, but tends to remain at a nearly constant temperature and doubtless, also, at a fairly uniform humidity. As W. S. Bristowe has pointed out, among the characteristic spiders of our British mountains are species of *Porrhomma* that are marked shade frequenters, and also forms like *Lepthyphantes pallidus* Camb., which are elsewhere common in cellars.

Most of the British spiders especially characteristic of mountains belong to a group of small, dark-coloured forms known as the Linyphiidae, including many types generally found in arctic regions. Amongst the 26 species given by Bristowe as particularly characteristic are five confined to the British Isles, their names being *Lepthyphantes whymperi* F. Camb., *Entelecera errata* Camb., *Stylocter monila* Camb., *Lycosa traillii* Camb., all of which are found throughout Great Britain, and *Eboria caliginosa* Falc., which is recorded only from Scafell Pike and Marsden Moor.

The fauna of flushes is perhaps not very well known and it possibly varies a good deal. Where the flush water issues from the mountain-top detritus, there are what are variously called " spring-heads " or " mossy flushes," which are perhaps generally of the type of the *liverwort flushes* mentioned in the vegetation section. But the flush water often trickles down damp and mossy steep rocks, " water drips " or small waterfalls, and this faunistically, at any rate, is *the* char-acteristic habitat of the high crags and it perhaps owes a good deal to the high atmospheric humidity. Certain predatory beetles are often noteworthy. Presumably they live on the larvae of small flies living in the damp moss. In Cumberland and the Pennines at least, *Dianous coerulescens* is almost universally present in this habitat, and it is often associated with other beetles, such as *Quedius auricomus*, *Q. umbrinus*, *Hydroporus nivalis* and *Lesteva pubescens*. Here also is to be found the " daddy," *Tipula cheethami*, especially noticeable because its pupal skins remain sticking to the moss.

The bulk of the population in the moss, however, is usually com-posed of midges (chironomids), of which *Orthocladius ictericus*, *Tanypus lentigenosus* and *T. notatus* are recorded from this habitat. Other midges equally favour the high spring-heads. From 2,500 ft. and upwards there are recorded as fairly common *Podonomus peregrinus* and *Syndiamesa pilosa*, of which the latter has already been encountered on heather-moor. Around the spring-heads also are other diptera, par-ticularly the tipulids *Trichyphona claripennis*, *T. unicolor* and *Dicranota guerini*. It is probable that the " snow flushes," already described on p. 95, have also a distinctive fauna, for certain of the high-level species of fly are described as numerous near melting snow. Here comes the empid, *Hydromyia nivalis*, with *H. wesmaeli* (also common near springs and steep flushes) and the anthomyiid, *Limnophora triangulifera*.

When the high flushes pass into permanent rivulets they almost always contain other animals besides fly larvae. Of these, the alpine flat-worm, *Planaria alpina*, is an especially constant inhabitant. It is a small slug-like creature under a quarter of an inch in length, which spends the day-time beneath stones. In the larger flushes and smaller streams, the amount of moss—with its attendant midge population— diminishes and here may also be found the larvae of stone-flies or may-flies. The latter include, according to D. E. Kimmins, species such as *Amelatus inopinatus* (going up to 2,000 ft.) and *Leptophlebia marginata* up to 3,000 ft. Mr. Kimmins has recently recorded a new species, *Protonemura montana*, from this type of habitat in the Lake District. At somewhat lower levels may be found *Baetis pumilus, B. tenax* and *Ephemerella ignita*. H. B. N. Hynes records the stone-fly, *Nemoura erratica*, as not uncommon in small streams of this type, and states that occasional individuals from 1,500 ft. were short-winged, a feature found regularly in allied species at high altitudes in Southern Europe.

There is thus a fairly distinct community of animals in this habitat, which would almost certainly repay further study. If the flushes and water-drips are excluded, we have as yet no record of any special alpine fauna on the high crags.

PLATE XXV

A. R. Thomson.

Field-vole, *Microtus agrestis*

PLATE XXVI

Pine-marten, *Martes martes*

Frances Pitt

CHAPTER 12

THE LARGER MAMMALS AND BIRDS

T H E second method of attacking the animal ecology of the uplands is that of enumerating the species usually present and then attempting to evaluate their ecological significance. The most obvious of the animals in the lists given below are unquestionably the herbivores, and, as might be expected, all of these tend to favour grasslands, although the three largest ones can maintain themselves on moorland in the strict sense. The predatory species, in contrast, occur wherever prey is to be found—though nowadays, one of them, the wild cat, is confined to the Northern Highlands. There the pine-marten and polecat are also to be found, though both of these also occur in the Lake District and North Wales.

The other mammalian species given in the list, like many of the birds, are of very wide distribution in Britain and not especially montane. The reason for their inclusion here is that they are commonly resident at altitudes of 1,000 ft. or more.

MAMMALS AND BIRDS BREEDING OR RESIDENT ABOVE 1,000 FT.

Fox, *Vulpes vulpes*
Pine-marten, *Martes martes*
Stoat, *Mustela erminea*
Weasel, *Mustela nivalis*
Polecat or foumart, *Mustela putorius*
Wild cat, *Felis silvestris*

Raven, *Corvus corax*
Hooded crow, *Corvus cornix*
Carrion-crow, *Corvus corone* (1,800)
Chough, *Pyrrhocorax pyrrhocorax*
  (returning)
*Twite, *Carduelis flavirostris*
Snow-bunting, *Plectrophenax nivalis*
Skylark, *Alauda arvensis* (2,600)
Meadow-pipit, *Anthus pratensis*
*Grey wagtail, *Motacilla cinerea*
Ring-ouzel, *Turdus torquatus* (2,000)
Buzzard, *Buteo buteo* (1,750)

Blue or mountain hare, *Lepus timidus*
Field-vole, *Microtus agrestis* (2,200)
*Mouse, *Apodemus sylvaticus*
Red deer, *Cervus elaphus*
Sheep, *Ovis aries*

Wheatear, *Oenanthe oenanthe* (3,000)
*Whinchat, *Saxicola rubetra*
*Stonechat, *Saxicola torquata*
*Wren, *Troglodytes troglodytes* (2,000)
*Dipper, *Cinclus cinclus*
*Cuckoo, *Cuculus canorus* (chiefly as
  parasite of meadow-pipit)
*Short-eared owl, *Asio flammens*
Peregrine, *Falco peregrinus*
*Merlin, *F. columbarius*
Kestrel, *F. tinnunculus* (1,700)
Golden eagle, *Aquila chrysaëtus*
Greenshank, *Tringa nebularia*

*Hen-harrier, *Circus cyaneus*
 Kite, *Milvus milvus* (formerly)
*Curlew, *Numenius arquata*
 Snipe, *Capella gallinago*
 Dunlin, *Calidris alpina* (2,800)
 Common sandpiper, *Actitis hypo-
 leucos* (2,300)
 Redshank, *Tringa totanus*

Golden plover, *Pluvialis apricaria*
 (2,900)
 Dotterel, *Eudromias morinellus* (3,500)
*Lapwing, *Vanellus vanellus* (2,500)
 Black-headed gull, *Larus ridibundus*
*Common gull, *L. canus*
 Red grouse, *Lagopus scoticus* (2,000)
 Ptarmigan, *L. mutus*

* Usually below 1,500 ft.   The figures are approximate upper-limits in feet.

The natural history of these species is in most cases recorded in the standard works on birds and mammals, and it is not proposed to refer to it in detail here. In the attempt to indicate the broader inter-relations between the species and their environments, it is of interest to try to delimit naturally occurring groups, which possibly we may be able to link with the vegetation or the physico-chemical environment. Of these possible animal groupings, three are at once distinct —grouse-moor, deer-forest and sheep-walk—and, because their history is that of the moors, they merit the separate descriptions given to them later. In addition, a new type of habitat is arising, the State Forest, created by man for economic reasons, which is perhaps going to replace as a habitat the upland forests we have lost, and we may, perhaps, reserve this also for later treatment. We are left then with the problem of distinguishing any other pertinent remaining grouping among our list of upland species.

A few, perhaps, fall into a group which we might regard as truly montane. Here come possibly the mountain hare, the ptarmigan, snow-bunting, and dotterel—all species living only among the high stony wastes and *Rhacomitrium*-heaths. The ptarmigan and snow-bunting formerly occurred in most of our high mountains, though they are, as breeding species, now confined to the Northern Highlands. The snow-bunting is still a regular winter resident in the high grasslands oı Southern Scotland and the Lake District, where it apparently feeds on the fruits of woodrush and *Juncus squarrosus*. In summer it feeds mainly on insects.

The mountain hare was for a time restricted in a like manner to the Northern Highlands, but it has been reintroduced elsewhere and has even spread freely. It is interesting, also, because it represents the tendency among the truly montane species to assume a white colora-tion in winter. This is not, however, observed in the dotterel, which migrates in winter. In the mountain hare, the colour change is due to the absorption of pigment in the existing hair and not to a moult, and it is often incomplete in individuals from the Southern Pennines and also in those from some of the Outer Isles—e.g. Harris and Lewis. On the present evidence it is not possible to say whether this tendency is due to a genetic difference or partly to the peculiarities of the habitat. It must be admitted that the full colour-change often appears to be most inappropriate against the background of dark-hued heather and cotton-sedge which covers so much of our moorland.

Stoats may possess a similar tendency towards the production of mountain races, or they may be especially responsive to changes in environment. The winter colour change towards white is rarely complete in lowland England but seems to be a constant feature above an altitude of 1,000 ft. It is stated, indeed, that stoats from high altitudes on Ben Nevis and other high Scottish mountains maintain a white coat even in the height of summer. If this is invariably the case, it strengthens the assumption that these changes in pigmentation are associated with variations in temperature. It may, perhaps, be noted here that one other moorland creature, the grouse, is derived from a northern form, the willow-grouse or ryper, which becomes white in winter. The British grouse is usually white-flecked to a variable degree, but this feature does not apparently vary with changes of locality or season in a manner which is easily correlated with habitat differences.

To the short list of truly montane species we may possibly add the creatures of the high crags and block-screes. They include the pine-marten and fox among mammals, and, among birds, the golden eagle, peregrine falcon, raven and possibly also the buzzard, though this inhabits mainly the lower crags. All of these are predatory except the raven, and even that is open to the suspicion of not always waiting until its meal is dead. These are all species which were formerly spread over a much wider range. No better example of this can be found than the kite, a species which in medieval times was so abundant in our towns, and particularly in London, as to excite the wonder and comment of foreign visitors. To-day it lingers in isolated mountain fastnesses, nesting in hanging oak-woods, and so nearly exterminated that its British representatives could probably be numbered on the fingers. Similarly, the raven, though now rarely seen far from the high hills, was in medieval times a characteristic bird of the smaller towns, if not of the larger also, and one which was protected in Northern Britain, probably because of its services as a scavenger.   The golden eagle, which nested in Derbyshire 250 years ago, and in the Lake District to within the last 150 years, is now confined to the Western Isles and Highlands.   It, like the peregrine falcon, has probably always been a bird of the high and inaccessible cliffs, but it has not received the measure of protection accorded to the peregrine, which, as a favourite hawk of kings and barons in medieval times, for long bred within the law. Of the species which we can regard as characteristic of the high crags, it is worthy of comment that only three are at present found in all of the main mountain areas—foxes, ravens and peregrines—and all of these have in some measure been protected at an earlier period of their history.

The typical bird population of some moorland areas has been reported on by David Lack, and Table 12 gives his records for five such areas.   Brow Grains is mixed Pennine moorland, heather and cotton-sedge, and Sleights Moor is in North-east Yorkshire and near the sea.   The Sleights Moor is a heather-moor, however, and its comparative richness in birds is probably typical both of this habitat and of North-east Yorkshire.   Certainly the twite is more characteristic of that area than of any other in Northern England, though it also occurs on the drier heathery parts of the western " mosses." The Letterfrack and Shetland moors were both low-lying, near the sea, and probably wet bog, with much *Molinia*, deer-sedge and little heather.   Grouse are not usually common on such moors, and indeed the bird population is often small.

There are two other features of the table worthy of comment. The abundance of skylarks in these figures is perhaps an unusual feature, while the larger number of species recorded for the Sleights Moor is probably due to the greater number of birds counted in that locality.

It appears from this table, and my own estimates agree, that the bird population of a typical upland moor would commonly lie between 20-50 adult birds per 100 acres.   Undoubtedly very great variations occur.   The more exposed areas and those with stunted vegetation (e.g. after burning) have a smaller population, while higher vegetation, especially when the continuity of the vegetation is broken by rocky outcrops, tends to have larger populations.   Here the ring-ouzel is likely to appear, especially where it can get the fruit (such as bilberry and rowan-berry) it likes.   Uniform areas of cotton-sedge, in particular, have little but meadow-pipits at a density of below 10 per 100 acres. On the whole, the extensive rough grasslands are not much better. When all is said, the meadow-pipit remains the most characteristic upland bird, though in winter many individuals leave the high moors for the lowland grass-fields and the coast.

The dampness of many moorlands is no doubt the reason why the list of birds includes a considerable proportion of wading and littoral species. There is, perhaps, no more characteristic introduction to the uplands in spring than the melancholy pipe of the curlew, though this is, on the whole, equally a bird of the grassy lower hills and of heathery moorland knolls that include a fair proportion of marshy ground. It

Table 12

BIRDS PRESENT IN DIFFERENT MOORLAND LOCALITIES AS NUMBERS PER 100 ACRES

	Brow Grains	Letterfrack Galway	Mainland Shetland	Sleights Moor	Dartmoor
Adults per 100 acres	22	56	69	151 (94*)	54
Altitude in feet	ca1,000	250	0-200	4-800	1,000-1,500
Meadow-pipit	7	8	23	43	29
Skylark	+	44	17	4	24
Ring-ouzel				+	
Twite			+	4	
Wheatear			5	3	
Wren				+	
Merlin				+	
Golden Plover		+	+	10	
Dunlin				+	
Curlew	4				+
Snipe					+
Grouse	7			57	
Hooded Crow			+		

* Excluding grouse as protected birds.

The following also were observed :

Shetland : Ringed Plover (11), Starlings
Sleights : Teal, Song-thrush
Dartmoor : Lapwing (16), Stonechat, Cuckoo
Brow Grains : Hedge-Sparrow

does not often nest above 1,500 ft. Somewhat similar is the lapwing, which is, however, on the whole, a grassland species. Although it may nest as high as 2,500 ft., it is more typical of the rough pastures near upland farms and generally nests well below 1,500 ft. To our list we could also add the common sandpiper, wherever there are mountain tarns with gravelly and sandy margins, and possibly the black-headed gull and redshank may ultimately have to be added. Colonies of the former are becoming so frequent near moorland pools (up to at least 2,000 ft.) as to be almost typical of any extensive stretch of moorland. The redshank is also spreading inland in Northern England, and perhaps generally along the western margins, though it rarely nests above 1,500 ft. The rare greenshank is a typical bird of the more remote deer-sedge " flows " in the Highlands. The common-gull is perhaps a more local nesting species than the black-headed gull, though apparently a long-established one and one which, though found at times in colonies and even with black-headed gulls, often nests in isolation.

EFFECTS OF GAME PRESERVATION

There is one other source of interesting evidence as to the original composition of the moorland animal communities—namely, the records of animals trapped, or slain by other methods, during the years when game preservation was in its infancy. The most complete list of this sort I have seen is one referring to the " vermin " trapped in Glen Garry (Inverness-shire) between Whitsunday 1837 and Whitsunday 1840. The numbers of individuals of the different sorts are given, as recorded opposite (Table 13.) The list includes all the species mentioned earlier as well as many which are nowadays never or very rarely seen.

The composition of such lists probably depends not only upon the nature of the surrounding terrain, but also on the methods of killing used. There are more general lists from various sources showing a considerable variety in the proportions of the main species recorded, and three of these, together with the summarised form of that given above, are included in Table 14 (p. 236). The figures refer to (i) five Aberdeenshire parishes near Braemar, 1776-86 ; (ii) the Langmill and Sandside estates in Sutherland, 1819-26 ; (iii) the Duchess of Sutherland's estate, 1831-34 ; and (iv) Glen Garry.

Table 13

ANIMALS TRAPPED IN GLEN GARRY, 1837-40

Foxes	11	Hawks, blue, or peregrine	
Wild cats	198	falcons	98
House-cats (going wild)	78	ash-coloured (probably	
Martens	246	cock hen-harriers)	9
Polecats	106	hobby†	11
Stoats and weasels	301	Falcons, jer§	6
Badgers	67	orange-legged*	7
Otters	48	Merlins	78
		Kestrels	462
		Buzzards, common	285
Eagles, golden	15	rough-legged§	371
white-tailed†	27	honey†	3
Ospreys†	18		
Goshawks†	63	Ravens	475
Kites†	275	Hooded or carrion-crows	1,431
Harriers, hen-	63	Owls, fern (short-eared)	71
marsh (probably		horned (long-eared)	35
Montagu's)†	5	golden (brown)	3

† Now extinct as breeding-species in Scotland.

§ Probably winter-visitors.

* Cannot certainly be identified ; the red-footed falcon, *Falco vespertinus*, recorded certainly only 3 or 4 times in the Highlands, is the only member of its genus on the British list whose legs can unequivocally, and for all seasons, stages and sexes, be described as orange.

In round figures, these suggest that for every eagle or two foxes killed, there would be perhaps four wild cats, polecats and martens, and nine or ten each of kites and hawks or ravens and crows.

The influence of this wholesale destruction of a part of the natural animal grouping must have been very large and the effects are worth examining, as far as we can trace them, while records remain in human memory. Perhaps the last area to show large-scale changes of which there is record may be the Border Country, for similar transformations in the Highlands have not always been pressed to completion. In the Border Country much of the final part of this transformation has been accomplished in the last 200 years or less, for this

Table 14

	(i)	(ii)	(iii)	(iv)
No. of years	*10*	*7*	*4*	*13*
Eagles	70	355	224	42
Hawks and kites	2,520	1,115	1,155	1,757
Ravens and hooded crows	1,347	1,962	936R	1,906
Foxes	634	546	193	11
Wild cats, polecats, martens	—	—	901	550
Carrion-crows and magpies	—	2,647	1,739	—

R, Ravens only.

was " debatable land " until long after the Union of Crowns in 1603, and it was only long after this that what had been a wild-cattle country with much scrub and " moss " was finally converted to sheep-walk.

The predatory animals of this area had formerly included at least the following : fox, badger, weasel, stoat (all of which still survive in small numbers), also the polecat or foumart (*Mustela putorius*), pine-marten (*Martes martes*) and wild cat (*Felis silvestris*). Dealing with the fate of these animals, there are available the records of the Candlemas Fur Fair, held annually at Dumfries. From these it appears that the wild cat had disappeared by the beginning of the nineteenth century, though the last actually recorded from the Border Counties was one killed in Berwickshire in 1849. At the Fur Fair in 1828, " foumart skins were unusually scarce." The actual decline is illustrated by somewhat irregular figures. In 1829-31 there were 400-600 skins, 168 for 1860 and none for 1869 and 1870.

In a similar manner the pine-marten has become extinct over most of the Border Country, and parallel decreases have taken place in the numbers and kinds of predatory birds. It has been recorded that in the 1830s all the following birds nested in the Parish of Eglingham in Northumberland : buzzard (very common), marsh- (probably an error for Montagu's, its distinction being then not widely known) and hen-harriers, kite, peregrine and raven. Of these, the first four have now absolutely disappeared as breeding species, though buzzards are still to be seen farther south in the Lake District and Craven Uplands, where, indeed, they have been increasing in number. The hen-harrier was originally one of the commonest moorland hawks. In four years, for example, 310 were killed in one estate in Ayrshire. They are now

PLATE XXVII

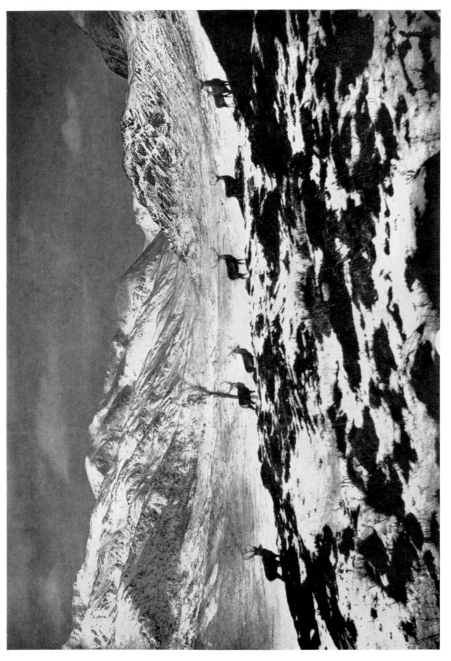

Robert Adam

Deer forest in winter, Inverness-shire

PLATE XXVIII

Eric Hosking

Meadow-pipit, *Anthus pratensis*, at its nest

never seen. The sort of wholesale massacre, indicated by the figures just mentioned, was no doubt due to the great improvements in fire-arms as well as to the spread of intensive game-preservation, but it originated also in the desire of the hill farmers to protect their lambs and poultry.

In the Gaelic, a hen-harrier is *Luch shealgair* or mouse-hawk, and both harriers, buzzards and kites are species feeding to a considerable extent on mice and voles. All of the mammals mentioned in a pre-ceeding paragraph also feed on these animals to some extent at least. After a wholesale extermination of these predators, such as that described above has taken place, it would not be surprising, therefore, to find a corresponding remarkable increase in the mice and voles which make up a considerable part of their food. There seems to be no doubt that such an increase has, in fact, taken place in the last 100 years. We know from Dr. A. S. Watt's investigations that it is now almost impossible for an English woodland to regenerate naturally, the reason being that the small rodents such as mice and voles are now so abundant as to destroy any tree seedlings during the first year or two of their life. On the uplands, voles are, probably, more numerous than mice, and as they are grass-eaters, they have presumably profited by the general extension of rough grasslands which has resulted from sheep-farming. Because of the absence of suitable cover, they are infrequent in pasture which is closely grazed by domestic animals. They are thus commonest in rough and tussocky upland grasslands, and these are the chief places which can support a continuous popula-tion. During the last 100 years, at least two severe vole-plagues have been recorded from the Border Country. They took place in 1875 and again in 1890-92, and Charles Elton, who gives a detailed analysis of these and other outbreaks, has remarked that " there is no record (in a region where memories and records are good) of any major vole-plague in the hundred years before 1870, while there have been two serious ones in the seventy years since." It seems likely then that the vole population now reaches generally higher levels in the absence of natural control by the original predators.

The vole-plague of 1890-92 in the Southern Uplands of Scotland was so large as to threaten the sheep-farmers with disaster. Voles burrow through the base of the grass tussocks and the surface soil, if dry enough, and bite through the young grass shoots, destroying far more than they eat. In 1890-92 they were so numerous in the Southern

Uplands as to destroy almost all the herbage of the upland sheep-walks. This destruction took place, moreover, throughout an area which can hardly have been less than a thousand square miles.

Both in 1875 and 1890-92, the period of abundance was followed by the temporary reappearance of buzzards in some places and by a great abundance of short-eared owls (called at the time " the *new* owl ") and kestrels. The disappearance of the voles at the end of these plagues was catastrophic in speed and probably due to epidemic disease. It was followed by as equally rapid decrease in the numbers of short-eared owls, whose young (particularly) died in dozens when their food disappeared. The causes and frequency of these vole-plagues and, indeed, the whole question of number fluctuations in animal populations, is being investigated by Mr. Elton and his associates, who have drawn attention to the similarity between the vole plagues and those of lemmings in arctic and alpine Scandinavia and in Canada. They have demonstrated the cyclic nature of the number fluctuations, with a tendency for high numbers to occur every three or four years. In undeveloped countries, these are followed by corresponding cycles of predators such as foxes and owls.

One special reason for inquiring into these problems has been the very great extension of tree-planting by the Forestry Commission on areas of moorland or rough pasture. In the absence of sheep-grazing, the greater luxuriance of the grasses is exceptionally favourable to the development of small rodents like voles, and during a hard winter they may severely damage the young trees. On the Argyll hills, of which we have spoken elsewhere, there is no doubt ". . . that the vole fluctuations determine the local abundance from year to year, of such predators as feed on them : short-and long-eared owls, common buzzard, kestrel, fox and weasel."

A. D. Middleton has shown that similar fluctuations occur among other moorland animals, particularly red grouse, black grouse, blue hares and weasels. His data for red grouse, taken from three widely different localities in Cumberland, Lanarkshire and Aberdeenshire, are presented in Fig. 43. They show that the periodicity tends to be of a similar type in different places and that the peaks tend to be separated by a somewhat longer period, averaging 5·9 years, than that mentioned above.

Undoubtedly these cyclic fluctuations in numbers are part of a general biological tendency, which, as we have seen, is shown also in the " plagues " of the heather-beetle (*Lochmaea suturalis*) and of other insects. Although pheasants, which are not normally inhabitants of grouse-moors, have been observed to feed freely on heather-beetles, plagues of this insect have not so far been associated with a corresponding abundance of predators. Other similar examples are recognised, however. In some years on the moors and high fells there are produced great hordes of daddy-longlegs (*Tipula* spp.), of the bibionid (*Bibio lepidus*) and of bracken-clocks (*Phyllopertha horticola*), events which every fly-fisherman on the mountain lakes and tarns welcomes. So, too, do the local black-headed gulls which congregate in immense numbers to feed on these insects. Of late years, great numbers of caterpillars of the antler-moth (*Cerapteryx gramineus*) have also appeared locally and at infrequent intervals on the high grasslands of the Lake District and North Wales, and on these also black-headed gulls have fed freely. Even in Britain, therefore, great number fluctuations among

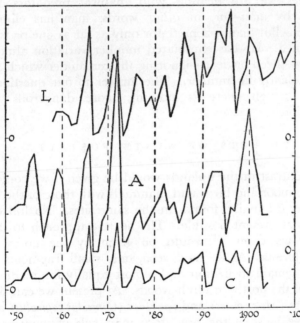

FIG. 44.—Periodic abundance and scarcity of grouse (data from Middleton). A, Aberdeenshire; C, Cumberland; L, Lanarkshire; Vertical scale-units are 1000 birds shot.

animals are not infrequent, and, of course, in arid and semi-desert countries, the great locust plagues have long excited wonder. The researches of Mr. Elton and his colleagues have led us to expect these large number fluctuations, but the question that is still awaiting solution is whether the fluctuations tend to become unusually large when the balance of nature is destroyed by the elimination of predators as in most of our British habitats.

We may suppose that in the natural state there is likely to be a number of species of predators preying on any one type of animal. If this latter type tends to increase greatly in number through some temporary change in environment or in its food supply, it seems reasonable to suppose that (as indeed is observed) its numbers will tend to be reduced by a greater production of its predators. In other words, the maximum number production of the animal preyed upon will be limited by the action of the predators—that is to say, the extreme oscillations in numbers will tend to be damped out. In the biotic communities we are dealing with, natural predators have been eliminated by man—or, in other words, man has eliminated his competitors. But man is a predator only as far as one or two animals are concerned. He has eliminated number variation almost entirely in his prey—sheep or deer—ignoring the remainder which apparently oscillate violently in number. The answer to our question seems to be clear, though there is nothing more dangerous than easy generalisation.

EFFECTS OF STATE FORESTS

The real contrast in the uplands would be given if we could compare the existing moorland birds and mammals with those of the woodlands which were, originally, found on the same sites. No full contrast of this type is at present possible. The nearest approach to the original woodlands we know of would be given by the north European coniferous forests. As we have seen, only small fragments of natural pine-forest remain in Britain and almost equally fragmentary are the remnants of the northern birch-woods. At present we can simply note that badgers (*Meles meles*) and roe-deer (*Capreolus capreolus*) are usually found, while most of the predatory mammals of moorland tend to find cover and shelter in our existing high-level woodlands—whether they are of pine or of birch or oak.

The old high-level forests in Britain were remnants of the northern forests mainly of pine, spruce and birch, which can still be studied elsewhere. In addition to the upland species still surviving and mentioned earlier, these usually contained :

Beaver, *Castor fiber*	Brown bear, *Ursus arctos*
Elk, *Alces alces*	Northern lynx, *Lynx lynx*
Swine, *Sus scrofa*	Wolf, *Canis lupus*
Wild ox, *Bos spp.*	

These existed, probably with red and roe-deer and many others, smaller ones of which we have no record. Four types of animals were probably sufficiently frequent to be important about the dawn of history—the two sorts of deer, swine, wolves and cattle. Of the latter, the original type of wild cattle was probably the urus (*Bos taurus primigenius*), a creature standing six feet high with long horns. There may also have been another less frequent species (*Bos frontosus*) with a heavy bone development between the horns. The Celtic ox (*Bos longifrons*), a smaller red-coloured beast, was probably introduced by Neolithic man.

The number of birds which may inhabit woodlands is, of course, very large, and we may perhaps be pardoned for limiting the present description, which must in any case be incomplete, to a very few essentials. The vestigial pine-forests contain certain distinctive birds—which are also equally characteristic of the northern coniferous forests. The characteristic birds of the Scottish pine-forests are the goldcrest (*Regulus regulus anglorum*), crested tit (*Parus cristatus scoticus*), siskin (*Carduelis spinus*), Scottish crossbill (*Loxia curvirostra scotica*), capercaillie (*Tetrao u. urogallus*), black grouse (*Lyrurus tetrix britannicus*), long-eared owl (*Asio o. otus*) and sparrow-hawk (*Accipiter n. nisus*).

Of these, the crested tit, crossbill and capercaillie are confined to this habitat. There are also many other birds which are numerous in these woods, especially perhaps the various tits and the tree-creeper (*Certhia familiaris*). Of the former, the great tit (*Parus major*), coal-tit (*P. ater*), blue tit (*P. caeruleus*) may be mentioned specially. Like the long-tailed tit (*Aegithalos caudatus*), these additional birds are widely spread in most upland woods, along with the chaffinch and willow-warbler (*Phylloscopus trochilus*), the latter of which, perhaps, prefers deciduous woodlands of oak and birch. The willow-tit (*Parus atricapillus*), in contrast, is confined to birch- and willow-woods.

M.M.   R

There is also another most interesting difference between the upland and lowland woods, partly exemplified in these pine-forests For the most part, the upland woods are poor in undergrowth and rarely have a shrub layer. It is generally found that the absence of this layer greatly reduces the bird fauna of a woodland. Thus conifer-woods, even at best, commonly have a much smaller bird population than do the mixed hardwood or deciduous woodlands of the lowlands. Such a wood might average one bird in a square with a side of about 30-35 yards, but in coniferous woodland the number is unlikely to attain even half this frequency.

It is probable that if estimates were available for the high-level oak or birch-woods a similar result would be obtained, for characteristics of these woods are the straight boles of the trees, the absence of shrubs and the somewhat uniform tree cover—all factors mitigating against the varied niches which woodland birds prefer.

One of the most recent of moorland transformations has been the tendency, especially during the last fifty years, towards the reafforesta-tion of British uplands. The numerous State Forests, in particular, are mainly on upland grasslands or on heather moorland, usually on land that has been woodland within the last thousand years or less. Hence they represent, in effect, the re-establishment of the original type of vegetation, though it must be remarked that, as we have seen, the tree species used are often exotic and that, in many cases, conifers are employed on what was originally deciduous woodland. Sheep are kept out of these plantations, and in their absence the grass grows thick, providing cover for small rodents, such as the field-vole (*Microtus agrestis*) and field-mouse (*Apodemus sylvaticus*), which thus tend to become very abundant, particularly where the plantation is introduced on grassland. This change in itself results in certain problems, for in developing their runways at and below the ground surface, the animals, particularly the voles, may damage the roots and, in severe winters particularly, they often eat the bark of the tree-seedlings. Considerable damage to the plantations may thus result, so much so, in fact, that in one district alone (Argyllshire) in 1929-30, a million young conifers were destroyed by voles. Associated with these in the plantations has been an abundance of owls, very often barn-owls at lower levels, or long-eared owls at higher levels, and in some cases short-eared owls feeding mainly on the voles.

The development of the plantation is, however, followed by

changes in the character of the animal population. When the trees are partly grown—five or six feet in height—the grass becomes shaded and there is a diminution in the population of ground animals and an increase in the birds, particularly of the willow-warbler (*Phylloscopus trochilus*). Still later comes a third phase when the trees are approaching their full stature, and at this time the lowest levels are nearly unoccupied, but wood-pigeons (*Columba palumbus*) and tits occupy the uppermost layers, often accompanied by the goldcrest. The natural history of these woodlands is thus not without ecologically distinctive features.

Still more interesting to naturalists has been a second result of increased afforestation ; a tendency for " dispossessed " species of animals to return to localities from which they had long been absent.

We already know that the increase in plantations of the last 50 years has led to great extensions of range by capercaillie (*Tetrao urogallus*), though, because of its fondness for nipping off the leading shoots of conifer stems, this bird is rather frowned upon by foresters. Jays and magpies, too, have spread, and the roe-deer, a small and mainly nocturnal forest species which perhaps survived as a native only in the Lake District and the Northern Highlands, is now reported from places whence there is no previous record. Similarly, the red squirrel, practically or quite extinct in Scotland, has now spread widely after reintroduction, showing a marked preference for coniferous woods.

It is likely also that species such as the badger, polecat and pine-marten, if not the wild cat, will develop greater frequency, and we may even hope to see such interesting northern birds as the common crossbill (*Loxia curvirostra*) as a more widely spread nesting species, though actually it is the continental form of this bird that shows a tendency to establish itself, while the Scots form shows little tendency to spread.

The practice of growing the trees in close canopy—so that they cast dense shade—means that there is neither shrub layer nor ground-flora. When such forests get above a certain size, therefore, they become extremely poor in bird life and, indeed, in the smaller woodland species of any sort, and they are from this point of view a new and still very unfavourable habitat.

Perhaps, however, if these forests finally come to be organised for continuous production and for constant regeneration, we may see something approaching their full fauna once more reconstituted.

CHAPTER 13

ANIMAL COMMUNITIES AND
THEIR HISTORY

GROUSE-MOOR

T H E red grouse (*Lagopus scoticus*) is unquestionably the most characteristic moorland bird in this country ; it has, moreover, the distinction of being our only *endemic* bird species—that is, one not found outside the British Isles. It is a species closely allied to the ryper or Scandinavian willow-grouse (*L. albus*), a sub-alpine and sub-arctic species which lives among the open margins of the northern forests. Red grouse lack the characteristic white winter plumage of the ryper, though they show a good deal of plumage variation, and white-flecked forms are not uncommon. While the ryper feeds on the young shoots and fruits of the willow, birch and bilberry, the red grouse feeds mainly on the young shoots of heather (*Calluna*) or crowberry (*Empetrum*), and it seems reasonable to associate its origin with the development of plant communities dominated by heather and with the replacement of former open woodland by heather-moor.

Because of their food requirements, grouse are found in the uplands wherever heather is abundant. The original natural habitat was no doubt heather-moor and the open heathery margins of the native pine-forests, and there are very extensive semi-natural heather-moors all down the eastern margin of the Highland zone in Britain, especially in Perthshire and Yorkshire. But sporting values have led to an enormous extension of this vegetation type in the interests of grouse preservation. Widespread drainage of the wetter moors has disturbed the natural balance of the vegetation, and, because the production of large numbers of grouse requires an abundant supply of young heather, frequent burning is resorted to, a practice which must have marked effects on the fauna and flora. There can be little doubt that this treatment has profoundly modified even the original heather-moors.

Grouse-moor is normally, therefore, a much modified relic of something which was once a natural vegetation and faunistic unit. The insect ecology of this type of vegetation has been dealt with elsewhere (see p. 222). But certain special creatures are directly associated with grouse on this type of moor. One of these is the beetle *Atomaria*

PLATE 29

John Markham

Northern eggar moth (*Lasiocampa callunae*), caterpillar. Forest of Bowland, October

PLATE 30

F. C. Pickering

PLATE 30   245
UPLAND MOTHS AND BUTTERFLIES

1
SCOTCH ARGUS
Erebia aethiops (Esper)

2
MOUNTAIN RINGLET
Erebia epiphron (Knoch)

3
BROAD-BORDERED WHITE
UNDERWING
Anarta melanopa (Thunb.)

4
SMALL DARK YELLOW
UNDERWING
Anarta cordigera (Thund.)

5
BEAUTIFUL YELLOW
UNDERWING
Anarta myrtilli (L.)

6
Coenonympha tullia
(Muller)

7
Coleophora caespititiella
(Zeller)

8
HAWORTH'S MINOR
Celaena haworthii
(Curtis)

9
SCOTCH OR MOUNTAIN
BURNET
Zygaena exulans
(Reiner and Hohenwarth)

10
FOX MOTH
Macrothylacia rubi (L.)

11
ARGENT AND SABLE
Eulype subhastata (Nolck.)

12
THE DRINKER
Philudoria potatoria (L.)

13
BLACK MOUNTAIN MOTH
Psodos coracina (Esper)

14
NORTHERN EGGAR
Lasiocampa callunae (Palmer)

15
NORTHERN DART
Amathes alpicola (Zett.)
subsp. *alpina* (Humphreys and Westwood)

gibbula, a form which lives only on the dung of grouse. An associated parasite is the thread-worm causing grouse-disease (*Trichostrongylus*), which lives on the heather and is taken into the digestive system of the birds. There it will pair with another individual and lay eggs that are passed out with the faeces. If conditions on the moor are not too dry, the thread-worm takes only a fortnight to reach maturity. Under modern conditions, moors are almost always overstocked for sporting purposes, and hence very rapid spreading of the disease takes place, so that a damp summer in particular is likely to cause widespread epidemics.

Some reference is desirable to the effects of grouse preservation on the moorland animals. Ruthless extermination has been the fate meted out to any bird or animal suspected of preying on either grouse or grouse eggs. The result is that out of the long list of birds and beasts of prey that formerly were to be found on our moorlands, only two, the kestrel and the merlin, are now to be seen regularly on grouse-moors. The former preys mainly on small rodents or on occasional birds, while the merlin is an interesting little hawk which feeds also to a considerable extent on small birds like meadow-pipits and on the larger insects, particularly large moths.

Although we can guess at the species formerly present, it is thus extremely difficult to imagine what proportions the fauna of a *natural* grouse-moor would show, for man has taken the place of the original predators and has, by measures of control such as frequent burning, no doubt greatly altered the minor faunal constituents. It is probable also that at present grouse-moors tend to be greatly over-stocked through artificial rearing and control of predators. A number of one to the acre has been recorded as possible in a good moor. It seems very unlikely that this is a natural density, and numbers in certain cases have fallen to one grouse to five acres, possibly a number more typical of a natural state. Our knowledge of other species suggests that each pair of birds will normally occupy a given territory and will do best if its normal density is not greatly exceeded. We provisionally say, then, that a square mile (640 acres) of heather-moor might contain as many as 320 grouse. It might probably also contain from 100 to 200 meadow-pipits and an unknown number of predatory mammals or birds.

DEER-FORESTS

The red deer (*Cervus elaphus scoticus*) is the largest native mammal found among our mountains and moorlands. Both the red deer and the roe-deer (*Capreolus capreolus*) are always regarded as true natives of Britain. Native roe-deer, however, now only survive among the older Lake District woodlands and in the remnants of the Scottish forests, though of late years they have tended to spread more widely once more. Red deer, on the other hand, are now an upland and moorland type not only in the Highlands of Scotland but also in the Lake District and as far south as Exmoor. There is no question about the continuity of the existing races of red deer and undoubtedly their survival has been due to their sporting value.

A characteristic deer-forest, in the Western Highlands for example, is generally composed mainly of some form of Scirpus-moor, with much sub-alpine grassland at higher levels, and generally also the remains of pine woodland (or plantations) and birch scrub just above the " straths " or valley bottoms. The amount of moorland varies a good deal ; it disappears on the steeper slopes (more than 1 in 4 or 5), and where the rocks are richer in lime or softer, more easily giving soil. Extensive areas of gently-sloping or flat moorland are not very suitable for deer, although the beasts resort to them in early spring to feed on the cotton-sedge. Usually deer-sedge (*Trichophorum caespitosum*) is a principal food-plant, but in high summer the deer move to the summits and so escape flies, and they then feed mainly on the grasses and mosses of the Rhacomitrium heaths and high grasslands.

These northern deer-forests are probably the least man-modified of our mountain or moorland areas. Here may still be seen the golden eagle, and occasionally near the coast, though it no longer breeds, the still larger sea-eagle, as well as smaller birds of prey. On the high tops are found the ptarmigan and the blue hare, both taking on a white coat in winter. The wild cat (*Felix silvestris*) is still frequent, and so, too, are ravens, carrion-crows and hooded crows, the last especially being often a pest along the seaward margins.

Few of these are large enough to affect red deer, and nowadays their principal enemies are probably foxes. These may attack the newly-born calves, when they are left alone for a time during the first three or four days after birth. Even at this stage the calf is generally too strong for wild cats to tackle, and the numbers killed by cats, and occasionally by eagles, are probably too small to have any serious consequences. In spite of the fact that large predators are nearly absent, it is estimated that under existing conditions only about half of the deer calves survive to the end of the first year of life, the other main cause of death being under-nourishment or disease at the end of the winter. Even so the population tends to increase slowly, and so a certain limited amount of shooting is necessary to prevent over-stocking. It is estimated that it is necessary to maintain about 25 deer on the forest for each one annually removed.

Fraser Darling's observations on a deer-forest show that the wild British red deer have a most interesting social organisation. It is based on the existence of small family groups, which include yearlings, two-year-olds and young hinds, all probably descendants of the oldest hind, which acts as leader of the group. Each group seems normally to keep to its own territory, especially during the colder months of the year. In high summer, however, when tabanid flies become a pest, it seems that the mountain summits are used more or less communally, the groups returning to their own territory as autumn comes. The stags tend to form small groups apart, commonly on quite different territories. Their groups break up when they join the hinds during the period of rut in October.

Darling suggests that this type of organisation has arisen in British red deer mainly because they have not been molested by animal predators (other than man) for the last 300 or 400 years. From ancient accounts of " tainchels," in which large numbers of deer were driven into a confined space and killed, there is some evidence that formerly British red deer lived in herds as do reindeer and other types of deer to-day. According to Darling, this herding tendency is observed in regions where the larger animal predators, wolves and the like, are still abundant, and he thinks that a similar tendency is noticeable among sheep. Our own moorland and mountain breeds of sheep are comparatively independent, often difficult to herd and roaming the hills in semi-isolation. Yet most other breeds of sheep, like the merino, show a marked tendency to flock, and these are the types used in countries where predators like wolves and pumas still exist.

The suggested change in the social organisation of red deer would undoubtedly agree with what we know of the history of the species in Scotland. Undoubtedly, very large changes in habit and habitat have taken place. J. Ritchie has pointed out that the modern red deer is small compared with those which were found in prehistoric times. The antlers of modern stags are often only one-half to two-thirds of the length of some of those recovered from peat. These may have from 19 to 22 points and exceed 3 ft. in length. A comparison of specimens in the Royal Scottish Museum showed that a good modern Royal, a 12-pointer, stood 3 ft. 5 in. high at the shoulder and was 5 ft. 7 in. long. A complete skeleton from a peat-moss in Haddingtonshire, also a 12-pointer and therefore a very moderate specimen compared with those mentioned above, nevertheless must have stood at least 4 ft. 6 in. at the shoulder and have had a body length of 7 ft. 10 in. In a word, it must have been at least a third as large again as a selected modern example and probably weighed twice as much. Undoubtedly, therefore, there has been a very great decrease in size in red deer as we know them to-day.

The red deer was, however, formerly a woodland animal, and in prehistoric times it was distributed over the whole country, lowland as well as upland. This is conclusively proved by the remains found in peat deposits and bogs and in the kitchen middens associated with prehistoric man, even if it were not well attested by historical evidence, such as the location of Norman deer-forests. Red deer have, then, been ousted from the woodlands and the lowlands, and Dr. Julian Huxley has shown that the altered habitat has been associated with reduced size and proportionate changes in antler type which can reasonably be attributed to the reduced fertility of the modern habitat. There are still to be found in the continental forests of Europe descendants of the native red deer (subspecies *Cervus elaphus typicus* and *C. elaphus germanicus*), which in size and antler-spread resemble those from prehistoric British specimens, and it seems, therefore, that the native red deer has retained its size where it has been allowed to remain in the original type of habitat. Moreover, even in Scotland to-day, a fair correlation can be made out between the vegetation types or fertility of the area and the size of the deer and antler types obtained from it. It has been stated on good authority that an experienced judge can name the particular Scottish deer-forest from which any given specimen of stag is derived.

Finally, when the Scottish red deer have been transported elsewhere into open woodland, a corresponding increase in size has taken place, a notable example being that of the Scottish red deer introduced in North Otago, New Zealand. These, at the end of 50 years after introduction, had entirely regained the original prehistoric standard of size and antler-spread.

There is one other curious feature of the modern red deer. They do not take kindly to crowding and consequently a density of about one deer to 30 acres is about the maximum number a deer-forest will normally support. On the stonier and poorer forests there are even fewer deer—not more than one to between 40 and 60 acres. It was found by H. Evans that on the Isle of Jura (27,500 acres) there were about 2,000 red deer. While the best areas carried one deer per 10 acres, a more common density was one to 20 acres. There is much evidence, however, that conditions on Jura were very favourable and that it was probably much overstocked.

It is noticeable also that red deer tend to avoid sheep-ground. Partly this may be due to the visits of the shepherds and their dogs, but even where those visits are infrequent, the more numerous sheep (one to every 3 to 5 acres) seem to "crowd out" the deer. This often has very striking results. For example, sheep have been introduced or increased in numbers on many forests during the late war. They tend to accumulate on the best grazing ground and, in consequence, to drive the deer from it. In some cases, noticeably on the island of Rhum, where human interference has been negligible, there has resulted a natural segregation of two almost completely distinct animal communities, deer-forests on the rockier or more peaty ground, and sheep-walk on the grass-covered slopes of Fionchre and Bloodstone Hill. This is, in origin, a geological separation—deer-forest on the poorer Torridonian sandstones and the harder igneous rocks, and sheep-walk on the softer and chemically richer basaltic rocks.

SHEEP-WALK

It is probable that this type of replacement has taken place very frequently in the past, and, if we may judge by the recent experiences mentioned above, it probably tended to take place to a greater or lesser extent wherever sheep were introduced. The extent to which replacement then took place would primarily depend on the general vegetation types. Areas with rocks tending to give soils richer in lime would, presumably, most easily become sheep-walk, irrespective of special efforts by man to convert them. On the other hand, large areas of the Highlands have maintained themselves as semi-natural deer-forests, in spite of determined efforts to convert them to sheep-walk in the early nineteenth century. Later, of course, the high sporting value which became attached to deer-stalking led to the maintenance of deer-forests in which sheep-rearing has been almost or entirely suppressed. In contrast to these areas, we observe that certain mountain areas have become almost wholly sheep-walk. These areas include much of the Welsh mountains, the Lake District and large areas in the Southern Uplands of Scotland, areas in which the underlying rocks, though hard, have a moderately high lime content and in which consequently the soils are often not excessively base-deficient. On these areas to-day, semi-natural Festuca-Agrostis grass-lands are the most important type of vegetation, covering all the steeper slopes and usually changing over, as the rainfall increases or the slope decreases, to wet Nardus-Juncus (*squarrosus*) grass-heaths or, on plateau-tops, to Scirpus or cotton-sedge moor. The whole tendency in the Lake District and the Welsh mountains (as in many parts of the Southern Uplands) seems to be to treat the mountain sheep-walk or farm as a natural unit. It is bought or sold with its native flock of sheep. They know its features and, in practice, each ewe, feeding singly or, more often, with a lamb and possibly last year's yearling, is generally to be found in the same localities. However, when bad weather is coming or is long continued, they will work down to lower and more sheltered regions. They are left more or less entirely to themselves. Formerly they were only brought down from the moun-tains twice a year, for lambing and for shearing, though nowadays round-ups for dipping against disease are also added. Under these conditions, a density of one sheep to three acres of mountain repre-sents a good average, which can be exceeded only on exceptionally good land or with the aid of winter feeding. Incidentally, it is of interest to note that the mountain-bred sheep are difficult to feed in this way as they often refuse hay or special foods.

Under the semi-natural conditions under which they are kept, mountain sheep are liable to various diseases and, like deer, par-ticularly to those caused by insects. To eliminate these, sheep-dipping is therefore almost universal under modern conditions and, of course, is compulsory in areas where " scab " is prevalent. The dips employed are usually arsenical solutions, primarily to prevent infection by

" scab " but also to keep down attacks by flies and sheep-ticks. Sheep-scab is due to small animals, mites (Acarina), that eat into the skin and cause a raw wound to develop. The sheep-tick (*Ixodes ricinus*) is also technically a mite that burrows into the skin and sucks blood from the animal, though incidentally it is not averse from human blood. Indeed it is difficult to control because it infests almost every moorland animal as well as some birds (e.g. grouse, crow, golden plover, kestrel and merlin) if not all. Apart from the drain on blood-supply that heavy infestation might produce, sheep-ticks are dangerous because they are also the carriers of two or three virus diseases that infect cattle and deer. The question of eliminating sheep-ticks is thus practically very important, made more difficult no doubt by the humid conditions which favour many forms of invertebrate life in the larval stages.

In addition to these mites, there are other parasitic creatures, particularly a wingless fly belonging to the Diptera (*Melophagus ovinus*) which lives on sheep in a somewhat similar manner. Finally, there is a blow-fly (the green bottle-fly, *Lucilia sericata*), whose larvae cause open wounds to develop, particularly on exposed, dirty or damaged places. All of these infections have their counterpart among deer.

There is, however, one disease of sheep which is not paralleled among deer : the malady known as " liver-rot." This is caused by the liver-fluke (*Fasciola hepatica*), a parasitic flatworm which lives in the liver of sheep and which formerly was responsible for losses in the United Kingdom amounting to a million or more sheep in the year. The liver-fluke is of interest because it has two main stages in the life-cycle. The eggs of the fluke are voided from the sheep in its faeces and they develop into a larval form which, for a time, swims about in water or in moisture films and dies unless it is able to reach its second host, a snail (*Limnaea truncatula*), which is common in fresh water or damp pastures. The larva enters the snail either by the pulmonary tract or by penetrating the tissues, and after passing through additional larval stages, it escapes as a mobile form which encysts on the water or on vegetation. Given suitable humidity, it may survive in the encysted form for as much as 12 months, and only develops further after being swallowed by the final host (normally a sheep). Considering the great humidity of so many upland habitats in Britain, the relative scarcity of liver-fluke in the upland sheep-

PLATE 31

B. A. Crouch

a. Keswick, Cumberland: Druids' Circle

F. Fraser Darling

b. Morven, Argyll: black-faced sheep at shearing-time

PLATE 32

John Markham

Penmachno, Caernarvonshire: State forest plantations

walks is rather surprising. No doubt it can be attributed very largely to the non-calcareous nature of the water supplies and the resultant scarcity or localised distribution of *Limnaea truncatula*.

It is unfortunate that sheep-breeding activities of the last 150 years have greatly obscured the history of our breeds of mountain sheep, for some of the " improved " breeds, though valuable enough in their respective spheres, have tended to lose the particular characteristics which seem to have been common to the original mountain races. As we know them, the original mountain types had in common a small size (ewes under 20 to 22 in.) and a somewhat light fleece which in the ewes weighed from 1½ to 2½ lb. The fleece had, moreover, two components, relatively long coarse hairs (" kemp ") and a short close wool. The fleece was often coloured, usually brownish or blackish, and the ewes had short horns. The small size of these sheep, of course, militates against their value as meat-producers, high although the quality of meat may be, while the short and coarse fleece only commands a good price in seasons of wool scarcity or when particular types of coarse cloth are fashionable. Nevertheless, experienced mountain farmers of Herdwicks or Welsh Mountain breeds consider that the character of the fleece, and particularly the presence of kemp, confers or is correlated with hardiness and an ability to withstand bad weather, which makes these breeds able to survive independently on the mountain.

We are not able to say whether our British sheep were derived from an indigenous wild form, feeding on the high crags and sub-alpine grasslands as do the wild sheep of to-day ; or whether they were already semi-domesticated when introduced. It is certain that the remains of Neolithic man in Britain and all over Europe are associated with a small goat-like sheep known as the peat sheep or Turbary sheep (*Ovis aries palustris*). It may be, then, that when Neolithic man came to Britain, he may have introduced this sheep even if a wild native race was already present. The nearest modern representative of the Turbary sheep seems to be the original native sheep of the Shetland Isles. The verbal descriptions already given of the common characters of the mountain races would fit both these breeds fairly well, although actually they are relatively long-legged and much more like a goat in build. The Shetland sheep also have short dun-coloured fleeces weighing only about 2 lb. and, like the Turbary sheep, have short tails containing only 13 vertebrae, in contrast to the 20 or more vertebrae in modern domestic breeds. The short goat-like cones in the horns of the ewes and the slender build no doubt accounts for the frequency with which the remains of Neolithic Turbary sheep are called " sheep or goats." Whenever they have been examined by experts, however, they have proved to be the bones of Turbary sheep, and in Britain they have been recorded not only with Neolithic man but also from Bronze Age finds, lake-dwellings and elsewhere, from Roman camps and Romano-British sites and from hill forts and " brochs," some of which were inhabited until the Middle Ages. Even much later, various details, remarked by medieval travellers in Britain, occasional complaints to the Cistercian abbeys about the quality of north-country wool and the like, all seem to suggest that the small-horned peat sheep, dun-coloured and hardy, were the immediate precursors of the mountain sheep as we know them to-day. Peat or Turbary sheep are only known in association with man but they bear a general resemblance in form to the wild Asiatic urial (*Ovis vignei*), and hence it is generally assumed that they were derived from a similar stock. The Urial is, however, a far larger beast, commonly standing 30-35 in. at the shoulder, while in its fleece the hair is much more prominent, with very short wool beneath. It has, however, the same type of horn as the peat sheep.

Another possible ancestral type of wild sheep is the now scarce mouflon (*Ovis musimon*), which still survives in Corsica and Sardinia. Principal differences from the urial are the smaller size (height about 25-29 in.), the absence of horns in the ewes and the foxy red of the colouring. It is considered probable that this is the type from which the Soay sheep have been derived. The uninhabited island of Soay, far out in the Atlantic, still supports a native race of sheep of distinctive characters which formerly are also believed to have been present in the neighbouring island of Hirta, another of the St. Kilda group. Before the evacuation of the inhabitants of the St. Kilda group in 1930, men from Hirta occasionally used to visit Soay to round up and pluck the wool of some of the sheep, but they are for all practical purposes wild. After the evacuation in 1930 Hirta, the only inhabited island of St. Kilda, was cleared of ordinary sheep and stocked with the animals from Soay; and the herds on Soay and Hirta now number some hundreds. The skeletal characters and goat-like movements of the Soay sheep are identical with those of the mouflon, but their fleeces differ markedly, in that a short and close wool is the predominant feature. The weight of the fleece, however, is generally less than 1 lb. One other feature of interest about these sheep is that there is evidence (*vide* Ritchie) that they have been the same essentially since the early sixteenth century, while the name of the island, Soay, is of Norse derivation, meaning Sheep Island.

HISTORY OF ANIMAL COMMUNITIES

The animal communities which have just been surveyed are, on the whole, man-induced ones, although probably each contains a nucleus of something which existed under wholly natural conditions. In the light of what we already know, it is interesting to try and trace the development of these faunistic groupings, even though we must often rely on vague indications of what actually happened. The general sequence of events can easily be outlined. There must always have been large expanses of upland bog and of mountain rocks, and below these the upland forests which have now vanished. The general trends in this topographical system have clearly been towards the extension of bog and *mor* soils and their associated vegetation. In a broad way, this has meant chiefly the disappearance of woodland, a vegetational change that has been accelerated by the effects of man and grazing animals, and which in turn has apparently led to further leaching and bog extension. This general drift must have thus followed an ecological pattern, and we are really concerned with the relation between this pattern and the animal groupings. Evidently, from what has already been said, the controlling influences have been not only the change in the vegetation, which affects shelter as well as the type of ecological niche available for animals, but there must also have been the immensely important decline in the size and nutritive value of the vegetation, which runs parallel to the progress of soil-leaching and the development of oligotrophic peats.

As far as primitive man was concerned, the great areas of peat-bog must have presented inherent stability on account of their size and volume. They included nothing attractive to man. Hence, modification must have been slow, marginal and often negligible. It could have resulted in little but a drift in the qualitative nature of the mainly plant-eating invertebrate fauna, though doubtless heather-eating insects and birds may also have become more numerous.

While the degeneration of upland woodlands produced more striking changes, it must not be considered as resembling the wholesale clearances which have followed agricultural exploitation in modern times, as, for example, in North America. Primitive man would, at first, be mainly a hunter and at most concerned with maintaining the animal stock, perhaps finally exerting the sort of control of forest resources that was practised by the native Indians in the forested uplands of New York State—a periodic burning of openings in the forest in order to maintain park-like grazing conditions attractive to deer. This is evidently a very ancient way of husbanding forest resources. From this to the development of a pastoral culture seems a small step. It means either the introduction of animals capable of domestication (cattle), or if they were present in the wild state, a weighting of faunistic development by favouring in some way the creatures useful to man. In the northern forests thes would be mainly cattle and swine. Presumably one way in which this was done was by eliminating the predators. So long as the larger predators, like wolves, remain, the possible domesticated animals are likely to be those which are to some degree capable of self-defence, as are herds of cattle. Sheep, among the most defenceless of creatures, are not likely to become abundant until the larger predators have become nearly eliminated. Moreover, and possibly partly for similar reasons, they are animals of open grasslands and low herbage. Thus the ecological pattern which must have been followed was probably of the general type :

forest $\longrightarrow$	*open woodland, scrub* $\longrightarrow$ *and parkland*	*grassland*
deer	cattle	sheep
swine	swine	
wild cattle	deer few	
predators typical and many	predators fewer	predators few or none

This is admittedly a crude representation, complicated by the probability of an altitudinal zonation which might have followed a similar pattern, for we know that the early inhabitants often lived among the open upper margins of the woodlands.

These changes of biological pattern do not take place rapidly; they are induced mainly by slow drifts in the balance of vegetation or of animal types. Even when man, with the acquisition of iron tools, obtained greater mastery over the forest, such drifts may have taken

PLATE XXIX

R. Brinsden

Evening cloud, Langdale, Lake District

PLATE XXX

Aerofilms

North Wales: aerial view SSW over the Llugwy valley from above Capel Curig. The peak on the right is Moel Siabod, and those in the left distance are Moelwyn and Cynicht. The view shows the middle hills which are "the traditional home of the original Celtic settlers" many generations rather than the one or two which have often sufficed for wholesale forest clearance in recent history. If, for example, we judge from what happened in Northern England, such changes may have taken, in some places, 2,000 or 3,000 years and at their most rapid (in Iron Age times) could not have occupied less than 300 or 400.

In lowland areas in North-west Europe, changes of this type generally began in Neolithic times and, as Dr. Grahame Clark has showed, they were generally becoming more or less complete by the time iron was being widely used. There was, of course, also an associated spread of agriculture in the lowlands, a feature which was probably much less general in the uplands on account of the unfavourable climate. Finally, when sheep became plentiful, the use of vegetable fibres for making fabrics diminished, wool becoming the commonest medium for this purpose. In England these changes can be traced on and around the downs, and presumably similar ones might have been found on the Derbyshire and Craven limestones.

Generally, however, in highland Britain, these processes went on more slowly and at widely different times. An interesting glimpse of them is that obtained from the study of animal remains in Neolithic kitchen-middens. An extremely complete series of these kitchen middens was discovered on the islands of Colonsay and Oronsay, off Western Scotland, and these were carefully explored by Mr. Symington Grieve. Colonsay and Oronsay are closely adjacent islands, and one can pass from one to the other, dry shod, at low tide. From the kitchen midden deposits examined, which were composed mainly of shells, it was possible to estimate the frequency of bones of different types of animals at different levels in the deposits.

The results of these observations showed that the original inhabitants of these islands were mainly hunters and shell-fish gatherers. They were dependent upon red deer and swine for their animal food, presumably hunting them in the woodlands which then covered the islands. In the upper deposits, however, cattle and sheep became common, while the bones of red deer and swine disappeared, with the obvious suggestion of a replacement comparable to that observed in recent times. We have, then, very interesting evidence of what looks like a transformation of a hunting into a pastoral people.

A second interesting feature of this example is the comparatively early date at which the change from one type to another took place.

M.M.   S

No doubt it would be much easier to eliminate predators (if present) at an early stage on islands, and this may be an additional reason for the early disappearance of forest all through the western isles.

At any rate, the process of forest degeneration was often, if not always, very much slower on the mainland, and an appropriate moment to examine its biological aspects is when written history first began to accumulate for the uplands, at the beginning of the twelfth century. Northern England at that time was still recovering from that " wasting of the north " by William the Norman, that has been compared in effect to the passing of an ice-age. Its recovery was based mainly on the establishment of huge cattle-farms or ranches, " vaccaries " in medieval Latin, which must ultimately have covered most of the upland margins and valleys as well, perhaps, as great areas of lowland. They left their mark particularly among the Central Pennines as place-names involving " stall " and " booth." Around these vaccaries the cattle wintered ; in summer they spread far over the higher hills.

In some areas, like Bowland Forest and Wyresdale in Lancashire, Inglewood Forest and other parts of Northumbria, this form of utilisation persisted long, and even to-day tradition and folk-lore tell of the fierce cattle which ran wild or semi-wild through the ancient valley woodlands. There are grounds for believing that north of the Border there were many similar areas.

Contemporaneous with these vaccaries was the establishment of royal and baronial forests (in the legal sense), which seems to suggest that the lowland woodlands were in a somewhat scrappy condition or so much disturbed that it was necessary to preserve certain areas for the hunting of deer and other game animals. At any rate, the sites of these hunting forests serve to indicate the places where deer, and normally their natural predators, were still abundant. In Northern Britain, the " forests " were already mainly confined to the foothills and the uplands or to occasional patches of poor soil outside the Highland zone, such as the poor gravels and sands of Sherwood and Delamere.

In most of Wales conditions seem to have been more settled and more populous than they were in Northern England. Cattle-rearing was the principal occupation, although the available references suggest that the animals were much more domesticated. The twelfth-century Giraldus Cambriensis tells us that the Welsh were indifferent to commerce and manufactures. They lived in a solitary manner among the woods, feeding on the produce of their herds, milk, cheese and butter, and eating flesh in larger proportions than their oaten bread. Their traditional home was the middle hills between the heights of 800 and 1,600 ft. (Pl. XXX, p. 257), now mostly moorland and damp grassland, but then presumably at least partly woodland. By the time we are speaking of however they were settling at lower levels, returning again to summer habitations, often apparently at a higher level or more exposed.

The other notable development of this period was one which was destined to change the face of Northern England completely. It was at this time (*ca.* A.D. 1130 to 1150) that the Cistercian monks began to found their abbeys. The generosity of their patrons seems to have been expressed mainly in grants of land outside the pale of such civilisation as existed, and in or on the margin of the uplands.

In the course of the next 100 years, these monasteries had acquired a wealth and an influence which seems remarkable when one considers that they were on the borders of the wild and that, often, as one ancient writer remarks, there was neither soil to grow crops nor sun to ripen them. At Jervaulx, indeed, said to be second richest abbey in Yorkshire at the time of the Dissolution, the country was so desolate that the parent body of Savigny could not believe that the abbey could ever become self-supporting and so, for long, refused to accept its incorporation. The list of assets proudly displayed at the time, by the Jervaulx monks, included 40 cows, 16 mares (recently given by their patron, Earl Conan), 5 sows, and 300 sheep. In the last item lay the clue to ultimate prosperity, for the wealth of the Cistercian abbeys in the north was founded on their sheep and on the wool trade resulting from them.

The spread of the Cistercian order seems to have been the most potent factor in the biological history of the highland zone or, at least, the factor whose importance we can most easily recognise. The Cistercians were predominantly farmers and by far the largest part of their income was derived from wool. In assessing their influence it should be remembered that their example was later followed by the abbeys of other monastic orders settled near the highland zone. Moreover, even the large flocks of sheep maintained by the great northern abbeys were quite insufficient to account for the extent of their trade in wool. They were evidently, although it was contrary to the rules of the order, wool merchants and exporters on a very large scale. Thus their influence spread through the whole rural economy. Instead of a mode of life in which a man maintained flocks sufficient for his own needs, a new system arose in which for the first time large-scale economic exploitation of the highland zone was possible.

So began the movement that in the next 500 years was finally to convert much of highland Britain into sheep-walk. Little by little the wandering ewes destroyed the oak-wood, the hazel and the birch scrub. The " golden hoof of the sheep," according to the Spanish proverb, turned mossland into cotton-sedge and heather-moor into mat-grass. The harassed deer, working from one fastness to another, became fewer and fewer, until finally, from Trent to Tweed, few or none remained.

The decay of the deer-forests thus proceeded steadily after the twelfth century, even in the wild north. Not only were the monastic sheep-runs ever expanding (like those of Fountains Abbey, for example, which had one of 100,000 acres in the Craven Uplands and controlled at least a million acres there), but men's minds revolted at the idea of nearly one-third of the country being alienated by the Crown from productive use. Moreover, even kings were not averse from following the profitable example of their monkish subjects, for we read of James V of Scotland, about 1530, running 10,000 sheep in his forest of Ettrick, when long continued peace had made this possible. It can hardly be doubted that others also sought to follow these examples. Thus by 1550, when Leland's *Itineraries* were compiled, the places where deer were still evident enough for comment were becoming few, and at the close of the Middle Ages we can picture the general distribution of deer in the middle part of the highland zone as shown in Fig. 45. This figure is probably reasonably complete for Northern England, but more data for Scotland would be welcome. Even so, it shows very clearly how deer had disappeared from the vicinity of the Cistercian abbeys, a distribution that is at least suggestive of the biological effects of the Cistercian rural economy.

The period figured—about 1550—is evidently a second one which might be usefully employed for a sort of biological stocktaking in Britain. At this time the Pennines had been almost wholly turned into sheep-walk, although the absence of near-by abbeys, as well as their natural characters, had to some extent preserved the Stainmore Bogs and the Bowland Forest area. In the Bowland Forest as well as in Northumbria much woodland and herds of semi-wild cattle still per-

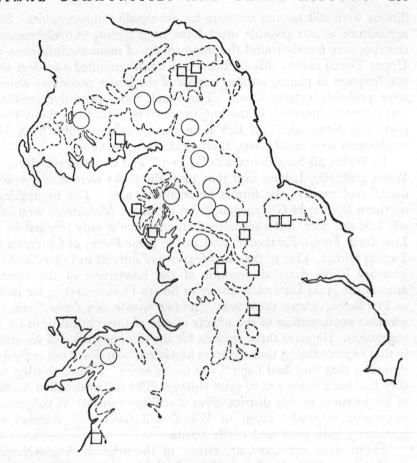

FIG. 45.—Distribution of red deer about 1550 A.D. (from Leland), as circles, and of Cistercian Abbeys (squares), suggesting that the latter as centres of sheep-rearing had limited the range of red-deer.

sisted. Over most of the Pennines, however, Leland's evidence alone shows that woodland remains could have been little more than scrub, while the wild red deer only persisted in the more remote areas. The Lake District woods must have been almost completely destroyed at this time and the hills were probably almost wholly sheep-walks, among which red deer lingered only in the wilder fastnesses of the Ennerdale and Martindale Fells. Along the Border, however, conditions were still far too insecure for wholesale improvements. Such agriculture as was possible must have been almost entirely pastoral, centring very largely round the main sphere of monastic influence, the Upper Tweed valley. Much forest and scrub remained and deer were still frequent in places, although most of the larger predatory animals were probably exterminated. The much more primitive condition was reflected, however, in the large exports of hides from the adjacent ports like Newcastle. At this time most southern ports from Hull southwards were wool ports, their trade still growing.

In Wales, all Snowdonia was " forest " and had still red deer. Of Wales generally, Leland says that even the parks were now " void of deer," and most of the forests he mentions also. The mountainous northern borders of Glamorgan, from the Black Mountains westward, still had red deer, but elsewhere their presence is only implied in the Llwydarth Forest, Pembroke, and in the great Forest of Clune on the English border. One of the chief features of interest in Leland's Welsh itinerary is his detailed account of the barrenness of the country around the great Cistercian abbey of Strata Florida and as far inland as Plynlimon, where there was " nother woode nor corne," an eye-witness's confirmation of the effects of one of these institutions on the vegetation. He gives three reasons for the disappearance of woodland in that region: firstly, that the trees had been " cut down not copsed " ; secondly, that they had been " too much eaten " ; and, thirdly, that they had been destroyed to evict thieves. The rather detailed account of his journeys in this district gives a striking contrast to the general impression otherwise given of Wales, still fairly well wooded and producing both corn and cattle pasture.

Sheep were unimportant, either in the original Anglo-Norman manorial tenure or in the traditional Welsh economy. Thus sheep-rearing did not become extensive in Wales until after the Dissolution of the monasteries when the small gentry acquired the monastic estates. They then adopted the practices of the monkish farmers and extended them to the whole country. The resultant extension of the wool trade brought them wealth. They built large houses in the valleys and finally cleared the valley bottoms. Thus rural life came more and more to desert the traditional home of the Celtic settlers, the rolling and boulder-clay covered uplands from 800 to 1,500 ft., although the utilisation of the uplands increased once more from then onwards. The clearing of the impenetrable valley woods sounded the death-knell of the remaining predators, and wolves finally became extinct about the end of the sixteenth century.

In contrast, the great mass of the Central Highlands of Scotland was still in a primitive state, mainly wild moorland or more dangerous forests in which still roamed innumerable wolves, many red deer, probably some bears and possibly even elks. Contemporary historians are at one in describing appalling conditions north of the Highland line, owing to the abundance of wolves. So dangerous was travelling in that area that the great pine forests of Rannoch and Lochaber were all but impassable, and hospices, or spittals (e.g. the Spittal of Glenshee) were set up for travellers caught by night in this region. For long, head-money had been offered for wolf-killing, but finally it seems to have been decided that only the destruction of the forests would abate the plague. So began burnings, attested both by local tradition and more definite record, that destroyed the forests round Lochaber and Loch Awe and through Rannoch and Atholl. A hundred years later, in 1680, the last wolf of which there is certain record was killed in Perthshire, though about the same time another had been slain in Forfarshire. Nevertheless, isolated individuals may have lingered in the far north, for persistent tradition maintains that another was killed by a hunter named Macqueen in 1743.

The state of the Scottish Highlands in the early sixteenth century suggests that these mountains were still in a very primitive condition, and from the little that is known of their animal life it seems that in addition to wolves, they still harboured the brown bear, and even the elk may have been present. At this time also, Bishop Leslie of Rosse has described very clearly the almost wild herds of cattle found in Argyll and Inverness, creatures avoiding man, subject to no control and receiving no shelter—though apparently they might be fed in bad weather. These were probably ancestors of the modern Highland Kyloe, and descendants, no doubt, of types such as the ancient Celtic cattle (*Bos taurus longifrons*), a race whose remains, like those of Turbary sheep, are generally associated with man.

Another very interesting contrast is implied in Bishop Leslie's records. For although he gives a very clear account of the great flocks of sheep to be seen in the Tweed valley, in the vicinity of several great abbeys among the southern uplands, he makes no reference to sheep in the Highlands but only to cattle. It is thus reasonable to assume that sheep, the most defenceless of animals in the presence of large predators, were absent in the conditions existing north of the Highland line. Wolves had been exterminated by this time in Northern England and the southern uplands of Scotland. These and other facts suggest that the Highlands were at that time passing through a biological phase, very near the phase of primary utilisation, characterised by frequent woodland remains, large predators, some like wolves, being numerous, and large herbivores like red deer and cattle but few of the smaller ones. In the next 200 years conditions steadily changed, and towards the latter part of the eighteenth century there remained only five ancient deer-forests, mostly high ground and poor, though deer were still frequent over a wide range in the high hills. Most of the rest of the land was held and used on a co-operative basis derived from the old clan system, in which communal grazings, mainly for cattle, figured prominently, and such arable land as was used was worked on the old run-rig system. This was essentially the traditional Celtic system, which we have already met in Wales as early as the twelfth century. It is probable that there was a slow drift towards the characteristic sheep-walk already predominant in other parts of the highland zone and even then operating in the Western Isles and along the western seaboard, where it had doubtless been developed by the Norse. If this drift existed, it was rudely accelerated after 1800 because of the high prices for wool and mutton induced by the Napoleonic wars. All over the Scottish Highlands there was the creation of large-scale sheep-farms, a development involving the eviction of the native population whose labour was no longer required, hurried through at a tremendous cost in human misery to forestall a possible collapse in prices.

The period that followed 1800 must, biologically, have resembled that following the economic developments instituted by the Cistercian abbeys in Northern England. It would probably be worth studying in detail from that point of view. The process, though much more intense, was, however, not allowed to go to completion. Before the Highlands had become wholly sheep-walk, the great wealth accruing to Victorian England from industrial expansion and, no doubt, the example of the Queen and Prince Consort in popularising country life and sports in the Highlands, led about the 1850s to an enormous extension of deer-forests and grouse-moors, and these have persisted until the present. The forests restricted to deer in the pre-1940 era numbered nearly 200 and covered approximately three and a half million acres—that is, about one-fifth of Scotland—and over the whole of this area sheep-rearing was practically suppressed.

The economic and social problems raised by these transformations, grave though they are, do not concern us here. The evidence suggests that the biological degeneration of the original forest-moor-mountain system in the highland zone has taken place in two well-marked stages, an earlier one in which persisted extensive fragments of forest and scrub peopled by large herbivores and numerous carnivores and by men with a Neolithic-Celtic mode of life, at first mainly upland. This no doubt would tend naturally but slowly to drift towards a later stage in which both woodland and to a large extent the original moors and mosses had been converted *by grazing pressure* to a form of sheep-walk, on which trees were absent and from which the larger predators were of necessity banished.

This survey of the history of our upland areas suggests not only that we can distinguish certain phases in this development under human influence, but also that the transformations have been characterised by certain ecological peculiarities. From this general biological point of view, it seems also that a reduction in the size of the dominant vegetation and the lowering of the nutritive levels has been correlated with a tendency towards decreased animal size. This is seen not only in comparing the more abundant animals with their successors, deer and cattle with sheep, wolves and bears with foxes, pine-martens and polecats with weasels and stoats, but it seems also to have characterised the sizes of individual species, as, for example, red deer, mountain-hares and wild cats (see Ritchie), although the danger here is obviously that of comparing animals nurtured in a lowland environment in prehistoric times with those now living on high and infertile moorlands or mountains. Nevertheless, if we survey the whole field of animal history in Northern Britain, it can be very clearly recognised that the tendency has been for the larger mammals to be replaced by smaller ones. This tendency can, perhaps, be made out in the lists of species already given.

The information derived from the study of the animal communities is of value in one other way. It gives us at least a preliminary basis for assessing the degree of modification the plant and animal communities have undergone. This is a very important feature in dealing with the vegetation, for to a very large extent the condition of the woodland and bog vegetation in the different parts of the highland zone reflects the amount of disturbance it has suffered, and the same conclusion seems to apply to the invertebrate fauna. Of course both climate and topography have also an effect in altering the rate of modification. However, if we can estimate the extent of human influence, however roughly, it should be possible to arrange the different upland regions in an order which would express approximately their place in the sequence of modification.

A principal factor in the past has been accessibility, and although almost every upland locality really requires individual treatment, it is possible to indicate in very broad outline certain features which should be considered in dealing with their relative status.

It has often been pointed out that the physical characters of the Cornish peninsula and of most of the Welsh uplands have always laid them open to human penetration. The early occupation by man, which is known to have resulted, makes it probable, therefore, as was first suggested by Clement Reid, that their plant and animal communities as a whole are far from primitive. In contrast, the Lake District and the Western Highlands in North Britain share a large measure of comparative inaccessibility from the eastern lowlands, as well as the barrier of a high annual rainfall, which is a most important distinguishing climatic feature. In early times this area apparently received its population mainly from the sea. The Neolithic settlers we have already met within the Lake District, spread in like manner into Galloway, Arran and the Firth of Clyde. They appeared also in Skye and the Outer Hebrides (Uist and Benbecula), while what was possibly a later or derived population left numerous traces in Caithness, Orkney and around the Moray Firth (see Fig. 47, p. 268). The main period of marked human influence in the west was, however, that of the Viking settlements in the ninth and tenth centuries. In contrast, this came southwards via the Orkneys and it heavily affected Caithness, Wester Ross and the outer islands, extending down the coastal fringe again as far as the Isle of Man and the Lake District (see Fig. 46, p. 267). The early pattern of human influence must thus have resembled that of the Lake District both in general character and in becoming severe after the Viking settlements. The curious reader will find it interesting to note the close relation of the distribution of the Viking occupation shown in Fig. 46, and the " grass-heath " described by Marcel Hardy, which occurs over precisely the same seaward and western margins north of the Great Glen. Later,

FIG. 46.—The Viking settlements of the western highlands and islands.

perhaps, exploitation lagged behind in the Scottish Highlands and human influence on the mainland must have remained small until iron-smelting spread inland on a larger scale in the eighteenth century with a consequent destruction of forest. In the western islands, however, legend ascribes to the Vikings and to the quarrels among their war-leaders, so much forest destruction that the present nearly treeless condition of the islands might well have resulted at an early date from the results of the Neolithic and Viking occupations.

FIG. 47.—The distribution of megalithic monuments.

The archæological records for Eastern Britain reveal a different state of affairs. There were both more extensive and more numerous influxes of human invaders between the Moray Firth and the Humber. The " Beaker " people and possibly others in the Bronze Age were followed by pre-Roman invaders using iron, and it is probable, as F. Elgee showed in north-east Yorkshire, that as the Iron Age invaders advanced, the earlier Neolithic peoples were driven into the moorland areas. In their turn, many of the irreconcilables among the pre-

Roman settlers became concentrated in the upland areas, certainly in many parts of Wales and also on the limestones of the Craven uplands —where Ingleborough itself is considered to have served as a central refuge. Finally, they were especially numerous in the centre and east of the southern Scottish uplands, which may have been profoundly affected by the considerable population there assembled. No doubt there was at that time much resemblance between the southern uplands and the other Border country, Wales, but in its multitude of little forts the southern uplands at this time seem most to have resembled another North-West Frontier of an era 1,600 years later.

The earlier settlers in eastern Scotland kept, on the whole, to the foothills and broader valleys, just as they did in Northumbria. It seems that there was little or no human occupation of the broad zone of high rainfall that runs down the western half of the country (cf. Fig. 14). Settlements in that part were confined to the less rainy areas along the western coasts, and this type of distribution has, of course, persisted even to-day. Thus, away from the sea, the Western Highlands have strong claims to be considered as the least modified of British mountain and moorland habitats, just as the Southern Pennines are probably the most modified. The exploitation of Northern England in general possibly started later than that of Wales and the Cornish peninsula, but it seems to have proceeded more rapidly and continuously since the time when much of the hill country was affected by the sheep-farming methods of the Cistercian abbeys. The Southern Pennines, later to be surrounded by large populations and readily traversed, now show far more extreme signs of biological change than those visible farther north, but signs of this were evident in Leland's day (Fig. 45). The border country apparently had a relatively large population in Roman times, but then and later, throughout the Middle Ages, may have been too much of a battle-ground to permit any steady increase of population or of agricultural amelioration. It was not until long after the union of crowns in 1603 that any extensive measures of " improvement " were possible, though there is reason to believe that the reclaiming of " waste " lands was especially rapid after that date. It is plain, then, that the man-induced modifications of the original biological units have proceeded at different times and at different rates in different parts of the highland zone.

CHAPTER 14

THE FUTURE—
CONSERVATION AND UTILISATION

A L A R G E part of what has already been written in these pages has been concerned with the past. Before we leave the story of the uplands, it would be fitting to glance, if nothing more, at the prospects of their future. Their present condition is, to a large extent, the results of man's activities, and it is equally certain that their future will be what man makes of them.

Two main types of solution have been suggested as possible answers to these problems of the future, although this is a subject on which considerable diversity of opinion has existed and will exist. There are some who would keep the high hills and moorlands simply as places for recreation, and these would view with disfavour any attempts to convert them partly or wholly to economic purposes. To these, and indeed to many of us, there are undoubtedly very strong grounds for preserving considerable areas for the recreation and exercise of those who must normally live in cities. Others, however, urge that much economic use might be made of these areas, pointing for justification to the basic economic factors which must now be considered. While Victorian Britain could afford to isolate a large part of a small island as game reserves for grouse and deer, it is now certain that we have to consider whether these reserves can be made to play any material part in national production, a role which is becoming a necessity as a result of increasing population and diminishing trade balances.

The alternatives presented are essentially those of conservation or of production, and it may seem to the onlooker that the choice between these possibilities is often based either on sentimental grounds or on purely commercial considerations. While both of these will doubtless continue to play their part in these matters, neither can be regarded as an altogether trustworthy guide, and it would certainly be an advantage if we could discover the principles which should form our decisions in such matters.

The principle of conservation has received widespread acceptance of recent years. Through the generosity of many private persons, beautiful places and large estates have passed into the hands of the National Trust to be administered and preserved on behalf of the

nation. Another form of conservation which received such strong
support as to lead to the introduction of legislation in 1949, was that of
creating a series of National Parks, areas of particular natural beauty,
controlled by public action in order to maintain existing amenities,
existing rural occupations and scenic beauty, whilst providing reasonable facilities for public access and enjoyment. Whilst most biologists
regard this as desirable, there is a real danger, if we stress the idea of
conservation too strongly, that we may lose sight of other and wider
possibilities. Of the English Lake District, it has been said most aptly
that its charm is very largely the result of what its inhabitants have
done in the past, and it is a fact that much of its present beauty is the
result of the romantic interest it has aroused in the last 150 years. Thus
it seems that what really matters in such an area is not only its conservation, for this should be the least we can do if we value it, but the
control of its further development.

Nature is never static, and to the ecologist in particular conservation means that the future is as important as the past. It is not
enough to conserve blindly, because the trends of soil and vegetation
operating to-day determine what the conserved site will be in the
future, and it will often be unlike what is there now. We must therefore
study these trends and be prepared to guide their development if we
are to reach the desired end. Moreover, if what we see in the uplands
to-day is often the degenerating remains of the former plant and
animal communities, we may naturally ask if there is any good reason
why this condition should remain. Should we not also consider the
possibility that the developments which we must in any case control,
if we are to maintain what is attractive or useful in such an area, can
equally easily be directed towards the regeneration of what is fast
disappearing or has already disappeared ?

This idea may be particularly attractive to the biologist, but it is
also at the root of any process of upland land utilisation and there is,
scientifically speaking, little to separate it from the point of view of
those who desire to see upland country become more productive, thus
to play a more important part in the national economy. From this
point of view, the chief biological difference between production and
conservation is that the former is likely to be more concerned with the
quantity of the biological material produced, while the latter will be
more insistent on some particular *quality*. In the former case also the
rate of production is important. In the latter case it may be possible,

and it will often be necessary, to wait for the desired result. Actually, of course, both cases involve each of these aspects.

As any treatment of upland country, for either of these two main purposes, will involve development, we may perhaps turn to discuss the problem of the possible lines of development from the biological point of view, leaving its other aspects until later. It is actually a particular form of a rather widespread problem in land utilisation— that of utilising to the best advantage a country with extreme climatic or other habitat conditions. Wide experience in other lands has shown that afforestation and pastoral forms of agriculture are usually the best forms of land utilisation under such conditions. Both history and recent experience suggest that either is quite practicable in Britain, except perhaps on bog soils, and the choice between them must be determined by other factors. We may note that elsewhere it has generally been found that afforestation is the more suitable form of utilisation in a wet climate, grazing being resorted to in dry climates, in which tree-growth is impossible or too slow.

The system we have to deal with is, however, a dynamic one, and in deciding on its most suitable form (forestry or grazing practice) we must take into account the trends of soil and of vegetation. Thus in the uplands it will be necessary to consider which method of land development will contribute most towards reducing the inherent tendencies towards leaching and soil waterlogging.

Finally, the question of the amount of production is economically important and should be considered if we are to assess fairly the prospects of development. From this point of view, we must note that most of the upland soils are in a run-down condition, exhausted by leaching. It seems reasonable to assume that an important step in development will be to build up in them a higher degree of soil fertility. Any continued form of economic production will depend on this being done and upon the possibility of maintaining the improved status.

GRAZING AND AFFORESTATION

In the more recent past, upland country has been used mainly for some sort of grazing. Deer-forests and grouse-moors, sheep-walks and hill cattle-pastures all come in this category—of which the essential feature is the attempt to take a crop in the form of some sort of animal,

PLATE XXXI

Edwin Broomer

Hay Tor, Dartmoor, showing the upland land forms associated with long-continued weathering and erosion

PLATE XXXII

C. H. Wood

Aerial view of Hawes Water, Lake District, showing ash-oak woodland on unstable slopes and moorland above on stable slopes; also the waterworks dam in course of construction the object being to produce as large a crop as is possible. This form of utilisation may thus be contrasted with those in which the crop is vegetable, the usual variants being agricultural or silvicultural. Arable cultivation is limited, being restricted to the best soils, and commonest is hay production, designed mainly to maintain the crop of grazing animals through the winter. Thus the principal form of vegetation cropping is often of trees, though, of course, there is no reason why this should always be so. We might perhaps envisage growing grass which could be used for paper-making or for some similar purpose, and the contrast would apply equally to crops of potatoes or oats. Are there any essential differences between these vegetable crops and those of animals obtained by the grazing method?

In the first place it should be noted that the two methods of cropping involve considerable quantitative differences. Roughly speaking, a grazing animal like a sheep eats during its growth about 8 to 10 times its own final weight, the weights being *dry* weights (i.e. excluding water which is present in varying amounts in different sorts of plant and animal tissues). For simplicity of argument, let us assume that the ratio of food weight to final weight is 10. Thus, if the whole of the herbage present on a given area were converted to sheep flesh and bone, the " crop " would only be one-tenth of the dry weight of grass which could be obtained. In actual fact, such a treatment is not possible ; we can only use as crop the *annual gain* in herbage or in a flock of sheep, and, in the latter case, the rest of the flock consumes large amounts of herbage and so reduces the proportion that can be cropped in the form of sheep. The type of difference, however, is quite a general one, and as an example we may say that if the total annual plant production (P) above that required to maintain the population were turned into grazing animals (GA), and these in turn formed food for predatory animals (Pred), say wolves, for example, the possible annual productions in dry weight (as percentages of the original plant material) would be of the order of

$$P \quad : \quad GA \quad : \quad Pred$$
$$100 \quad : \quad 10 \quad : \quad 1$$

and for the reasons indicated above, the productions would tend to be considerably less than these possible figures. At each step in the food-chain there is, therefore, a very large loss in production. Moreover, carnivores and other similar predators are clearly a highly uneconomic form of production. Now man is a predator, and one, moreover, who can feed at two levels in the above food-chain—either directly on plant materials (e.g. potatoes or oats) or on the flesh of grazing animals. Clearly we might feed many more men on vegetable crops than those we could feed on flesh alone. Of course we should have to allow in practice for other considerations, both dietary and agricultural. Nevertheless, the argument shows that there are obvious advantages in concentrating on plant crops rather than on animal where other considerations allow, and the suggestion can clearly be made that where high productivity is the aim, grazing would have its role mainly as a method of cropping soils or places not easily cropped in any other way.

Of course trees are plants, and the same arguments apply to timber production as to any other form of vegetable cropping, even although the crop is not edible in this instance. Timber has an added advantage as a crop. Wood is a plant tissue that is composed almost entirely of cellulose and its derivatives, carbonaceous compounds which include a minimum of elements such as nitrogen or indeed of any form of mineral ash. Thus when a timber crop is taken, a minimum of these valuable substances is taken from the site. In a tree most of the components valuable to living organisms are in the leaves and young shoots. These are generally left on the site and the materials they contain return to the soil.

On the other hand, animal flesh and wool and hide consist of proteins, substances rich in nitrogen, and including also sulphur and phosphorus. Animal bone is largely calcium phosphate. Thus an animal crop incorporates very large amounts of nitrogen, phosphorus and calcium—derived from the soil via the grass. The result of taking such crops, then, is a constant drain being made on the soil fertility. Thus grazed areas in the long run lose their fertility unless measures (such as manurial treatment) are continually taken to renew it.

This is an important point to bear in mind, for it suggests that in the long run grazing may be more exhausting to the soil than afforestation would be. On the other hand, however, the higher yield of timber crops reduces the differences between the two sorts of crop ; there are, however, hardly any British data which would enable us to compare the relative effects under British conditions. The point of view is, nevertheless, an important one. The soil is our capital and its assets may not be dissipated.

TYPES OF PLANTING

Similar considerations should be applied in deciding on what form of grazing is used, or on what types of tree are to be planted. The latter point is perhaps more pertinent to the present discussion. The choice of trees lies mainly between coniferous trees, softwoods like pines and firs, and deciduous trees, hardwoods like oak, ash and beech. The decision must obviously depend on which trees maintain the character of the soil best as well as on their relative cropping capacity. There is probably little doubt that an equivalent crop of useful timber would be produced more rapidly by coniferous trees, so that in that respect they merit first choice. But many conifers, when grown in British uplands, produce on the soil surface an acid layer of " mor " humus, which tends to accelerate the leaching of the mineral soil. This being the case, it might be permissible to plant conifers of this type on acid " mor " soils, but to do so on soils of the brown-earth and " mull " type would be to dissipate soil assets and thus to violate the principles already laid down. This type of planting, which has been all too common, thus runs counter to any rational policy of land utilisation and should not be undertaken without corresponding remedial measures.

Forest policy in the uplands should thus be directed especially towards the maintenance of soil status. Because trees are inevitably long-term crops, they offer unusual opportunities for long-term planning, and because they often draw their minerals from the deeper layers of soil, they also often offer a natural method of replenishing the surface layers of soil with salts, and thus of rehabilitating run-down soils. It would obviously be the proper policy to plant trees which, either because of their deep roots or of their high base requirement, would be most efficient in drawing up bases from the deeper layers of soil, and in yielding them to the soil humus. Such trees normally form " mull " humus. In a general way, deciduous or hardwood trees usually do this best, though there is a good deal of variation between different species.

All of this does not mean that conifers should never be planted. They are the natural forest trees to plant on " mor " soils and on drained acid peats. Probably they could also be used profitably, especially in mixed plantations, to establish woodland again on some of the poorer, leached grasslands. Permanent improvements should be aimed at in such a case as the last, by the gradual establishment of *mull*-forming trees, though it might prove necessary to use manurial treatments in order to bring this about. Lime, with or without phosphate in addition, is generally the treatment used. It should perhaps be added that we know very little about the types of litter and humus formed by different trees under British conditions. There may be softwood trees which can act as mull-formers. We have already seen that juniper apparently has this capacity, and it might be a useful shrub to use in establishing plantations—either as a soil-improver or to provide initial shelter for larger trees.

The advantages of afforestation in upland country are not confined only to the production of increased and less exhausting crops. A reduction of leaching and of soil erosion also follows the establishment of forest cover, although these benefits can readily be lost if clear felling is resorted to when crops are taken. It has often been argued that woodlands also have a beneficial effect on rainfall, though most of what has been written on this debatable subject refers to the drier types of climate. In wet climates it is a general opinion among people with practical experience that, on the average, soils under woodland conditions are drier, and there is a well-known Swiss experiment in which it has been found that the " run-off " in streams and drains is much less under forest conditions. Presumably the forest cover both intercepts and evaporates more water. It is a very material point in making such comparisons between woodland and grassland, that in grasslands the organic matter (plant and litter) is concentrated in a narrow zone at the soil surface. Thus there is produced a turfy, water-holding mat as well as a layer of peat, both of which may accumulate water and cut down evaporation. In woodland, the whole organic production is widely spaced out in the vertical direction, much of it in the timber, and there is thus less obstacle to a higher rate of decay in the soil surface. Considering the matter from a purely biological point of view, it looks as though the accumulation of cellulosic vegetable products (wood in trees and fibres in grasses) can take place either in the form of wood *above* the soil surface or of peat *at* the soil surface. The advantages of the former method under conditions favouring peat accumulation are obvious. This sort of conclusion, like many of those we can arrive at by such *a priori* arguments, needs to be based on careful comparative studies, for it would be a matter of great importance in long-term policy if a method could be obtained of slowing down peat accumulation and with it the tendency towards increased waterlogging. It is probable that many areas of existing grassland would require draining before they could be planted with trees, but if the above arguments are correct these areas would probably maintain themselves under woodland without further attention.

The difficulties that arise in upland country during afforestation come not only from the soil trends associated with wet climates, but also from the fact that we are dealing with soils that are already badly run down, introducing other special problems. Probably most natural soils reach their maximum fertility under forest, and continuous agriculture is only possible where natural climatic conditions frequently induce water movements towards the soil surface or where irrigation or cultural operations can be devised to maintain the surface fertility. There are many border-line soil types and climates (particularly wet ones) where this is not practicable, and the maintenance of a reasonable fertility is only possible under forest. In such places, forest clearance results in so much soil degeneration that even the return to forest after agricultural clearance proves very difficult. A large part of the British uplands falls into this latter category, and is evidently the type of country that should never have been cleared.

PASTURE IMPROVEMENT

Reforestation is not the only possible solution of this problem of soil regeneration. Sir George Stapledon has suggested an alternative one —which, like afforestation, also has the merit of having behind it a very large practical experience. Experiments on the improvement of hill pastures, carried out in Wales under the Cahn hill pasture scheme, have shown that by suitable treatment of these pastures it is possible greatly to increase stock yields and also to re-establish a higher status of soil and of vegetation cover. The method is mainly one of manurial treatment, using particularly lime and phosphate manures, followed by controlled grazing. On gentle slopes it can often be accelerated by ploughing and putting down leys of suitable grass mixtures. The methods derived are effective partly in increasing the base and nitrogen status of the soil, partly and most noticeably in leading to the replacement of the poorer grasses by more productive ones. The spread of leguminous plants like clover is particularly noticeable, and as these have nitrogen-fixing bacteria associated with their roots, a considerable enrichment of the soil with this element follows. The methods of grassland improvement developed by Sir George Stapledon and his colleagues have come to stay. They will probably play an increasing part in the development of upland areas. No doubt they will involve a programme of frequent manurial treatment, and in this respect they may demand more than forest-lands which, so far as we know at present, are more likely—once established—to maintain the *status quo* without extra treatment. The choice between forests and grasslands, however, involves not only the questions of cost and of quantities of production like those already discussed, and of the effects of the method on the soil, but also the place of the products in the local and national economy. If any considerable number of people is to live in the uplands, it would be desirable to have a considerable area devoted to food production. On national grounds, the question also arises whether some division of agricultural interest might not allot a larger role in the nation's agricultural production to upland country. In general terms, it might be argued that lowland country might most profitably concern itself mainly with the production of such crops as cereals and sugar-beet, while a larger share in the national production of animal materials and dairy produce could be allotted to the uplands where, in general, cereal and beet cultivation is difficult or impossible. Thus even the solution of the biological problems of utilisation is hardly one that can be solved by considering upland Britain alone, although what is possible and profitable in the uplands must play a great part in arriving at a decision.

OTHER FORMS OF UTILISATION

In practice, of course, the utilisation of upland country does not only involve biological consideration. In addition to the possibility of crop production, there are mineral resources which have in the past received attention, and which may do so again. The chief minerals used at present are mainly the rocks, of which many different types are of value, partly on account of their hardness, for road metal or building stone. The limestone areas in particular are in great demand for supplying lime and baryta. Enormous quantities of china-clay, a decomposition product of granite, are also obtained in the south-west, and formerly large quantities of slates. On a smaller scale, tin and copper and lead have been mined, though not in quantity since the opening of richer mines abroad, from the seventies onward. Time has healed most of the scars caused by these industries, though the limestone regions are still often unduly disfigured by cement works and their chimneys.

Another natural product very easily obtained from upland country is water, and since the middle of last century increasing areas have been taken as catchment basins, while reservoirs have been constructed or lake levels raised by damming to store the impounded water. A large part of this water goes to great cities for human consumption and industrial uses, but there is now an increasing tendency to employ it for power-production, and the great hydro-electric schemes in Galloway and in different parts of the Scottish Highlands promise to improve the conditions of life very considerably in these mountain areas and they may also lead to industrial developments. There is one obvious advantage, the high rainfall, that makes upland regions very suitable for water-supply projects.

Of course, there is also the second one that this form of utilisation can generally be combined with other forms of production. Hydro-electric schemes, in particular, have little effect on the utilisation of the remaining countryside. When water is required for human consumption, however, it has been usual to put considerable limitation on the activities allowed in the catchment basin. Human habitations have normally been removed, grazing is generally stopped and access by visitors prevented. The effect of these measures is partly to sterilise the area and to this extent to reduce its productivity. On the other hand, some form of afforestation is usual in these catchment areas. There were perfectly good reasons for these steps. Upland water was first chosen as desirable for human consumption when it was realised that certain epidemic diseases like typhoid and dysentery might be water-borne, the causative agents being bacteria which reached the supply as the result of contamination of some water source by human excreta. It is with the object of preventing any chance of this happening that catchment areas are now isolated. The actual danger is slight, and it depends chiefly on the existence of persons who may act as " carriers," though not themselves showing any signs of disease. In actual fact, most bacteria die in water which stands exposed to light and air, and this is one reason why there should be little danger of infection in any case where prolonged storage is possible. The danger of harmful pollution by grazing animals is also rather slight, but the bacteriological tests used to detect pollution in the water-supply depend on the presence of certain forms of bacteria that are almost universally present in animal faeces, so that it is most convenient to eliminate obvious sources of this type of pollution. The attempts made to sterilise catchment areas in this way have resulted in afforestation being the only other form of utilisation that is usually attempted, and on the whole the association of water-supply and afforestation makes a very satisfactory combination.

The amount of water available in upland Britain is quite considerable, apart from the new reservoirs. Its area has been estimated at more than 500 sq. m., and the possibility of its productive utilisation is thus quite a material problem. Its further extension by the conversion of valleys into impounding reservoirs might also be important because this process submerges the fertile parts of the upland region —the valley alluvia and the lower soils of brown-earth type. This must greatly reduce the possible productivity of the valley, and it usually rules out any possibility of worth-while agricultural yield. The question is whether the water itself can be made productive by taking crops from it—of fish, for example. In actual fact, impounded water usually produces a floating crop of small plants called algae, as well as others on the shores, and there is also an animal population, composed partly of small animals such as insect larvae, free-swimming crustacea and snails, and partly of fish. There are two points of view about this population. Its size depends ultimately on the fertility of the water draining from the surrounding soil and thus upon the fertility of the soils themselves. Thus if we succeed in raising the general standard of fertility in the surrounding country, we shall automatically increase the gross production, e.g. of fish, in the lakes and reservoirs. This might be worth doing, for fresh water is potentially nearly as productive as an equal area of good land, and by using it to advantage we could make sure that manures, etc., used on the land were not wasted by leaching. On the other hand, there is an objection to heavy production if the water is wanted for human use. The water-living creatures and a good deal of resultant detritus have to be filtered off before it is used and this is often a cause of very considerable expense. For this reason a low production is preferred and, speaking generally, the use of a given area for water-supply purposes may not be compatible with its full development for most forms of biological production.

PEAT

The last common upland product is peat, and this is a material which can be considered under almost every heading. It is a biological product, and as the accumulated remains of plants it represents a large store of reserve substance which has only to be broken down to make a productive soil. It is, of course, not easy to do this in nature. The peat must be drained and it must then be limed in order to neutralise its acidity. The nature of the site and climate are usually against the first measure, and the cost of transport against the second. Thus often the only reasonable way of handling it is to try to drain it and to grow on it *mor* plants like pines. However, given a sufficient expenditure on manures, it is practicable to improve it sufficiently to convert its vegetation to useful pastures.

Peat is, of course, also useful as a fuel. Here the difficulties are the labour costs of cutting, drying and transporting. It has a very low calorific value by weight as sold, about one-third that of coal, so that it is only worth using where coal has to be transported a long way. It would be worth cutting as fuel only if it could be used with little transport—that is, if there was a considerable population near at hand.

Finally, peat is a strong absorbent, readily removing substances from solution or suspension. It is perhaps likely that it could be made extremely useful if available to industries near-by, but the cost of transport of such a heavy material rules out this use elsewhere.

When all is said and done, peat has a great virtue not often realised : that of storing water in a catchment area and releasing it continuously long after rain and floods have ceased. To put it plainly, other forms of peat utilisation are likely to be expensive and no clear-cut solution of the problem is likely to be found.

POLICY

Though it is clear that there are certain forms of land-utilisation which can and should be used in upland country, it seems reasonable to suppose that the choice would be affected by the diversity of character of the main upland areas. Moreover, there still remains the need for the formulation of an overall policy which would not only allow for the development of the potentialities of each area, but permit them to fall into place in a comprehensive and balanced plan.

One difficulty in the way of proper development is likely to be that of finance. The suggestion that the developments must be State controlled, while desirable in the interests of national planning and of a long-term policy, tends merely to shift the financial burden on to the shoulders of the long-suffering taxpayer without providing for its objective solution. It seems probable that relatively low initial expenses and an early financial return may prove to be essential parts of any realistic plan. This may suggest, perhaps, that the most plausible method of attack would be to extend the existing schemes of re-afforestation and grassland improvement, for it is known that both of these can give a reasonably rapid return. The danger in both cases is that their use for this purpose might easily degenerate into mere catch-crop exploitation. The redevelopment of soil fertility and its maintenance when developed, is likely to be an essential part of any permanent scheme of amelioration. This object should be kept in mind at all stages, even if it involves additional cost

Another obvious danger is that the use of methods of utilisation such as sheep-rearing should be considered desirable simply because of the small labour costs involved. This particular type of utilisation has its value in certain cases, particularly as a part of a more complete system which will enable otherwise unreachable areas to be cropped. It will need to be considered not only for this reason, but also because some form of food production will be a necessary part of any development which aims at the establishment of human beings in the uplands. Nevertheless, the history of sheep-rearing in the British uplands, particularly during the last 100 years, has been a deplorable one, and it has been mainly responsible for their present depopulation and run-down condition. Its lessons will need to be considered and acted upon.

REPOPULATION

The present and still increasing depopulation of the highland zone in Britain is one of the most distressing features of its present condition, the more so because the scale of the problem is generally quite ignored. Almost half of Great Britain is included in it, and this half has a population of less than five persons to the square mile, most often at the average level of one or two to the square mile. Moreover, even this low figure is to an increasing extent composed of the people of the higher age-groups. Thus one of the most encouraging signs of recent years has been the considerable measure of re-population that has followed afforestation, and with the development of forests capable of being continuously cropped a still larger upland population should be possible. Whereas only one worker is required for about 3 sq. ml. of sheep-walk, about 15 would find occupation on recently afforested land (say 5 per square mile) ; while for mature European forests in full production, with associated industries, the labour requirement rises to between 20 and 30 per square mile. This is, of course, a level that could not be reached for some years—not until the forests were regularly producing timber and not until a fair degree of soil fertility had been reconstituted. Nevertheless, it is useful as a guide as to what is certainly possible.

It is unlikely that forestry alone will provide a complete solution of the problem of repopulation. Two other features of a satisfactory solution will probably include the provision of sources of power and also of some measure of food production. Other industries will then come to be associated with forestry. The ideal no doubt will finally prove to be an economy founded not on one industry alone but with the possibility of several or many products, so that any depression in the demand for any one of them would not throw too great a strain on the system as a whole. It thus seems probable that the unit of development, whatever it may be, must be a reasonably large one, so that it will be possible to include a suitable diversity of occupation and at the same time a sufficiently high degree of mechanisation, without undue duplication of machinery, either implemental or administrative. It is assumed that much mechanisation will be inevitable both to reduce labour costs and to maintain a good standard of leisure. It seems axiomatic that the day of the crofter or small-holder is past, except at a level of living which would be quite unattractive to men of the requisite type.

Nothing is to be gained by trying to elaborate the details of the developmental process, without practical acquaintance with the inevitable difficulties. Even the information necessary for planning is almost always lacking, so that the project is one likely to require both vision and patience: vision in drawing up an initial scheme and patience because it will take a generation for the whole to become effective. But it can confidently be said that whether the aim is primarily to make an upland area productive or to conserve it and so improve the amenities for visitors, the effect will be to make it more attractive to man. The ideal will prove to be successful in so far as it provides numerous niches into which human life and activity can be fitted. Here lies the best prospect for the future.

CHAPTER 15

THE NATURE CONSERVANCY

In Chapter 14, Professor Pearsall wrote of the future of our mountains and moorlands as he saw it in the later nineteen-forties. As examples of the active practice of conservation, he instanced the National Trust and the creation of National Parks. Since his completion of the manuscript of this book, which was first published in 1950, a new chapter in conservation has opened with the establishment of the Nature Conservancy in 1949. Since Professor Pearsall was much concerned with this body, and with the whole subject of conservation, it seemed appropriate to add to the revised edition of *Mountains and Moorlands* a brief account of the activities of the Nature Conservancy in Highland Britain during the years 1949-1966.

The functions of the Conservancy, as summarised in its Charter, are: "to provide scientific advice on the conservation and control of the natural flora and fauna of Great Britain; to establish, maintain and manage nature reserves in Great Britain, including the maintenance of physical features of scientific interest; and to organise and develop the research and scientific services related thereto".

In the period since 1949, the Conservancy has been able to establish Nature Reserves in many parts of Highland Britain, and the position of these reserves is shown on the map, Fig. 1a, page 3. Either by purchase or by arrangement with the landowners, protection of the flora and fauna from destructive agencies is now assured. The two largest reserves in England and Wales, both in the northern Pennines,—Moor House in north-east Westmorland, and, only two miles to the south-east of it, the Upper Teesdale Reserve—together include within their boundaries almost all types of moorland vegetation. The Upper Teesdale Reserve includes some of the most interesting plant communities and some of the rarest plants in Highland Britain. Other sites of rare mountain plants and large areas of characteristic mountain vegetation are included in the large Scottish Nature Reserves established in the Cairngorms, at Inverpolly and at Beinn Eighe in the north-west Highlands, on Rannoch Moor, on the Durness limestone at Inchnadamph, on the island of Rhum, and in many smaller reserves.

The maintenance and management of these reserves is carried out by the Conservancy staff of Regional Officers and Wardens, and scientific research by ecologists on the Conservancy's staff goes on in all of them. Most of the reserves are freely open to anyone wishing to walk over them, if application is made to the Warden. The exceptions are enclosed areas where experimental work is going on, or where the flora and fauna require special protection from disturbance. Field laboratories have been established at Moor House and at Anancaun on the shore of Loch Maree in the Beinn Eighe reserve, and provide facilities for visiting research workers as well as for the Conservancy's scientific staff.

Among the general subjects on which research is going on at nearly all the reserves are reasearch on climate, including data on the micro-climates of various habitats, work on evaporation and run-off at upland stations, and vegetation surveys combined with geological field-work. Specific projects include investigation of the biology of several members of the native fauna of mountains and moorlands, such as the Red deer and Red grouse, and co-ordinated team-work on such problems as the present altitudinal limit of tree growth in the British highlands, and the factors which now govern the growth and erosion of peat. In the mountainous island of Rhum in the Inner Hebrides, which was acquired by the Conservancy in 1957, integrated studies are proceeding on methods of land use and land management, including afforestation, with the aim of discovering how far it might be possible to improve the capacity of such marginal land to support a flourishing human population.

The following brief account of the most important Nature Reserves in Highland Britain will show that examples of all the various plant and animal communities described by Professor Pearsall in earlier chapters of this book are now safeguarded under the protection of the Nature Conservancy. More detailed accounts of the reserves, together with discussion of the principles involved in determining the type of management to be practised, can be found in the Annual Reports of the Nature Conservancy.

The mountain vegetation discussed in Chapter 5 is found on many summits of the Cairngorm Reserve of nearly 40,000 acres—from which indeed many of the examples and illustrations in Chapter 5 are taken. The main function of this reserve is to safeguard the characteristic wild life of this mountain massif—not only the vegetation, but the highly characteristic fauna which includes Red and Roe deer, the wild cat, and an assemblage of birds comparatively rare in Britain, including the Golden Eagle, the Ptarmigan, Dotterel, Snow Bunting, Greenshank, Scottish Crossbill and Crested Tit (see Plate 25).

In Chapter 5, it is stressed how many of the rarer and more interesting plants of the montane flora are restricted in their present distribution to habitats rich in bases, especially lime. The mountain Nature Reserves at Cwm Idwal in Snowdonia, Cader Idris in Merioneth, Upper Teesdale, the mountains of Rhum, and at Inchnadamph, all lie on base-rich rocks and include rare arctic and alpine plants within their boundaries. On the basic lavas of Cwm Idwal and Cader Idris are the southernmost stations for several plants—the beautiful Mountain Avens (Plate 16b) in Cwm Idwal, and the Welsh Poppy and Mountain Sorrel on Cader Idris. The unique sugar-limestone habitats of Upper Teesdale probably include more rare plants than any other area of similar size in Great Britain; among these plants are the Spring Gentian and the Teesdale Violet, and the rare sedge *Carex capillaris*. Of even greater interest than the rare plants of Teesdale is the preservation there of plant communities which probably represent the nearest surviving approach to the vegetation which was widespread in Britain in Late-glacial times about 10,000 years ago. Recent threats to adjoining parts of Teesdale by the plan to construct a reservoir at Cow Green emphasise the vital importance of the Conservancy's function in safeguarding these rare plants and vegetation types in its Reserve. On the strongly basic plutonic rocks of the mountains of Rhum, other rare mountain plants are found, including the Norwegian sandwort, *Arenaria norvegica*. In the Inchnadamph Reserve, the Durness limestone forms bare scarps and pavement in a landscape otherwise dominated by blanket peat, and on the limestone is found a type of willow scrub almost unique in Britain, though found in Scandinavia, and "a rich woodland flora of northern character including the Globe flower, *Trollius europaeus*," and the rare grass *Agropyron donianum*.

The upland woodlands described in Chapter 7 represent surviving relics of the forest of the mid-Post-glacial period, which was once, between five and eight thousand years ago, continuous over the landscape up to about 2,500 feet, and has since been progressively destroyed by the growth of blanket peat and the destructive activities of man and his grazing animals. The Beinn Eighe Reserve in Wester Ross includes the wood Coille na Glas Leitire, one of the surviving remnants of the ancient Scottish pine forest (others are found on the Cairngorms and on Rannoch Moor). At Coille na Glas Leitire, the Conservancy's ecologists are studying the conditions under which Scots pine is able to regenerate; this includes a study of soil conditions and of the grazing activities of members of the native fauna, notably the Red Deer. The Pine Marten (see Plate XXVI) is a characteristic member of the fauna of this wood, and studies on its biology are in progress. In these three Scottish reserves, protection is now assured to surviving fragments of this undoubtedly native forest type, which in other areas had suffered reduction and alteration by the demands for home-grown timber. In the Inverpolly Reserve, north of Beinn Eighe, are surviving fragments of Highland birch forest, a vegetation type which over great areas has been destroyed by the accumulating mantle of blanket peat, as discussed in Chapters 7 and 10. Most of the peat-forming types of vegetation are also found in the 26,000 acres of deer forest of the Inverpolly Reserve, which includes country typical of the glaciated Lewisian gneiss and, rising from it, steep mountains of Torridonian sandstone like Cul Mor, shown in Plate III.

On the Moor House Reserve, on the high North Pennine plateau, the vegetation types described in Chapter 8 under the heading Moorlands and Bogs are well represented, and are being investigated from many aspects. Observations on rainfall evaporation, and run-off suggest that at Moor House today conditions approach the threshold for the maintenance of blanket peat in an actively growing condition.

The Reserve is therefore well situated for investigation of the relationship between the common practices of moorland management—burning and draining—and the onset of peat erosion, and the problems discussed under this heading in Chapter 10 are being studied. Other investigations of moorland biology are concerned with the effect of moor-burning on the composition of vegetation and on the general fertility of the moorland. Such burning is of course common practice wherever the moorland is managed to provide grazing for sheep or for grouse.

Finally, the activities of the Nature Conservancy, both in directly sponsoring research and by encouraging independent workers to carry out research on nature reserves, have stimulated the publication of much recent work on mountains and moorlands. Some of the results of Conservancy work in Scotland have been incorporated by Morton Boyd into the revised edition of *The Highlands and Islands* by himself and Fraser Darling, in this series. The Conservancy has initiated the publication of a series of monographs on special topics. The first, *Plant communities of the Scottish Highlands* by D. N. McVean and D. A. Ratcliffe, a survey of native woodland vegetation and upland vegetation above the tree limit, provides a "background of knowledge against which reserve management policies may be planned and detailed research on vegetation carried out. It should provide a basis too for a land utilisation survey dealing with the connections between land management practices on the one hand, and vegetation, soils and productivity on the other." The use of the methods of phytosociology to describe and classify the mountain vegetation types presents an interesting contrast to the ecological methods used by Professor Pearsall in the present book. The second monograph, *Geology of Moor House* by Johnson and Dunham, includes results which have already been discussed in Chapter 10.

BIBLIOGRAPHY

AVEBURY, LORD (1888). The Scenery of England and Wales. London.

BEAUCHAMP, R.S.A. (1935). The rate of movement of *Planaria alpina*. *J. Exper. Biol.* 12 : 271.

(193). The rate of movement and rhaeotaxis in *Planaria alpina*. *J. Exper. Biol.* 14 : 104.

BOWEN, E. G. (1941). Wales—a study in geography and history. Cardiff.

BRÖGGER, A. W. (1929). Ancient emigrants : a history of the north settlements of Scotland. Oxford.

BUCHAN, A., & OMOND, R. T. (1905). The Meteorology of the Ben Nevis Observatories, Part III. *Trans. Roy. Soc. Edin.* 43 : 1-565.

BURNETT, J. H. Ed. (1964). The vegetation of Scotland. Oliver and Boyd.

BURR, S., & TURNER, D. M. (1933). British Economic Grasses. London.

CAMERON, A. E. (1938). The Antler Moth in Scotland. *Scot. Nat.* 1938 : 125.

CAMERON, A. E., McHARDY, J. W., & BENNETT, A. H. (1944). The Heather Beetle (*Lochmaea suturalis*), its biology and control. Petworth.

CARR, H. R. C., & LESTER, G. A. (1930). The Mountains of Snowdonia. London.

CHEETHAM, C. A. (1942-43). Heather-Moor Ecology. *Naturalist*, 1942 : 162 and 1943 : 72.

CHILDE, V. GORDON (1935). The Prehistory of Scotland. London.

CHISLETT, R. Yorkshire Birds. Brown, Hull.

CLARK, GRAHAME (1947). Sheep and swine in the husbandry of prehistoric Europe. *Antiquity*, 21 : 122.

COLLINGWOOD, R. G. (1933). An Introduction to the Prehistory of Cumberland, Westmorland and Lancashire north of the Sands. *Trans. Cumb. Westmd. Antiq. Arch. Soc.* 33 : 163.

COLLINGWOOD, W. G. (1925). Lake District History. Kendal.

CONWAY, V. M. (1947). Ringinglow Bog, near Sheffield. *J. Ecol.* 34 : 149

(1954). Stratigraphy and pollen analysis of Southern Pennine blanket peats. *J. Ecol.* 42 : 1 : 117.

CRAMPTON, C. B. (1911). The Vegetation of Caithness considered in relation to the Geology. Cambridge.

(1912). Stable and Migratory Plant Formations. *Scot. Bot. Rev.* 1912.

CRUMP, W. B. (1913). The Coefficient of Humidity. *New Phytol.* 12 : 125.

DARBY, H. C. (1936). The Historical Geography of England before 1800. Cambridge.

DARLING, F. FRASER (1937). A Herd of Red Deer. Oxford.

(1947). Natural History in the Highlands and Islands. London.

EDWARDS, F. W. (1933). Some Perthshire Diptera. *Scot. Nat.* 1933 : 87 and 113.

ELGEE, F. (1912). The Moorlands of North-eastern Yorkshire. London.

(1930). Early man in North-east Yorkshire. Gloucester.

ELTON, C. (1938). Notes on the ecological and natural history of Pabbay. *J. Ecol.* 26 : 275.

(1942). Voles, mice and lemmings: Problems in population dynamics. Oxford.

EVANS, E. PRICE (1945). Cader Idris and Craig-y-Benglog. *J. Ecol.* 32 : 167.

FAGAN, T. W. (n.d.). The nutritive value of grasses. *Bull.* 2, *Univ. Coll. Wales.* Aberystwyth.

FAREY, J. (1813). A general view of the Agriculture of Derbyshire. London.

FIRBANK, T. (1940). I bought a mountain. London.

FORD, E. B. (1945). Butterflies. London.

FRASER, G. K. (1933). Studies of Scottish moorlands in relation to tree growth. *Bull. Forest. Comm.* 15.

(1943). Peat deposits of Scotland, Part I (Mimeographed). *H.M. Geol. Surv., Wartime Pamphlet,* 36.

FURNESS COUCHER (1924 onwards). Ed. J. C. Atkinson, for the Cheetham Society, Manchester.

GIRALDUS CAMBRIENSIS (1908). Itinerary through Wales. (Everyman's Edition). London.

GLASSPOOL, J. (1937). The wettest place in the British Isles. *Meteorol. Mag.* 72 : 142.

GODWIN, H., & MITCHELL, G. F. (1938). Stratigraphy and development of two raised bogs near Tregaron, Cardiganshire. *New Phytol.* 37 : 425.

GODWIN, H. (1956). History of the British Flora. Cambridge.

GORDON, S. (1928). The Cairngorm Hills of Scotland. London.

GRIMSHAW, P. (1910). The insect fauna of grouse-moors. *Ann. Scot. Nat. Hist.* 1910 : 149.

M.M.   U

GRAHAM, R. (1939). An essay on English monasteries. London.

HARKER, A. (1941). The West Highlands and the Hebrides. Cambridge.

HARDY, M. (1904). Esquisse de la géographie et de la végétation des highlands d'Ecosse. Paris.

HAY, T. (1937). Physiographical notes on the Ullswater area. *Geogr. J.* 90 : 426.

HEADLAM, SIR CUTHBERT (1930). The Three Northern Counties of England. Newcastle.

HOLLINGWORTH, S. E. (1934). Some solifluction phenomena in the northern part of the Lake District. *Proc. Geol. Assoc.* 15 : 167.

HUXLEY, J. S. (1932). Problems of Relative Growth. London.

JOHNSON, D. (1938). Landslides and related phenomena. New York.

JOHNSON, G. A. L. and DUNHAM, K. C. (1963). The Geology of Moor House. Monograph of the Nature Conservancy Two. H.M. Stationery Office.

LACK, D. (1935). Breeding bird population of British Heaths and Moorlands, *J. Anim. Ecol.* 4 : 43.

LELAND, JNO. (1535-43). Itinerary.

LESLIE, A. S., & SHIPLEY, A. E. (1932). Grouse in health and disease. London.

LEWIS, F. J. (1904). Geographical distribution of vegetation of the basins of the Rivers Eden, Tees, Wear and Tyne. *Geogr. J.*, 1904.
(1905-11). Plant remains in the Scottish peat-mosses, I-IV. *Trans. Roy. Soc. Edinb.* 41 : 699, 45 : 335, 46 : 33, 47 : 793.

LEWIS, P. & E. (1935). The Land of Wales. Cardiff.

MACNAIR, P. (1893). The geological factors in the distribution of the alpine plants of Perthshire. *Trans. Perthsh. Soc. Nat. Sci.* 2 : 240.

MANLEY, G. (1942). Dun Fell, 2,735 ft. *Quart. J. Roy. Meteorol. Soc.* 68 : 151.

MARR, J. E. (1920). The Scientific Study of Scenery. London.

MATTHEWS, J. R. (1937). Geographical relationships of the British Flora. *J. Ecol.* 25 : 1.

MCVEAN, D. N. and RATCLIFFE, D. A. (1962). Plant Communities of the Scottish Highlands. Monograph of the Nature Conservancy One. H.M. Stationery Office.

MIDDLETON, A. D. (1934). Periodic fluctuations in British game populations. *J. Anim. Ecol.* 3 : 231.

MOSS, C. E. (1913) The Vegetation of the Peak District. Cambridge.

PEARSALL, W. H. (1938). The soil complex in relation to plant communities, III, Moorlands and Bogs. *J. Ecol.* 26 : 298.

(1941). The " Mosses " of the Stainmore District. *J. Ecol.* 29 : 161.

PEARSALL, W. H., GARDINER, A. C. & GREENSHIELDS, (1946). Freshwater biology and water supply in Britain. *Freshw. Biol. Assoc. Biol. Publ.* No. 11.

PEARSALL. W. H., & LIND, E. M. (1941). A note on a Connemara bog type. *J. Ecol.* 29 : 62.

PEARSALL, W. H., & PENNINGTON, W. (1947). Ecological History of the English Lake District. *J. Ecol.* 24 : 137.

PENNINGTON, W. (1943). Lake Sediments : Bottom Deposits of the North Basin of Windermere. *New Phytol.* 42 : 1.

PENNINGTON, W. (1965). The interpretation of some post-Glacial vegetation diversities at different Lake District sites. *Proc. Roy. Soc. B.* 161 : 310.

PRAEGER, R. L. (1934). The Botanist in Ireland. Dublin.

POLUNIN, N. (1939). Arctic Plants in the British Isles. *J. Bot.* 1939 : 270.

POWER, EILEEN (1941). The Wool Trade in English Medieval History. London.

RAINFALL ATLAS OF BRITISH ISLES (1926). Roy. Meteorol. Soc., London.

RAISTRICK, A. (1947). Malham and Malham Moor. Clapham via Lancaster.

REID, CLEMENT, AND OTHERS (1912). Geology of Dartmoor. *Mem. Geol. Surv.* 338.

RITCHIE, J. (1919). The influence of man on animal life in Scotland. Cambridge.

SAMUELSON, G. (1910). Scottish Peat Mosses. *Bull. Geol. Inst. Univ. Upsala.* 10 : 197.

SIMPSON, J. B. (1932). Stone Polygons on Scottish Mountains. *Scot. Geogr. Mag.* 48 : 37.

SMITH, R. (1900). Botancial Survey of Scotland, II. North Perthshire District. *Scot. Geogr. Mag.* 16 : 441.

SMITH, W. G., & MOSS, C. E. (1903). Geographical distribution of vegetation in Yorkshire, I. Leeds and Halifax. *Geogr. J.* 22 : 1903.

SMITH, W. G., & RANKIN, W. M. (1903). Geographical distribution of vegetation in Yorkshire, II. Harrogate and Skipton. *Geogr. J.* 22 : 1903.

SMITH, W. G. (1918). The distribution of *Nardus stricta* in relation to peat. *J. Ecol.* 6 : 1.

STAMP, L. D. (1946). Britain's Structure and Scenery. London.

STAPLETON, R. G. (1914). The sheep-walks of Mid-Wales. Aberystwyth.

(1936). A survey of the agricultural and waste lands of Wales. London.

SUMMERHAYES, V. S. (1941). The effect of voles (*Microtus agrestis*) on vegetation. *J. Ecol.* 29 : 14.

TALLIS, J. H. Studies on southern Pennine peats. I, II, III, and IV. *J. Ecol.* 52 : 2 & 53 : 2.

TANSLEY, A. G. (1939). The British Islands and their Vegetation. Cambridge.

THOMAS, B. (1935). The Composition of Draw Moss. *J. Min. Agric.* 42 : 458.

(1936). The Stool Bent or Heath Rush. *J. Min. Agric.* 43 : 262.

(1937). The Composition and feeding value of Heather. *J. Min. Agric.* 43 : 1050.

THOMAS, B., & DOUGALL, H. W. (1938). The Blaeberry. *J. Min. Agric.* 45 : 546.

(1939). Flying Bent. *J. Min. Agric.* 46 : 277.

TOUGH, D. L. W. (1919). The last years of a frontier. London.

TURNER, J. (1964). The anthropogenic factor in vegetational history I. Tregaron and Whixall mosses. *New Pyht.*, 63.

TURNER, J. (1965). A contribution to the history of forest clearance. *Proc. Roy. Soc. B.* 161.

WATSON, H. C. (1835). The New Botanist's Guide to the Localities of the Rarer Plants of Britain. London.

WATT, A. S. (1919). On the causes of failure of natural regeneration in British Oakwoods. *J. Ecol.* 7 : 173.

(1947). Pattern and Process in the Plant Community. *J. Ecol.* 35 : 1.

WILSON, A. (1931-33). The Altitudinal range of British Plants. *Northw. Nat.* 5 and 6.

WOODHEAD, T. W. (1929). History of the vegetation of the Southern Pennines. *J. Ecol.* 17 : 1.

WRIGHT, W. B. (1936). The Quaternary Ice Age. London.

WROOT, H. E. (1930). The Pennines in History. *Naturalist*, 1930 : 45 and 105.

ZEUNER, F. E. (1963). A history of domesticated animals. London.

GLOSSARY

aerobic, describing organisms requiring air (containing oxygen) to live in, also the conditions when such air is present.

amorphous, lacking evident form and structure.

anaerobic, describing conditions in which oxygen is absent or the organisms living in such conditions.

apogamous, describing reproduction without the fusion of gametes, e.g. of sperm and egg-cell.

basalt, a dark-coloured and compact basic rock of volcanic origin.

base, used in the chemical sense to mean a substance neutralising an acid, e.g. (in soils) lime or potash.

base-deficient, referring to soils in which the soil or humus material is not completely saturated with bases.

Beaker people, Neolithic invaders of southern and eastern Britain who used pottery of a characteristic pattern.

bergschrund, a gap between the snow or rock on a mountain and the ice of a glacier.

blanket-bog, a bog not confined to a basin but also covering undulating or sloping country.

Bronze Age, period when men used bronze tools, perhaps not before 1800 B.C. in the Pennines.

brown-earth, a name given to the characteristic forest-soil type in temperate climates like that of Western Europe.

colloidal, solids in the non-crystalline state, e.g. like jelly or flint.

coniferous, describing cone-bearing trees like pines and firs.

corrie, a circular or basin-shaped valley cut back into a high mountain slope (=cwm or cirque).

creep-soil, a soil formed from downward-moving rock or soil particles.

deciduous, describing trees whose leaves fall off (in winter in Britain).

Diptera, two-winged flies.

drift, disintegrated rock material deposited elsewhere, usually by moving ice.

eutrophic, with high nutritional requirements.

flush, an area of soil enriched by transported materials, either soil or dissolved mineral salts.

gill, a northern name for a small, steep-sided stream-valley.

gley, a permanently waterlogged mineral soil with a characteristic blue-grey or mottled colour.

gneiss, a rock composed mainly of quartz, felspar and mica, differing from granite mainly in the laminated appearance of the crystals.

gravel-slide, an unstable and continually moving slope of fine rock detritus.

grits, coarse sandstones, especially if the grains are rough.

haggs, erosion channels in peat or sometimes cuttings from which peat has been removed.

humus, the soil organic matter derived from decomposing plant remains.

humified, describing partly decomposed vegetable matter.

humification, the process of decomposition yielding humus.

hydrolytic, describing chemical changes brought about by the action of water.

igneous, used to describe rocks erupted from the heated lower layers of the earth's crust.

insolation, exposure to the sun's rays.

Iron Age, the era of men using iron tools, perhaps generally Roman in time or even later in much of upland Britain.

iron-pan, a layer of red-brown material rich in iron sometimes found in soils.

leached, washed by water which removes soluble salts.

leaching, the process by which soluble salts are removed from soil.

lichen, a composite plant consisting of fungal and algal components.

mor, an especially infertile and acid type of humus.

moss, a kind of spore-forming plant lacking flowers.

moss or *peat-moss*, a northern name for peaty land formed mainly by bog-moss.

mull, a fertile type of humus, like well-rotted leaf-mould.

Neolithic, pertaining to men who used stone implements of a particular pattern and who possessed some agricultural knowledge, probably reaching north-west Britain by 3000 B.C.

nevé, solidified snow, usually granular, but not completely turned into ice.

nivation, weathering processes associated with rock and soil above the usual snow level.

nunatak, land or hill projecting through a continental ice-sheet.

oligotrophic, with low nutritional requirements.

oxidation, the process of combining with oxygen or its chemical equivalent.

oxidizing, causing the process of oxidation.

pan, dense or hardened soil layers of iron or humus compounds.

phyllites, slaty rocks, usually splitting readily and showing a crystalline structure containing mica.

phytophagous, describing insects which feed on plants.

plutonic, describing igneous rocks that have solidified and consolidated at some distance below the earth's surface.

podsol, a soil type in which the layers below the surface are much leached.

raised-beaches, ancient sea-beaches above the present sea-level.

raised-bog, a peat-bog with a convex surface.

reducing, causing chemical changes equivalent to a reduction in the oxygen content of the substance affected.

roches moutonnées, ice-rounded rocks.

run-off, that part of the rainfall that runs off as surface water without penetrating the soil or rock cover.

schist, a highly foliated and splittable rock.

scree, *scree-slope*, rock detritus below an outcropping rock.

sedimentary, describing rocks laid down by deposition in water.

shales, soft rocks formed from the consolidation of clays.

solifluction, soil-flowing, normally associated with a high water-content and often with a frozen sub-soil.

stone-polygon, an arctic soil formation in which a central area of soil or mud is surrounded by polygonally arranged rows of stones.

stone-stripes, parallel rows of stones running down a slope and separating areas of soil or fine gravel.

striped-scree, scree-slopes in which the larger stones are arranged in parallel rows as above.

tuffs, the finer sorts of volcanic debris, e.g. ashes.

INDEX

Arabic figures in heavy type refer to plate numbers of photographs in colour. Roman numerals in heavy type refer to plate numbers of photographs in black and white.